ALMOST PERIODIC FUNCTIONS

A. S. BESICOVITCH
Fellow of Trinity College
Cambridge

DOVER PUBLICATIONS, INC.

This new Dover edition is a
reissue of the first edition republished
through special permission of Cambridge University Press.

Printed and Bound in the United States of America

CONTENTS

PREFACE

THE theory of almost periodic functions, created by H. Bohr, has now completed two stages of its development.

Almost periodicity, as a structural property, is a generalisation of pure periodicity and Bohr's original methods for establishing the fundamental results of the theory were always based on reducing the problem to a problem of purely periodic functions. But though the underlying idea of Bohr's method was clear and simple, the actual proofs of the main results were very difficult and complicated. New methods were given by N. Wiener and H. Weyl, by which the results were arrived at in a much shorter way. But these methods have lost the elementary character of Bohr's methods. It was C. de la Vallée Poussin who succeeded in giving a new proof (based partly on H. Weyl's idea), which was very short and at the same time based entirely on classical results in the theory of purely periodic functions.

This represents one stage in the development of the theory of almost periodic functions.

Bohr's theory of *a.p.* functions was restricted to the class of uniformly continuous functions. Then efforts were directed to generalisations of the theory. Thanks to the work of W. Stepanoff, N. Wiener, H. Weyl, H. Bohr and others, generalisations may be considered to have reached a certain completeness.

This was the second stage in the development of the theory.

These circumstances suggest that the present moment is not unfavourable for writing an account of the theory.

In Chapter I of this account we develop the fundamental part of the theory of *a.p.* functions of a real variable—the theory of uniformly *a.p.* functions. In the main problems of this chapter we adopt the methods of H. Bohr, de la Vallée Poussin, Weyl and Bochner.

Chapter II is devoted to a systematic investigation of generalisations of the theory.

In Chapter III we develop the theory of analytic *a.p.* functions, which in essentials remains unaltered as it was published by H. Bohr.

This account is not encyclopaedic. Our aim is to give the fundamental results of the theory, and we have omitted all discussion of certain special problems. Thus the work of Bohr, Neugebauer, Walter and Bochner on differential equations and difference equations has not been considered in this book, nor has the theory of harmonic *a.p.* functions developed by J. Favard in his interesting paper. For all these questions the reader is referred to the original papers.

A. S. B.

INTRODUCTION

THE theory of almost periodic functions was created and developed in its main features by H. Bohr during the last decade. Like many other important mathematical discoveries it is connected with several branches of the modern theory of functions. On the one hand, almost periodicity as a structural property of functions is a generalisation of pure periodicity: on the other hand, the theory of almost periodic functions opens a way of studying a wide class of trigonometric series of the general type and of exponential series (Dirichlet series), giving in the latter case important contributions to the general problems of the theory of analytic functions.

Almost periodicity is a generalisation of pure periodicity: the general property can be illustrated by means of the particular example

$$f(x) = \sin 2\pi x + \sin 2\pi x \sqrt{2}.$$

This function is not periodic: there exists no value of τ which satisfies the equation

$$f(x+\tau) = f(x)$$

for all values of x. But we can establish the existence of numbers for which this equation is approximately satisfied with an arbitrary degree of accuracy. For given any $\epsilon > 0$ as small as we please we can always find an integer τ such that $\tau\sqrt{2}$ differs from another integer by less than $\epsilon/2\pi$. It can be proved that there exist infinitely many such numbers τ, and that the difference between two consecutive ones is bounded. For each of these numbers we have

$$\begin{aligned} f(x+\tau) &= \sin 2\pi(x+\tau) + \sin 2\pi(x+\tau)\sqrt{2} \\ &= \sin 2\pi x + \sin(2\pi x\sqrt{2} + \theta\epsilon) \qquad (|\,\theta\,| \leqq 1) \\ &= f(x) + \theta'\epsilon. \qquad (|\,\theta'\,| \leqq 1) \end{aligned}$$

Almost periodicity of a function $f(x)$ in general is defined by this property:

The equation

$$f(x+\tau)=f(x)$$

is satisfied with an arbitrary degree of accuracy by infinitely many values of τ, these values being spread over the whole range from $-\infty$ to $+\infty$ in such a way as not to leave empty intervals of arbitrarily great length.

Almost periodicity is a deep structural property of functions which is invariant with respect to the operations of addition (subtraction) and multiplication, and also in many cases with respect to division, differentiation, integration and other limiting processes.

To the structural affinity between almost periodic functions and purely periodic functions may be added an analytical similarity. To any almost periodic function corresponds a "Fourier series" of the type of a general trigonometric series

$$(1) \qquad f(x) \sim \sum_{n=1}^{\infty} A_n e^{i\Lambda_n x}$$

(Λ_n being real numbers and A_n real or complex): it is obtained from the function by the same formal process as in the case of purely periodic functions (namely, by the method of undetermined coefficients and term-by-term integration). The series (1) need not converge to $f(x)$, but there is a much closer connection between the series and the function than we have yet seen. In the first place Parseval's equation is true, i.e.

$$M\{|f(x)|^2\}=\Sigma\,|A_n|^2,$$

from which follows at once the uniqueness theorem, according to which there exists at most one almost periodic function having a given trigonometric series for its Fourier series. Parseval's equation constitutes the fundamental theorem of the theory of almost periodic functions. Further, the series (1) is "summable to $f(x)$," in the sense that there exists a sequence of polynomials

$$\sum_{n=1}^{\infty} p_n^{(k)} A_n e^{i\Lambda_n x} \qquad (k=1,2,\ldots)$$

(where $0 \leqq p_n \leqq 1$, and where for each k only a finite number of the factors p differ from zero) which

(*a*) converge to $f(x)$ uniformly in x, and

(*b*) converge formally to the series (1),

by which is meant that for each n

$$p_n^{(k)} \to 1, \text{ as } k \to \infty.$$

Conversely, any trigonometric polynomial is an almost periodic function, and so is the uniform limit of a sequence of trigonometric polynomials. It is easily proved that the Fourier series of such a limit function is the formal limit of the sequence of trigonometric polynomials. Thus the class of Fourier series of almost periodic functions consists of all trigonometric series of the general type

$$\Sigma A_n e^{i\Lambda_n x},$$

to which correspond uniformly convergent sequences of polynomials of the type

$$\Sigma p_n^{(k)} A_n e^{i\Lambda_n x}, \qquad (k = 1, 2, \ldots)$$

formally convergent to the series. Thus the theory of almost periodic functions opened up for study a class of general trigonometric series: the extent of this class will be discussed later on.

The first investigations of trigonometric series other than purely periodic ones were carried out by Bohl. He considered the class of functions represented by series of the form

$$\sum_{(n)} A_{n_1, n_2, \ldots, n_l} e^{i(n_1 a_1 + n_2 a_2 + \ldots + n_l a_l)x},$$

where $a_1, a_2, \ldots, a_l$ are arbitrary real numbers, and $A_{n_1, n_2, \ldots, n_l}$ real or complex numbers. The necessary and sufficient conditions that a function is so representable are that it possesses certain quasi-periodic properties which are at first glance very similar to almost periodicity; but Bohl's restriction on the exponents of the trigonometric series places his problem in the class of those whose solution follows in a more or less natural way from existing theories rather than of those giving rise to an entirely new theory.

A quite new way of studying trigonometric series is opened up by Bohr's theory of almost periodic functions. We indicated above the class of trigonometric series which correspond to almost periodic functions: we have not yet indicated how wide the class is. It is not possible to give any direct test for a series to be the Fourier series of an almost periodic function, nor can the similar problem be solved for the class of purely periodic continuous functions. But when the property of almost periodicity is properly generalised, then the corresponding class of Fourier series acquires a rather definite character of completeness.

The original work of Bohr was confined to the almost periodicity defined above. Thereafter work was done in the way of generalisation of the property by Stepanoff, Wiener, Weyl, Bohr and others. The new types of almost periodic functions were represented by new classes of trigonometric series

$$\Sigma A_n e^{i\Lambda_n x}.$$

As before, to a series of one of the new classes still corresponds a convergent series of polynomials

$$\Sigma p_n^{(k)} A_n e^{i\Lambda_n x}, \qquad (k = 1, 2, \ldots)$$

but to each new type of almost periodicity corresponds a different kind of convergence of this sequence—not uniform convergence, although the convergence always has some features of uniformity. In fact there exists a strict reciprocity between the kind of almost periodicity of a function and the kind of convergence of the corresponding sequence of polynomials.

When these generalisations are taken into consideration some answer can be made to the above question of the extent of the class of trigonometric series which are Fourier series of almost periodic functions. This answer is given by the Riesc-Fischer Theorem:

Any trigonometric series $\Sigma A_n e^{i\Lambda_n x}$, *subject to the single condition that the series* $\Sigma \mid A_n \mid^2$ *is convergent, is the Fourier series of an almost periodic function.*

This is completely analogous to the Riesc-Fischer Theorem for the case of purely periodic functions. Generalisations of this result similar to those for purely periodic functions are possible.

Thus the Fourier series of all almost periodic functions form as large a subset of the class of all trigonometric series of the general type as the Fourier series of purely periodic functions do of the class of all trigonometric series of the ordinary type.

There is no doubt whatever that a trigonometric series of the general type

$$\Sigma A_n e^{i\Lambda_n x}$$

(with no restriction on the coefficients), in general does not represent a function (is not "summable") in any natural way, and it may be that almost periodicity is the decisive test for a non-artificial summability.

Almost periodicity is generalised in a natural way to the class of analytic functions in a strip $a < Rz < b$ by the condition that the approximate equation

$$f(z+\tau i) = f(z), \qquad (\tau \text{ real})$$

must be satisfied in the whole strip. One of the main features of the theory of analytic almost periodic functions is the existence of the "Dirichlet series" $\Sigma A_n e^{\Lambda_n z}$, which corresponds to the Fourier series of almost periodic functions of a real variable. The consequence is the same as in the case of almost periodic functions of a real variable. We get a possibility of enlarging the class of exponential series accessible to investigation. While in the case of ordinary Dirichlet series $\Sigma A_n e^{\Lambda_n z}$ the exponents are subject to the condition of forming a monotone sequence, there is no restriction of this kind on Dirichlet series of almost periodic functions. In fact any set of real numbers may form Dirichlet exponents of an analytic almost periodic function.

The connection between analytic functions and their Dirichlet series is even deeper than between almost periodic functions of a real variable and their Fourier series. The behaviour of almost periodic functions and the character of their singularities at infinity are defined by the nature of their Dirichlet series.

The study of harmonic and doubly periodic functions has also brought interesting and important results.

Applications of almost periodic functions have been made to linear differential and difference equations, and undoubtedly further development of the theory will lead to wider applications.

CHAPTER I

UNIFORMLY ALMOST PERIODIC FUNCTIONS

§ 1. Definition and elementary properties.

1°. *A set E of real numbers is said to be relatively dense (r.d.) if there exists a number $l>0$ such that any interval of length l contains at least one number of E. Any such number l is called an inclusion interval of the set E.* Thus the sets of numbers (i) $\pm n$, (ii) $\pm \sqrt{n}$, where n takes all the positive integral values, are both *r.d.* On the other hand, neither of the sets (iii) of all positive numbers, (iv) of all prime numbers $\pm p_n$ is *r.d.*

2°. Let $f(x)$ be a real or complex function defined for all real values of x. *A number τ is called a translation number of $f(x)$ belonging to $\epsilon \geqq 0$ if*

$$\underset{-\infty<x<+\infty}{u.b.} \quad |f(x+\tau)-f(x)| \leqq \epsilon.$$

From this definition we deduce the following properties of translation numbers of the same function.

(i) *A translation number belonging to ϵ belongs also to any $\epsilon' > \epsilon$.*

(ii) *If τ is a translation number belonging to ϵ, then so is $-\tau$.*

(iii) *If τ_1, τ_2 are translation numbers belonging respectively to ϵ_1, ϵ_2, then $\tau_1 \pm \tau_2$ is a translation number belonging to $\epsilon_1+\epsilon_2$.*

We denote the set of all the translation numbers of a function $f(x)$ belonging to ϵ by $E\{\epsilon, f(x)\}$. We deduce from (i) that

$$E\{\epsilon', f(x)\} \supset E\{\epsilon, f(x)\}^*$$

for any $\epsilon' > \epsilon$, and from (ii) that the set $E\{\epsilon, f(x)\}$ for any $\epsilon \geqq 0$ and for any $f(x)$ is symmetrical with respect to the point O.

* The formulae $A \supset B$, $A \subset B$ are read respectively: A contains B, A is contained in B.

3°. *A continuous function* $f(x)$ *is called uniformly almost periodic (u.a.p.) if for any* $\epsilon > 0$ *the set* $E\{\epsilon, f(x)\}$ *is r.d.*

We shall always denote by l_ϵ an inclusion interval of $E\{\epsilon, f(x)\}$. From the definition it follows at once that any continuous purely periodic function $f(x)$ is *u.a.p.*, since for any ϵ the set $E\{\epsilon, f(x)\}$ contains all numbers np (p a period of $f(x)$, n integer) and thus is *r.d.*

We shall now prove several theorems, which establish elementary properties of *u.a.p.* functions.

4°. THEOREM. *Any u.a.p. function* $f(x)$ *is bounded.*

For, put $\epsilon = 1$ and denote by M the maximum of $|f(x)|$ in an interval $(0, l_1)$. It can be easily seen that corresponding to any x we can define a number τ of $E\{1, f(x)\}$, such that $x + \tau$ belongs to $(0, l_1)$, and consequently that

$$|f(x+\tau)| \leqq M.$$

But

$$|f(x+\tau) - f(x)| \leqq 1,$$

thus

$$|f(x)| \leqq M + 1,$$

for all values of x, which proves the theorem.

5°. THEOREM. *Any u.a.p. function is uniformly continuous.*

For, given $\epsilon > 0$, take an $l_{\epsilon/3}$ and let $\delta\,(0 < \delta < 1)$ be a number such that $|f(x_1) - f(x_2)| < \frac{1}{3}\epsilon$ for any x_1, x_2 belonging to the interval $(0, l_{\epsilon/3} + 1)$ if only $|x_1 - x_2| < \delta$. Let now x', x'' be any two numbers such that $|x' - x''| < \delta$. There exists a number τ of the set $E\{\frac{1}{3}\epsilon, f(x)\}$ such that both the numbers $x' + \tau$, $x'' + \tau$ belong to the interval $(0, l_{\epsilon/3} + 1)$. We have then

$$|f(x'+\tau) - f(x''+\tau)| < \tfrac{1}{3}\epsilon.$$

On the other hand

$$|f(x+\tau) - f(x)| < \tfrac{1}{3}\epsilon$$

for any x. Thus

$$|f(x') - f(x'')| \leqq |f(x') - f(x'+\tau)| + |f(x'+\tau) - f(x''+\tau)| + |f(x''+\tau) - f(x'')| < \epsilon,$$

which proves the theorem.

Corollary. *If* $f(x)$ *is u.a.p., then to any* $\epsilon > 0$ *corresponds a number* $\delta = \delta(\epsilon) > 0$ *such that the set* $E\{\epsilon, f(x)\}$ *contains all numbers of the interval* $(-\delta, +\delta)$.

6°. Theorem. *If $f(x)$ is u.a.p., then $cf(x)$ (c any constant), $\bar{f}(x)$ (the conjugate function of $f(x)$), $\{f(x)\}^2$ are also u.a.p.*

For, if
$$|f(x+\tau)-f(x)| \leqq \epsilon,$$
then
$$|cf(x+\tau)-cf(x)| \leqq |c|\,\epsilon,$$
$$|\bar{f}(x+\tau)-\bar{f}(x)| \leqq \epsilon,$$
$$|\{f(x+\tau)\}^2-\{f(x)\}^2| \leqq 2M\epsilon,$$
where
$$M = \underset{-\infty<x<+\infty}{u.b.} |f(x)|.$$
Thus each of the sets
$$E\{|c|\,\epsilon, cf(x)\}, \quad E\{\epsilon, \bar{f}(x)\}, \quad E\{2M\epsilon, \{f(x)\}^2\},$$
contains the set $E\{\epsilon, f(x)\}$ and consequently is *r.d.*, which proves the theorem, since ϵ is arbitrary.

7°. Theorem. *If $f(x)$ is u.a.p. and if*
$$\underset{-\infty<x<+\infty}{l.b.} |f(x)| = m > 0,$$
then $1/f(x)$ is also u.a.p.

For, if
$$|f(x+\tau)-f(x)| \leqq \epsilon,$$
then
$$\left|\frac{1}{f(x+\tau)}-\frac{1}{f(x)}\right| = \left|\frac{f(x+\tau)-f(x)}{f(x+\tau).f(x)}\right| \leqq \frac{\epsilon}{m^2}.$$
Thus $E\left\{\frac{\epsilon}{m^2}, \frac{1}{f(x)}\right\}$ contains $E\{\epsilon, f(x)\}$ and consequently is *r.d.* This being true for an arbitrary ϵ the theorem is proved.

Remark. The last two theorems are particular cases of the following

Theorem. *If $f(x)$ is u.a.p., then any uniformly continuous function of $f(x)$, $F\{f(x)\}$ is also u.a.p.*

8°. Theorem. *If a sequence of u.a.p. functions $\{f_n(x)\}$ converges uniformly in the whole interval $-\infty < x < +\infty$ to a function $f(x)$, then $f(x)$ is also u.a.p.*

For, given ϵ, there exists a function $f_{n_0}(x)$ such that
$$|f(x)-f_{n_0}(x)| < \frac{\epsilon}{3}$$
for all values of x. Let now τ be a number of $E\{\tfrac{1}{3}\epsilon, f_{n_0}(x)\}$.

Then

$$|f(x+\tau)-f(x)| \leq |f(x+\tau)-f_{n_0}(x+\tau)| + |f_{n_0}(x+\tau)-f_{n_0}(x)| + |f_{n_0}(x)-f(x)| < \epsilon,$$

which shows that

$$E\{\epsilon, f(x)\} \supset E\{\tfrac{1}{3}\epsilon, f_{n_0}(x)\}.$$

Thus $E\{\epsilon, f(x)\}$ is *r.d.* This being true for any ϵ we conclude that $f(x)$ is *u.a.p.*

9°. In 6° and 7° we established almost periodicity of functions of one *u.a.p.* function. We pass now to functions of more than one *u.a.p.* function. We shall first establish some properties of translation numbers of *u.a.p.* functions.

Lemma. *Given any two positive numbers ϵ_1, ϵ_2 ($\epsilon_1 < \epsilon_2$), there exists a number $\delta(\epsilon_1, \epsilon_2) > 0$ such that $E\{\epsilon_2, f(x)\}$ contains every number whose distance from the set $E\{\epsilon_1, f(x)\}$ is not greater than $\delta(\epsilon_1, \epsilon_2)$.*

By the corollary of 5° there exists a number $\delta = \delta(\epsilon_2 - \epsilon_1) > 0$ such that $E\{\epsilon_2 - \epsilon_1, f(x)\}$ contains all numbers of the interval $(-\delta, +\delta)$.

But by (iii) of 2° the sum of any two numbers taken one from each of the sets $E\{\epsilon_1, f(x)\}$, $E\{\epsilon_2 - \epsilon_1, f(x)\}$ and *a fortiori* from each of the sets $E\{\epsilon_1, f(x)\}$, $(-\delta, +\delta)$ belongs to the set $E\{\epsilon_2, f(x)\}$, which proves the lemma.

10°. **Lemma.** *If ϵ, δ are two arbitrary positive numbers and $f_1(x)$, $f_2(x)$ two u.a.p. functions, then the set of numbers of $E\{\epsilon, f_1(x)\}$ whose distances from the set $E\{\epsilon, f_2(x)\}$ are less than δ, is r.d.*

Consider the sets $E\{\tfrac{1}{2}\epsilon, f_1(x)\}$ and $E\{\tfrac{1}{2}\epsilon, f_2(x)\}$, and let a number $l = k\delta$ (k integer) be an inclusion interval of each of these sets. Divide the whole interval $(-\infty, +\infty)$ into intervals $\{(n-1)l, nl\}$, where n takes all integral values. Inside every interval $\{(n-1)l, nl\}$ we can find numbers $\tau_1^{(n)}$, $\tau_2^{(n)}$ belonging respectively to $E\{\tfrac{1}{2}\epsilon, f_1(x)\}$, $E\{\tfrac{1}{2}\epsilon, f_2(x)\}$. We shall have

$$-l < \tau_1^{(n)} - \tau_2^{(n)} < +l.$$

Denote by λ_i the interval $(i-1)\delta \leqq x < i\delta$, so that the difference $\tau_1^{(n)} - \tau_2^{(n)}$ always belongs to one of the intervals λ_i $(i = -k+1, \ldots, k)$. Obviously there exists an integer n_0 such that to any integer n corresponds an integer n' $(-n_0 \leqq n' \leqq n_0)$ for which the difference $\tau_1^{(n')} - \tau_2^{(n')}$ belongs to the same interval λ_i as the difference $\tau_1^{(n)} - \tau_2^{(n)}$. Thus we have

$$\tau_1^{(n)} - \tau_2^{(n)} = \tau_1^{(n')} - \tau_2^{(n')} + \theta\delta, \quad (-1 < \theta < +1)$$

or

$$\tau_1^{(n)} - \tau_1^{(n')} = \tau_2^{(n)} - \tau_2^{(n')} + \theta\delta.$$

But by (iii) of 2° the numbers $\tau_1^{(n)} - \tau_1^{(n')}$, $\tau_2^{(n)} - \tau_2^{(n')}$ belong respectively to $E\{\epsilon, f_1(x)\}$, $E\{\epsilon, f_2(x)\}$. Thus the distance of every number $\tau_1^{(n)} - \tau_1^{(n')}$ $(-\infty < n < +\infty)$ from the set $E\{\epsilon, f_2(x)\}$ is less than δ. The modulus of the difference of the values of $\tau_1^{(n)} - \tau_1^{(n')}$ for any two consecutive values of n is easily seen to be less than $(2n_0+3)\,l$, and thus the set $\{\tau_1^{(n)} - \tau_1^{(n')}\}$ $(-\infty < n < +\infty)$ is *r.d.*, which proves the lemma.

11°. THEOREM. *For any $\epsilon > 0$ and for any two u.a.p. functions $f_1(x)$ and $f_2(x)$ the set* $E\{\epsilon, f_1(x)\} . E\{\epsilon, f_2(x)\}$ is relatively dense.*

Take a positive number $\epsilon_1 < \epsilon$. By the lemma of 9° there exists a $\delta > 0$ such that all numbers whose distance from the set $E\{\epsilon_1, f_1(x)\}$ is less than δ, belong to $E\{\epsilon, f_1(x)\}$. Now by the preceding lemma the set G of the numbers of $E\{\epsilon_1, f_2(x)\}$ whose distances from the set $E\{\epsilon_1, f_1(x)\}$ are less than δ, and which consequently belong to $E\{\epsilon, f_1(x)\}$, is *r.d.*, i.e. the set $E\{\epsilon, f_1(x)\} . E\{\epsilon_1, f_2(x)\}$ is *r.d.*, and *a fortiori* so is the set $E\{\epsilon, f_1(x)\} . E\{\epsilon, f_2(x)\}$.

12°. THEOREM. *The sum of two u.a.p. functions $f_1(x)$, $f_2(x)$ is u.a.p.*

For, taking an arbitrary $\epsilon > 0$, let τ be any number of the set

$$E\{\tfrac{1}{2}\epsilon, f_1(x)\} . E\{\tfrac{1}{2}\epsilon, f_2(x)\}.$$

Then
$$|f_1(x+\tau) + f_2(x+\tau) - f_1(x) - f_2(x)| \leqq \epsilon,$$
which shows that τ belongs to $E\{\epsilon, f_1(x) + f_2(x)\}$. Thus

$$E\{\epsilon, f_1(x) + f_2(x)\} \supset E\{\tfrac{1}{2}\epsilon, f_1(x)\} . E\{\tfrac{1}{2}\epsilon, f_2(x)\},$$

so that $E\{\epsilon, f_1(x) + f_2(x)\}$ is *r.d.*, which proves the theorem.

* A and B being two sets we denote by $A . B$ (or by $A \times B$) the set of all common elements of A and B.

The theorem can be generalised immediately to the case of the sum of any finite number of *u.a.p.* functions.

Corollary. *A uniformly convergent series* $\sum_{n=1}^{\infty} a_n e^{i\lambda_n x}$, *where* $\lambda_1, \lambda_2, \ldots$ *are real, is a u.a.p. function.*

For, each term of the series being a *u.a.p.* function (in fact a purely periodic function), the sum of the first n terms $s_n(x)$ is a *u.a.p.* function, and the sum $s(x)$ of the series being the uniform limit of $s_n(x)$ is also a *u.a.p.* function (on account of the theorem of 8°).

13°. THEOREM. *The product of two u.a.p. functions* $f_1(x), f_2(x)$ *is a u.a.p. function.*

By the preceding theorem the functions $f_1(x)+f_2(x)$ and $f_1(x)-f_2(x)$ are *u.a.p.*, and by the theorem of 6° their squares are also *u.a.p.* functions. Thus $f_1(x).f_2(x)$ can be represented as the sum of two *u.a.p.* functions

$$f_1(x).f_2(x) = \tfrac{1}{4}\{f_1(x)+f_2(x)\}^2 - \tfrac{1}{4}\{f_1(x)-f_2(x)\}^2,$$

which proves the theorem.

Corollary. *If* $f_1(x), f_2(x)$ *are u.a.p. and if l.b.* $|f_2(x)|$ *is positive, then* $f_1(x)/f_2(x)$ *is u.a.p.*

For by the theorem of 7° $1/f_2(x)$ is *u.a.p.*, and thus

$$f_1(x)/f_2(x) = f_1(x).\frac{1}{f_2(x)}$$

is the product of two *u.a.p.* functions.

14°. We shall now establish, under certain conditions, the almost periodicity of the derivative and of an integral of a *u.a.p.* function.

BOCHNER'S THEOREM. *If the derivative of a u.a.p. function* $f(x)$ *is uniformly continuous, then it is u.a.p.*

Take a sequence $\{h_n\}$ of real numbers converging to zero. We write

$$\frac{f(x+h_n)-f(x)}{h_n} = f'(x+\theta h_n). \quad (0<\theta<1)$$

The expression on the left being the difference of two *u.a.p.* functions is *u.a.p.* Thus $f'(x+\theta h_n)$ $(n=1, 2, \ldots)$ form a sequence of *u.a.p.* functions uniformly convergent to $f'(x)$ (on account of the uniform continuity of $f'(x)$). Consequently $f'(x)$ is *u.a.p.*

15°. THEOREM. *If an indefinite integral of a u.a.p. function $f(x)$ is bounded, then it is a u.a.p. function.*

Obviously we may assume $f(x)$ to be real. We write

$$F(x)=\int_a^x f(x)\,dx,$$

where a is a constant, and assume $F(x)$ to be bounded, so that both of the two numbers

(1) $$k_1 = l.b.\, F(x), \quad k_2 = u.b.\, F(x)$$

are finite. We have to prove that $F(x)$ is *u.a.p.*, i.e. that the set $E\{\epsilon, F(x)\}$ is *r.d.* for any $\epsilon>0$. The numbers τ of this set are defined by the condition that they satisfy the inequality

(2) $$|F(x+\tau)-F(x)| = \left|\int_x^{x+\tau} f(x)\,dx\right| \leqq \epsilon$$

for all x.

Now given an $\eta>0$ we can always define numbers x_1 and x_2 to satisfy the inequalities

(3) $$F(x_1) < k_1+\eta, \quad F(x_2) > k_2-\eta.$$

Take now an arbitrary $\epsilon'>0$ and let τ' be any number of $E\{\epsilon', f(x)\}$. Writing $|x_1-x_2|=d$ we shall have

$$\left|\int_{x_1+\tau'}^{x_2+\tau'} f(x)\,dx - \int_{x_1}^{x_2} f(x)\,dx\right| = \left|\int_{x_1}^{x_2}\{f(x+\tau')-f(x)\}\,dx\right| \leqq \epsilon' d,$$

i.e. $$|F(x_2+\tau')-F(x_1+\tau')-F(x_2)+F(x_1)| \leqq \epsilon' d,$$

whence

$$F(x_1+\tau') \leqq F(x_2+\tau') - \{F(x_2)-F(x_1)\} + \epsilon' d.$$

But by (1) and (3)

$$F(x_2+\tau') \leqq k_2, \quad F(x_2)-F(x_1) > k_2-k_1-2\eta,$$

thus

(4) $$F(x_1+\tau') < k_1 + 2\eta + \epsilon' d.$$

Take now an $\epsilon'' > 0$ which will be defined later on. Let τ'' be any number of $E\{\epsilon'', f(x)\}$. Analogously to (4) we have (observing that $\tau' + \tau'' \subset E\{\epsilon' + \epsilon'', f(x)\}$)

(5) $$F(x_1 + \tau' + \tau'') < k_1 + 2\eta + (\epsilon' + \epsilon'')\, d.$$

We shall now consider the integral $\int_x^{x+\tau''} f(x)\, dx$. Defining a τ' satisfying the inequality

(6) $$x < x_1 + \tau' < x + l_{\epsilon'},$$

we write

$$\int_x^{x+\tau''} f(x)\, dx = \int_{x_1+\tau'}^{x_1+\tau'+\tau''} f(x)\, dx + \int_x^{x_1+\tau'} \{f(x) - f(x+\tau'')\}\, dx.$$

By (1), (4), (5),

$$\left| \int_{x_1+\tau'}^{x_1+\tau'+\tau''} f(x)\, dx \right| = |F(x_1 + \tau' + \tau'') - F(x_1 + \tau')| < 2\eta + (\epsilon' + \epsilon'')\, d,$$

and by (6)

$$\left| \int_x^{x_1+\tau'} \{f(x) - f(x+\tau'')\}\, dx \right| < \epsilon'' l_{\epsilon'}.$$

Hence

(7) $$\left| \int_x^{x+\tau''} f(x)\, dx \right| < 2\eta + (\epsilon' + \epsilon'')\, d + \epsilon'' l_{\epsilon'}.$$

Given an $\epsilon > 0$ we put

$$\eta = \frac{\epsilon}{6}, \quad \epsilon' = \frac{\epsilon}{6d}, \quad \epsilon'' = \min.\left(\epsilon', \frac{\epsilon}{3l_{\epsilon'}}\right);$$

we obtain from (7)

(8) $$\left| \int_x^{x+\tau''} f(x)\, dx \right| < \epsilon,$$

for all x and for all $\tau'' \subset E\{\epsilon'', f(x)\}$. Hence by (2)

$$E\{\epsilon, F(x)\} \supset E\{\epsilon'', f(x)\},$$

which shows that $E\{\epsilon, F(x)\}$ is *r.d.*

16°. Some elementary properties of sets $E\{\epsilon, f(x)\}$ can be obtained by considering S. Bochner's *translation function.*

Given a *u.a.p.* function $f(x)$ we define the translation function $v_f(\tau)$ of $f(x)$ by the equation

$$v_f(\tau) = \underset{-\infty < x < +\infty}{u.b.} |f(x+\tau) - f(x)|.$$

Evidently the set $E\{\epsilon, f(x)\}$ is identical with the set $E\{v_f(\tau) \leqq \epsilon\}$ of values of τ for which $v_f(\tau) \leqq \epsilon$.

The function $v(\tau) = v_f(\tau)$ *satisfies the following conditions:*

(*a*) $v(\tau) \geqq 0, \ v(0) = 0$,

(*b*) $v(-\tau) = v(\tau)$,

(*c*) $v(\tau_1 + \tau_2) \leqq v(\tau_1) + v(\tau_2)$,

(*d*) $v(\tau)$ is *u.a.p.*

The properties (*a*), (*b*), (*c*) are obvious. To prove (*d*) we write

$$v(x+\tau) \leqq v(x) + v(\tau),$$

$$v(x) \leqq v(x+\tau) + v(-\tau) = v(x+\tau) + v(\tau),$$

whence

$$|v(x+\tau) - v(x)| \leqq v(\tau).$$

For $x = 0$ we have

$$|v(\tau) - v(0)| = v(\tau),$$

thus

(1) $$\underset{-\infty < x < +\infty}{u.b.} |v(x+\tau) - v(x)| = v(\tau),$$

i.e. $$u.b.|f(x+\tau) - f(x)| = u.b.|v(x+\tau) - v(x)|.$$

From this equation we conclude that $v(x)$ is a uniformly continuous function, and that

$$E\{\epsilon, v(x)\} = E\{\epsilon, f(x)\}$$

for all ϵ, which proves (*d*).

The converse can be easily proved, that

Any function $v(\tau)$ *satisfying the conditions* (*a*), (*b*), (*c*), (*d*) *is a translation function of a u.a.p. function.*

In fact the equation (1) follows from (*a*), (*b*), (*c*), and it shows that $v(\tau)$ is its own translation function.

§ 2. Normality of *u.a.p.* functions.

1°. S. Bochner has introduced a certain property (called normality), based on the convergence of sequences of functions, derived in a special way from a given function, and has proved that this property belongs to all *u.a.p.* functions and to no others, so that *u.a.p.* functions may be defined as functions possessing this property.

DEFINITION. *A continuous function $f(x)$ is called normal, if, given any sequence $\{h_i\}$ of real numbers, there exists a subsequence $\{h_{n_i}\}$ such that the sequence of functions $\{f(x+h_{n_i})\}$ is uniformly convergent.*

We shall prove that the class of normal functions and the class of *u.a.p.* functions are identical.

2°. **Lemma.** *Given a u.a.p. function $f(x)$ and a sequence $\{h_i\}$ of real numbers, then to any $\epsilon > 0$ there corresponds a subsequence $\{h_{n_i}\}$ such that the modulus of the difference of any pair of functions $f(x+h_{n_i})$ is less than ϵ.*

Any h_i can be represented in the form

$$h_i = \tau_i + r_i,$$

where τ_i belongs to $E\{\frac{1}{4}\epsilon, f(x)\}$ and r_i satisfies the inequality $0 \leqq r_i \leqq l_{\epsilon/4}$. For each h_i we consider only one representation in this form. Let r be a limit point of the set of all r_i. Define a number δ such that

$$|f(x'')-f(x')| < \epsilon/2,$$

if only
$$|x''-x'| < 2\delta.$$

Then the set of all h_i for which $r-\delta < r_i < r+\delta$ satisfies the condition of the lemma. For let h_j, h_k be two such values. We have

$$\begin{aligned} u.b.\,|f(x+h_j)-f(x+h_k)| &= u.b.\,|f(x+\tau_j-\tau_k+r_j-r_k)-f(x)| \\ &\leqq u.b.\,|f(x+\tau_j-\tau_k+r_j-r_k)-f(x+r_j-r_k)| \\ &\quad + u.b.\,|f(x+r_j-r_k)-f(x)|; \end{aligned}$$

each of the last two terms is less than $\epsilon/2$, since $\tau_j-\tau_k$ is a translation number belonging to $\epsilon/2$ and $|r_j-r_k| < 2\delta$. Thus

$$|f(x+h_j)-f(x+h_k)| < \epsilon.$$

3°. THEOREM. *Any u.a.p. function $f(x)$ is normal.*

For, let $\{h_i\}$ be a sequence of real numbers. By the preceding lemma we can choose a subsequence $\{h_{n'_i}\}$ such that for any two positive integers j, k and for all x

$$|f(x+h_{n'_j})-f(x+h_{n'_k})|<1.$$

Similarly we can choose a subsequence $\{h_{n_i^{(2)}}\}$ of the sequence $\{h_{n'_i}\}$ such that for any two positive integers j, k and for all x

$$|f(x+h_{n_j^{(2)}})-f(x+h_{n_k^{(2)}})|<\tfrac{1}{2}.$$

We then choose a subsequence $\{h_{n_i^{(3)}}\}$ of the sequence $\{h_{n_i^{(2)}}\}$ such that

$$|f(x+h_{n_j^{(3)}})-f(x+h_{n_k^{(3)}})|<\tfrac{1}{3},$$

and so on. Take now the sequence of functions

$$(1) \qquad f(x+h_{n_1'}), \quad f(x+h_{n_2^{(2)}}), \quad f(x+h_{n_3^{(3)}}), \quad \ldots.$$

Let j, k $(j<k)$ be two positive integers. We obviously have

$$|f(x+h_{n_j^{(j)}})-f(x+h_{n_k^{(k)}})|<\frac{1}{j},$$

which shows that the sequence (1) is uniformly convergent. As the sequence $\{h_i\}$ was arbitrary, the theorem is proved.

4°. CONVERSE THEOREM. *Any normal function $f(x)$ is u.a.p.*

For, assume the contrary: suppose $f(x)$ is not a *u.a.p.* function. Then there exists an $\epsilon>0$ such that the $E\{\epsilon, f(x)\}$ is not *r.d.*

Take now an arbitrary real number h_1 and let (a_2, b_2) be an interval of length $>2|h_1|$ which does not contain any number of $E\{\epsilon, f(x)\}$. Denote by h_2 the centre of this interval. Evidently h_2-h_1 belongs to the interval (a_2, b_2), and *a fortiori* does not belong to $E\{\epsilon, f(x)\}$. Define now an interval (a_3, b_3) of length $>2(|h_1|+|h_2|)$ which does not contain any number of $E\{\epsilon, f(x)\}$. Let h_3 be the centre of (a_3, b_3). For the same reason as before the numbers h_3-h_1, h_3-h_2 do not belong to $E\{\epsilon, f(x)\}$. In a similar way we define $h_4, h_5, \ldots$ so that none of the numbers h_i-h_j belongs to $E\{\epsilon, f(x)\}$. Thus for any i, j

$$u.b.\,|f(x+h_i)-f(x+h_j)|=u.b.\,|f(x+h_i-h_j)-f(x)|>\epsilon.$$

Thus we arrive at the conclusion that no subsequence of the sequence $\{f(x+h_i)\}$ is uniformly convergent, which is in contradiction with the assumption that $f(x)$ is normal, and the theorem is therefore proved.

The proofs given in this section are due to J. Favard.

§ 3. Mean values of *u.a.p.* functions and their Fourier series.

1°. *U.a.p.* functions, like purely periodic functions, can be "represented by their Fourier series." To establish this we have to consider certain limiting expressions—*mean values of u.a.p. functions.* Let $f(x)$ be a real *u.a.p.* function. We consider the integral

$$\frac{1}{X}\int_0^X f(x)\,dx,$$

and we call its upper limit and its lower limit, as $X\to+\infty$, *the upper and the lower mean value of the function* $f(x)$, and we denote them by

$$\overline{M}\{f(x)\},\quad \underline{M}\{f(x)\}.$$

If they are equal we call their common value *the mean value of* $f(x)$, and we denote it by $M\{f(x)\}$. It is obvious that the mean value of any integrable purely periodic function exists. If instead of $f(x)$ we have a function of two or more variables, then we indicate the variable with respect to which the mean value is taken by a suffix: we write for instance $M_x\{f(x, y)\}$.

In the case of a complex function $f(x)$ we define only *the mean value* $M\{f(x)\}$ by the limit of

$$\frac{1}{X}\int_0^X f(x)\,dx, \quad \text{as } X\to+\infty.$$

2°. Theorem. *The mean value of any u.a.p. function* $f(x)$ *exists.*

Let T, ϵ be two positive numbers and n a positive integer. We write

$$\frac{1}{nT}\int_0^{nT} f(x)\,dx = \sum_{k=0}^{k=n-1}\frac{1}{nT}\int_{kT}^{(k+1)T} f(x)\,dx.$$

Denote as usual by l_ϵ an inclusion interval of $E\{\epsilon, f(x)\}$, and let τ_k be a number of $E\{\epsilon, f(x)\}$ included in the interval $(kT, kT+l_\epsilon)$. We have

$$\begin{aligned}\int_{kT}^{(k+1)T} f(x)\,dx &= \int_{kT-\tau_k}^{(k+1)T-\tau_k} f(x+\tau_k)\,dx \\ &= \int_0^T f(x)\,dx + \int_0^T \{f(x+\tau_k)-f(x)\}\,dx \\ &\quad + \int_{kT-\tau_k}^{0} f(x+\tau_k)\,dx + \int_T^{(k+1)T-\tau_k} f(x+\tau_k)\,dx \\ &= I_1+I_2+I_3+I_4.\end{aligned}$$

Evidently $|I_2| < \epsilon T$. Now writing

$$A = \underset{-\infty<x<+\infty}{u.b.} |f(x)|,$$

and observing that the length of the range of integration in I_3 and I_4 is less than l_ϵ, we have $|I_3| < Al_\epsilon$, $|I_4| < Al_\epsilon$. Hence

$$\int_{kT}^{(k+1)T} f(x)\,dx = \int_0^T f(x)\,dx + \theta(\epsilon T + 2Al_\epsilon), \quad (|\theta| \leqq 1)$$

and thus

$$(1) \qquad \frac{1}{nT}\int_0^{nT} f(x)\,dx = \frac{1}{T}\int_0^T f(x)\,dx + \theta\left(\epsilon + \frac{2Al_\epsilon}{T}\right)^*.$$

Let now η be a positive number as small as we please. Taking in the above formula

$$\epsilon < \frac{\eta}{8}, \quad T > \frac{16Al_\epsilon}{\eta},$$

we shall have

$$(2) \qquad \frac{1}{nT}\int_0^{nT} f(x)\,dx = \frac{1}{T}\int_0^T f(x)\,dx + \theta\frac{\eta}{4}.$$

Corresponding to any positive number X, define the integer n by the condition

$$(2.1) \qquad nT \leqq X < (n+1)T.$$

From the boundedness of $f(x)$ we conclude

$$\lim\left\{\frac{1}{X}\int_0^X f(x)\,dx - \frac{1}{nT}\int_0^{nT} f(x)\,dx\right\} = 0, \text{ as } X \to \infty.$$

* In the course of proof θ denotes different values satisfying the conditions $|\theta| \leqq 1$.

Consequently there exists a number $X_0 > 0$ such that

$$(2.2) \qquad \left| \frac{1}{X} \int_0^X f(x)\, dx - \frac{1}{nT} \int_0^{nT} f(x)\, dx \right| < \frac{\eta}{4}$$

for all $X > X_0$.

Let X', X'' be any two numbers greater than X_0 and n', n'' the corresponding values of n in (2.1). By (2), (2.2)

$$\begin{aligned} \left| \frac{1}{X'} \int_0^{X'} f(x)\, dx - \frac{1}{X''} \int_0^{X''} f(x)\, dx \right| & \\ \leqq \left| \frac{1}{n'T} \int_0^{n'T} f(x)\, dx - \frac{1}{n''T} \int_0^{n''T} f(x)\, dx \right| & \\ + \left| \frac{1}{X'} \int_0^{X'} f(x)\, dx - \frac{1}{n'T} \int_0^{n'T} f(x)\, dx \right| & \\ + \left| \frac{1}{X''} \int_0^{X''} f(x)\, dx - \frac{1}{n''T} \int_0^{n''T} f(x)\, dx \right| & < \eta, \end{aligned}$$

which proves that the limit of

$$\frac{1}{X} \int_0^X f(x)\, dx$$

exists, as $X \to \infty$.

Thus the theorem is proved.

Taking the limit of the left-hand side of (1) we obtain

$$(3) \qquad M\{f(x)\} = \frac{1}{T} \int_0^T f(x)\, dx + \theta \left(\epsilon + \frac{2Al_\epsilon}{T} \right),$$

which is true for any $\epsilon > 0$, $T > 0$. The second term on the right-hand side is the error of the representation of $M\{f(x)\}$ by the integral $\frac{1}{T} \int_0^T f(x)\, dx$ and depends on ϵ, A, l_ϵ and T, of which ϵ, T are independent of $f(x)$ and l_ϵ, A are defined by $f(x)$. Evidently for the function $f(x+a)$, where a is an arbitrary real number, the numbers l_ϵ, A are the same as for $f(x)$. Consequently we may write

$$M\{f(x+a)\} = \frac{1}{T} \int_0^T f(x+a)\, dx + \theta \left(\epsilon + \frac{2Al_\epsilon}{T} \right).$$

But evidently

$$M\{f(x+a)\} = M\{f(x)\},$$

hence

$$(4) \qquad M\{f(x)\} = \frac{1}{T}\int_a^{a+T} f(x)\,dx + \theta\left(\epsilon + \frac{2Al_\epsilon}{T}\right),$$

i.e. the integral $\frac{1}{T}\int_a^{a+T} f(x)\,dx$ tends to $M\{f(x)\}$ uniformly in a, even if a varies together with T, so that we can write, for instance,

$$M\{f(x)\} = \lim_{T\to\infty} \frac{1}{T}\int_{-(T/2)}^{+(T/2)} f(x)\,dx.$$

3°. Consider now the product $f(t+x)\bar{f}(t)$. It is a *u.a.p.* function of t. Taking an arbitrary $\epsilon' > 0$ and denoting by $\bar{l}_{\epsilon'}$ an inclusion interval of $E\{\epsilon', f(t+x)\bar{f}(t)\}$ and by $\bar{A}$ the upper bound of $|f(t+x)\bar{f}(t)|$, we apply formula (4) of 2° to $f(t+x)\bar{f}(t)$:

$$M_t\{f(t+x)\bar{f}(t)\} = \frac{1}{T}\int_0^T f(t+x)\bar{f}(t)\,dt + \theta\left(\epsilon' + \frac{2\bar{A}\bar{l}_{\epsilon'}}{T}\right).$$

Obviously $\bar{A} \leq A^2$. Putting $\epsilon' = 2A\epsilon$ and observing that

$$E\{\epsilon', f(t+x)\bar{f}(t)\} \supset E\{\epsilon, f(t)\},$$

we see that l_ϵ is an inclusion interval of $E\{\epsilon', f(t+x)\bar{f}(t)\}$. Thus we may put $\bar{l}_{\epsilon'} = l_\epsilon$. We then write

$$(1) \quad M_t\{f(t+x)f(t)\} = \frac{1}{T}\int_0^T f(t+x)\bar{f}(t)\,dt + \theta\left(2A\epsilon + \frac{2A^2 l_\epsilon}{T}\right).$$

Writing

$$M_t\{f(t+x)\bar{f}(t)\} = g(x), \quad \frac{1}{T}\int_0^T f(t+x)\bar{f}(t)\,dt = G(x),$$

we have

$$(2) \qquad g(x) = G(x) + \theta\left(2A\epsilon + \frac{2A^2 l_\epsilon}{T}\right).$$

Taking in this equation ϵ sufficiently small, and T sufficiently large, we can make the second term of the right-hand side as small as we please.

Thus $G(x)$ *tends to* $g(x)$ *uniformly in* x, *as* $T \to \infty$.

Let τ be any number of the set $E\{\epsilon, f(t)\}$; we have

$$|G(x+\tau)-G(x)| \leqq \frac{1}{T}\int_0^T |f(t+x+\tau)-f(t+x)| \cdot |\bar{f}(t)|\, dt$$

$$\leqq A \underset{-\infty<t<+\infty}{u.b.} |f(t+\tau)-f(t)| \leqq A\epsilon,$$

i.e.
$$E\{A\epsilon, G(x)\} \supset E\{\epsilon, f(t)\},$$

which shows that $G(x)$ *is a u.a.p. function*. In the same way (or by 8°, § 1) we see that $g(x)$ is a *u.a.p.* function. The functions $G(x)$, $g(x)$ will play an important part in the proof of the fundamental theorem on *u.a.p.* functions.

Problem. Prove that

$$M_x[M_t\{f(t+x)\bar{f}(t)e^{-i\lambda x}\}] = M_t[M_x\{f(t+x)\bar{f}(t)e^{-i\lambda x}\}],$$

where $f(x)$ is *u.a.p.* and λ is real.

4°. We shall now consider approximation to *u.a.p.* functions by trigonometrical (exponential) polynomials. Observe first that for any real λ, $e^{i\lambda x}$ is a purely periodic (and *a fortiori u.a.p.*) function, and that

$$M\{e^{i\lambda x}\} = 0 \quad \text{for} \quad \lambda \gtrless 0,$$
$$= 1 \quad \text{for} \quad \lambda = 0.$$

Let now $f(x)$ be a *u.a.p.* function. For any real λ the function $f(x)e^{-i\lambda x}$, being the product of two *u.a.p.* functions, is a *u.a.p.* function and consequently the mean value

$$M\{f(x)e^{-i\lambda x}\} = a(\lambda)$$

exists.

Theorem. *Let $f(x)$ be a u.a.p. function, $\lambda_1, \lambda_2, \ldots, \lambda_N$ N arbitrary real numbers different from one another, and $b_1, b_2, \ldots, b_N$ N arbitrary complex (or real) numbers. Then*

$$(1) \quad M\left\{\left|f(x)-\sum_{n=1}^{N} b_n e^{i\lambda_n x}\right|^2\right\}$$

$$= M\{|f(x)|^2\} - \sum_{n=1}^{N} |a(\lambda_n)|^2 + \sum_{n=1}^{N} |b_n - a(\lambda_n)|^2.$$

We write

$$M\left\{\left|f(x)-\sum_{n=1}^{N} b_n e^{i\lambda_n x}\right|^2\right\}$$

$$=M\left[\left\{f(x)-\sum_{n=1}^{N} b_n e^{i\lambda_n x}\right\}.\left\{\bar{f}(x)-\sum_{n=1}^{N} \bar{b}_n e^{-i\lambda_n x}\right\}\right]$$

$$=M\{f(x)\bar{f}(x)\}-\sum_{n=1}^{N} \bar{b}_n M\{f(x)e^{-i\lambda_n x}\}$$

$$-\sum_{n=1}^{N} b_n M\{\bar{f}(x)e^{i\lambda_n x}\}+\sum_{n_1=1}^{N}\sum_{n_2=1}^{N} b_{n_1}\bar{b}_{n_2} M\{e^{i(\lambda_{n_1}-\lambda_{n_2})x}\}.$$

As $M\{e^{i(\lambda_{n_1}-\lambda_{n_2})x}\}$ differs from nought (and is equal to 1) only for $n_1=n_2$ the last sum reduces to the sum $\sum_{n=1}^{N}|b_n|^2$. Thus

$$M\left\{\left|f(x)-\sum_{n=1}^{N} b_n e^{i\lambda_n x}\right|^2\right\}$$

$$=M\{|f(x)|^2\}-\sum_{n=1}^{N}\bar{b}_n a(\lambda_n)-\sum_{n=1}^{N} b_n\bar{a}(\lambda_n)+\sum_{n=1}^{N} b_n\bar{b}_n$$

$$=M\{|f(x)|^2\}-\sum_{n=1}^{N} a(\lambda_n)\bar{a}(\lambda_n)+\sum_{n=1}^{N}\{b_n-a(\lambda_n)\}.\{\bar{b}_n-\bar{a}(\lambda_n)\}$$

$$=M\{|f(x)|^2\}-\sum_{n=1}^{N}|a(\lambda_n)|^2+\sum_{n=1}^{N}|b_n-a(\lambda_n)|^2.$$

The equation (1) is called *the equation of approximation in mean.*

5°. From the last theorem we see that the polynomial $\sum_{n=1}^{N} b_n e^{i\lambda_n x}$ with fixed exponents λ_n gives the best approximation in mean to $f(x)$ (i.e. the least value of the right-hand side of (1) 4°) if $b_n=a(\lambda_n)$ for all n, in which case we have

$$M\{|f(x)-\sum_{n=1}^{N} a(\lambda_n)e^{i\lambda_n x}|^2\}=M\{|f(x)|^2\}-\sum_{n=1}^{N}|a(\lambda_n)|^2.$$

The left-hand side of this equation being non-negative, we conclude that

$$(1) \qquad \sum_{n=1}^{N} |a(\lambda_n)|^2 \leqq M\{|f(x)|^2\}.$$

This inequality being true for an arbitrary number N of real numbers λ_n, we conclude that to any positive ϵ corresponds at most a finite number of values of λ for which $|a(\lambda)| > \epsilon$. All $a(\lambda)$ different from nought satisfy one of the enumerable set of inequalities

$$|a(\lambda)| > 1, \quad \frac{1}{n} \geqq |a(\lambda)| > \frac{1}{n+1}. \quad (n = 1, 2, \ldots)$$

Each of these inequalities being satisfied by at most a finite number of values of λ, we deduce the

THEOREM. *There exists at most an enumerably infinite set of values of λ for which $a(\lambda)$ differs from nought.*

6°. Denote these values of λ by Λ_1, Λ_2, ..., and write $a(\Lambda_n) = A_n$ for all n. We call the numbers Λ_1, Λ_2, ... *Fourier exponents* and the numbers A_1, A_2, ... *Fourier coefficients* of the function $f(x)$. The formal series

$$A_1 e^{i\Lambda_1 x} + A_2 e^{i\Lambda_2 x} + \ldots = \Sigma A_n e^{i\Lambda_n x}$$

is called the *Fourier series* of the function $f(x)$, and we write

$$f(x) \sim \Sigma A_n e^{i\Lambda_n x}.$$

By (1) we have

$$(2) \qquad \Sigma |A_n|^2 \leqq M\{|f(x)|^2\}.$$

This is the Bessel inequality for u.a.p. functions.

7°. Let $f(x)$ be a purely periodic function with period 2π. Its Fourier series in the ordinary sense is defined by $\sum_{-\infty}^{+\infty} A_n e^{inx}$, where

$$(1) \qquad A_n = \frac{1}{2\pi} \int_0^{2\pi} f(x) e^{-inx} \, dx,$$

and these coefficients satisfy the *Parseval equation*

$$(2) \qquad \Sigma |A_n|^2 = \frac{1}{2\pi} \int_0^{2\pi} |f(x)|^2 \, dx.$$

But for the case of a purely periodic function

$$\frac{1}{2\pi}\int_0^{2\pi} f(x)\, e^{-inx}\, dx = M\{f(x)\, e^{-inx}\},$$

$$\frac{1}{2\pi}\int_0^{2\pi} |f(x)|^2\, dx = M\{|f(x)|^2\}.$$

Thus the coefficients (1) (which are different from nought) are also Fourier coefficients of $f(x)$ in the new sense, and from (2) we see that there cannot be any other Fourier coefficient in the new sense. Thus *in the case of purely periodic functions the ordinary definition of the Fourier series coincides with the new one.*

8°. THEOREM. *The Fourier series of a u.a.p. function represented by the sum of a uniformly convergent trigonometric series* $f(x) = \sum_{n=1}^{\infty} a_n e^{i\lambda_n x}$ *coincides with this series.*

The series $\sum_{n=1}^{\infty} a_n e^{i(\lambda_n - \lambda)x}$ is uniformly convergent for any real λ. Therefore

$$M\{f(x)\, e^{-i\lambda x}\} = \sum_{n=1}^{\infty} a_n M\{e^{i(\lambda_n - \lambda)x}\}.$$

Hence $$M\{f(x)\, e^{-i\lambda x}\} = 0$$

for λ different from all λ_n, and

$$M\{f(x)\, e^{-i\lambda_n x}\} = a_n$$

for any n, which proves the theorem.

9°. In 6° we showed that for *u.a.p.* functions the Bessel inequality holds. In fact it will be shown in § 4 that the *Parseval equation*

$$\Sigma\, |A_n|^2 = M\{|f(x)|^2\}$$

is true for any *u.a.p.* function. This is *Bohr's Fundamental Theorem.* By means of this theorem it will be shown that two different *u.a.p.* functions cannot have the same Fourier series. Thus not only does a *u.a.p.* function define its Fourier series but also a Fourier series defines uniquely a *u.a.p.* function.

10°. We shall now prove a theorem, which will be required for the proof of the fundamental theorem.

THEOREM. *If the mean value of a real non-negative u.a.p. function $f(x)$ is nought, then $f(x) = 0$ for all x.*

Suppose that the theorem is not true and that at some point x_0 $f(x_0) = m > 0$. Then there exists a $\delta > 0$ such that

$$f(x) > \tfrac{2}{3} m$$

in the interval $(x_0 - \delta, x_0 + \delta)$.

Take now an $l_{\frac{1}{3}m} > 2\delta$. Any interval of length $l_{\frac{1}{3}m}$ contains at least one number of the form $x_0 + \tau$, where τ belongs to $E\{\frac{1}{3}m, f(x)\}$ and *a fortiori* at least one of the intervals

$$(x_0 + \tau - \delta,\ x_0 + \tau), \quad (x_0 + \tau,\ x_0 + \tau + \delta).$$

In each of these intervals, which are the intervals $(x_0 - \delta, x_0)$, $(x_0, x_0 + \delta)$ translated through τ, we have

$$f(x) > \frac{m}{3}.$$

Thus in each interval of length $l_{m/3}$ there exists a sub-interval of length δ, where $f(x) > m/3$. Consequently

$$\int_a^{a + l_{m/3}} f(x)\, dx > \frac{m\delta}{3}$$

for any a. We have now

$$0 = M\{f(x)\} = \lim \frac{1}{n l_{m/3}} \int_0^{n l_{m/3}} f(x)\, dx \geqq \frac{m\delta}{3 l_{m/3}},$$

and thus we have arrived at a contradiction, which proves the theorem.

11°. The Fourier series of a *u.a.p.* function $f(x)$ has been defined as the aggregate of all the " terms "

$$a(\lambda)\, e^{i\lambda x}, \qquad (a(\lambda) = M\{f(x)\, e^{-i\lambda x}\})$$

where $a(\lambda) \neq 0$. Sometimes it is convenient to add to this aggregate some terms for which $a(\lambda) = 0$. This enlarged aggregate is still called the Fourier series of the function. We never add more than an enumerable set of terms with coefficients equal to zero.

Let $\{f_k(x)\}$ be an enumerable set of *u.a.p.* functions. The set of the Fourier exponents of all the functions of the set is enumerable. Denote them by $\Lambda_n (n=1, 2, \ldots)$. Then the Fourier series of each function of the set may be represented in the form

$$f_k(x) \sim \Sigma A_n^{(k)} e^{i\Lambda_n x}.$$

THEOREM. *If a sequence*

$$(1) \qquad f_k(x) \sim \Sigma A_n^{(k)} e^{i\Lambda_n x} \qquad (k=1, 2, \ldots)$$

of u.a.p. functions converges uniformly to a function $f(x)$, *then the Fourier series of* $f(x)$ *is given by the equation*

$$(2) \qquad f(x) \sim \Sigma A_n e^{i\Lambda_n x},$$

where $A_n = \lim A_n^{(k)}$, *as* $k \to \infty$, *for all* n; *in other words the series* (2) *is "the formal limit" of the series* (1), *as* $k \to \infty$.

For, we have for any λ

$$|M\{f_k(x)e^{-i\lambda x}\} - M\{f(x)e^{-i\lambda x}\}| \leq \underset{-\infty<x<+\infty}{u.b.} |f_k(x) - f(x)| \to 0,$$

as $k \to \infty$.

§4. Fundamental theorem of the theory of *u.a.p.* functions.

1°. If for a *u.a.p.* function $f(x)$

$$a(\lambda) = M\{f(x)e^{-i\lambda x}\} = 0$$

for all real values of λ, we say that *the Fourier series of* $f(x)$ *is equal to nought.*

We shall first prove the fundamental theorem for such functions, and then it will be easy to extend it to the general case. In the case of a function $f(x)$ with Fourier series equal to nought the Parseval equation takes the form

$$M\{|f(x)|^2\} = 0.$$

We prove this result by considering an auxiliary purely periodic function $F(x)$ with period T equal to $f(x)$ for $0 \leq x < T$. We shall first prove that for large T all Fourier coefficients of $F(x)$ are small. We prove this proposition by proving a more general

Lemma. *If $f(x)$ is a u.a.p. function with Fourier series equal to nought, then*

$$\frac{1}{T}\int_0^T f(x)\, e^{-i\lambda x}\, dx \to 0,$$

as $T\to\infty$, uniformly in λ, i.e. given an $\epsilon>0$ there exists a $T_0>0$ such that for all $T>T_0$ and for all real λ

$$\left|\frac{1}{T}\int_0^T f(x)\, e^{-i\lambda x}\, dx\right| < \epsilon.$$

We shall first prove the following lemmas.

2°. **Lemma.** *If $f(x)$ is a u.a.p. function, then*

$$\phi(\lambda, T) = \frac{1}{T}\int_0^T f(x)\, e^{-i\lambda x}\, dx \to 0,$$

as $\lambda\to+\infty$, or $\lambda\to-\infty$, uniformly in $1 \leqq T < \infty$.

We write

$$\phi(\lambda, T) = -\frac{1}{T}\int_{\pi/\lambda}^{T+(\pi/\lambda)} f\left(x-\frac{\pi}{\lambda}\right) e^{-i\lambda x}\, dx$$

$$= -\frac{1}{T}\int_0^T - \frac{1}{T}\int_{\pi/\lambda}^0 - \frac{1}{T}\int_T^{T+(\pi/\lambda)},$$

and thus

$$\phi(\lambda, T) = \frac{1}{2T}\int_0^T \left\{f(x) - f\left(x-\frac{\pi}{\lambda}\right)\right\} e^{-i\lambda x}\, dx$$

$$-\frac{1}{2T}\int_{\pi/\lambda}^0 f\left(x-\frac{\pi}{\lambda}\right) e^{-i\lambda x}\, dx$$

$$-\frac{1}{2T}\int_T^{T+(\pi/\lambda)} f\left(x-\frac{\pi}{\lambda}\right) e^{-i\lambda x}\, dx = I_1 + I_2 + I_3.$$

Writing

$$A = \underset{-\infty<x<+\infty}{u.b.} |f(x)|, \quad \omega(\delta) = \underset{-\infty<x<+\infty}{u.b.} |f(x+\delta) - f(x)|,$$

we shall have

$$|I_1| \leqq \frac{1}{2}\,\omega\left(\frac{\pi}{|\lambda|}\right), \quad |I_2| \leqq \frac{A\pi}{2T\,|\lambda|}, \quad |I_3| \leqq \frac{A\pi}{2T\,|\lambda|}.$$

Hence
$$|\phi(\lambda, T)| \leqq \frac{1}{2}\omega\left(\frac{\pi}{|\lambda|}\right) + \frac{A\pi}{|\lambda| T}$$
$$\leqq \frac{1}{2}\omega\left(\frac{\pi}{|\lambda|}\right) + \frac{A\pi}{|\lambda|},$$
which proves the lemma.

3°. **Lemma.** *If $M\{f(x)\} = 0$, then given $\epsilon > 0$ there exist two positive numbers δ, T_0, such that*
$$\left|\frac{1}{T}\int_0^T f(x)\, e^{-i\lambda x}\, dx\right| < \epsilon$$
for all $T > T_0$ and for all λ in the interval $(-\delta, +\delta)$.

By (4) 2°, §3, there exists a number $T_0 > 0$ such that

(1) $$\left|\frac{1}{H}\int_0^H f(x+s)\, dx\right| < \frac{\epsilon}{2},$$

for all s and for all $H > \frac{1}{2}T_0$. Now any $T > T_0$ can be represented by $T = nH$, where n is an integer and H satisfies the condition $\frac{1}{2}T_0 < H < T_0$.

Now define δ by the condition that

(2) $$|e^{-i\lambda x} - 1| < \epsilon/2A$$

for $|\lambda| < \delta$ and for $0 \leqq x \leqq T_0$ (and *a fortiori* for $0 \leqq x \leqq H$).

We write

(3) $$\frac{1}{T}\int_0^T f(x)\, e^{-i\lambda x}\, dx = \frac{1}{nH}\sum_{k=0}^{n-1} e^{-i\lambda kH}\int_0^H f(x+kH)\, e^{-i\lambda x}\, dx.$$

By (1), (2)
$$\left|\frac{1}{H}\int_0^H f(x+kH)\, e^{-i\lambda x}\, dx\right|$$
$$\leqq \left|\frac{1}{H}\int_0^H f(x+kH)\, dx\right| + \left|\frac{1}{H}\int_0^H f(x+kH)(e^{-i\lambda x} - 1)\, dx\right|$$
$$< \frac{\epsilon}{2} + \frac{\epsilon}{2} = \epsilon.$$

Hence by (3)

$$\left|\frac{1}{T}\int_0^T f(x)\, e^{-i\lambda x}\, dx\right| < \epsilon$$

for $T > T_0$ and $|\lambda| < \delta$, which proves the lemma.

4°. **Lemma.** *If* $M\{f(x)e^{-i\mu x}\} = 0$, *then given* $\epsilon > 0$ *there exist numbers* $T_\mu > 0$ *and* $\delta_\mu > 0$, *such that*

$$\left|\frac{1}{T}\int_0^T f(x)\, e^{-i\lambda x}\, dx\right| < \epsilon$$

for $T > T_\mu$ *and for* $\mu - \delta_\mu < \lambda < \mu + \delta_\mu$.

This lemma reduces to the preceding one applied to the function $f(x)\, e^{-i\mu x}$, which is also *u.a.p.*

5°. We can now prove the lemma of 1°. We have to prove that given $\epsilon > 0$ there exists $T_0 > 0$, such that

$$\left|\frac{1}{T}\int_0^T f(x)\, e^{-i\lambda x}\, dx\right| < \epsilon \tag{1}$$

for all λ and for all $T > T_0$.

By the lemma of 2° there exists a $\lambda_0 > 0$ such that (1) is satisfied for $T > 1$ and for $|\lambda| > \lambda_0$.

By the lemma of 4° to any μ of the interval $-\lambda_0 \leqq \mu \leqq +\lambda_0$ corresponds a $T_\mu > 0$ and an interval $(\mu - \delta_\mu, \mu + \delta_\mu)$, such that (1) is satisfied for any $T > T_\mu$ and for any λ of this interval. By the Heine-Borel theorem there exists a finite number of points $\mu_1, \mu_2, \ldots, \mu_n$, such that the intervals corresponding to these points cover the whole interval $-\lambda_0 \leqq \mu \leqq +\lambda_0$. For λ in each of the intervals $(\mu_k - \delta_{\mu_k}, \mu_k + \delta_{\mu_k})$, (1) is true for $T > T_{\mu_k}$. Thus, taking $T_0 > \max.(1, T_{\mu_1}, T_{\mu_2}, \ldots, T_{\mu_n})$, we see that for $T > T_0$ the inequality (1) will be satisfied for $|\lambda| > \lambda_0$ and for λ belonging to any of the intervals $(\mu_k - \delta_{\mu_k}, \mu_k + \delta_{\mu_k})$, i.e. for all values of λ.

6°. We now pass to the proof of the Parseval equation

$$M\{|f(x)|^2\} = 0 \tag{1}$$

for a function $f(x)$ with Fourier series nought. We consider the purely periodic function $F(x)$ introduced in 1°. We write

$$F(x) \sim \sum_{k=-\infty}^{+\infty} A_k e^{i\frac{2\pi k x}{T}}.$$

For $F(x)$ the Parseval equation holds:

$$(2) \qquad \frac{1}{T}\int_0^T |F(x)|^2 dx = \sum_{-\infty}^{+\infty} |A_k|^2 \leqq A^2.$$

But

$$\frac{1}{T}\int_0^T |F(x)|^2 dx = \frac{1}{T}\int_0^T |f(x)|^2 dx \to M\{|f(x)|^2\},$$

as $T \to \infty$. The equation (1) would be proved if we could prove that

$$\Sigma |A_k|^2 \to 0,$$

as $T \to \infty$. We cannot prove this, but we can easily see that

$$(3) \qquad \Sigma |A_k|^4 \to 0,$$

as $T \to \infty$. For, by the preceding lemma to any $\epsilon > 0$ corresponds a $T_0 > 0$, such that for any $T > T_0$, all $|A_k|$ are less than ϵ. By (2)

$$\Sigma |A_k|^4 < \epsilon^2 \Sigma |A_k|^2 \leqq \epsilon^2 A^2,$$

which proves (3). We shall prove (1) by expressing the sum $\Sigma |A_k|^4$ in terms of $f(x)$.

We introduce two new purely periodic functions

$$(4) \qquad G(x) = \frac{1}{T}\int_0^T F(x+t)\bar{F}(t)\,dt,$$

and

$$(5) \qquad H(x) = \frac{1}{T}\int_0^T G(x+t)\bar{G}(t)\,dt,$$

and we define the Fourier series.

Inverting the order of integration in the formula for the Fourier coefficients of $G(x)$, we shall have

$$\frac{1}{T}\int_0^T G(x)\,e^{-i\frac{2\pi kx}{T}}\,dx$$

$$= \frac{1}{T}\int_0^T \bar{F}(t)\,e^{i\frac{2\pi kt}{T}}\,dt\,\frac{1}{T}\int_0^T F(x+t)\,e^{-i\frac{2\pi k(x+t)}{T}}\,dx.$$

On account of the periodicity of $F(x)$, we have

$$\frac{1}{T}\int_0^T F(x+t)\,e^{-i\frac{2\pi k(x+t)}{T}}\,dx = \frac{1}{T}\int_0^T F(x)\,e^{-i\frac{2\pi kx}{T}}\,dx = A_k.$$

Further it is obvious that

$$\frac{1}{T}\int_0^T \overline{F}(t)\, e^{i\frac{2\pi kt}{T}}\, dt = \overline{A}_k,$$

and thus
$$\frac{1}{T}\int_0^T G(x)\, e^{-i\frac{2\pi kx}{T}}\, dx = \overline{A}_k A_k = |A_k|^2.$$

Thus the Fourier series of $G(x)$ is

$$G(x) \sim \Sigma\, |A_k|^2 e^{i\frac{2\pi kx}{T}}.$$

As the function $H(x)$ was formed from $G(x)$ in the same way as $G(x)$ from $F(x)$, we see that the Fourier series of $H(x)$ is given by the equation

$$H(x) \sim \Sigma\, |A_k|^4 e^{i\frac{2\pi kx}{T}}.$$

But it is a well-known theorem that if the Fourier series of a continuous function is uniformly convergent, then its sum is equal to the function. Thus

$$H(x) = \Sigma\, |A_k|^4 e^{i\frac{2\pi kx}{T}},$$

and
$$H(0) = \Sigma\, |A_k|^4.$$

By (3)
$$\lim H(0) = 0,$$

as $T \to \infty$, and by (5)

(6)
$$\lim \frac{1}{T}\int_0^T |G(x)|^2\, dx = 0,$$

as $T \to \infty$.

Take a sequence

$$0 < T_1 < T_2 < \dots, \quad T_n \to \infty,$$

such that, for any n, T_n is a translation number of $f(x)$ belonging to $\frac{1}{n}$. By (6)

(7)
$$\lim \frac{1}{T_n}\int_0^{T_n} |G(x)|^2 dx = 0.$$

Observe that the integrand in this formula varies with n, as the definition of $G(x)$ depends upon T.

Putting in (4) $T = T_n$, we shall have for $0 \leqq x \leqq T_n$

(8) $$G(x) = \frac{1}{T_n}\left\{\int_0^{T_n - x} f(x+t)\bar{f}(t)\,dt + \int_{T_n - x}^{T_n} f(x+t-T_n)\bar{f}(t)\,dt\right\} = \frac{1}{T_n}\int_0^{T_n} f(x+t)\bar{f}(t)\,dt + \frac{\theta A}{n}.$$

Take now the *u.a.p.* function

$$g(x) = M_t\{f(x+t)\bar{f}(t)\}.$$

By 3°, § 3,

(9) $$\underset{-\infty < x < +\infty}{u.b.} \left| \frac{1}{T_n}\int_0^{T_n} f(x+t)\bar{f}(t)\,dt - g(x)\right| = \epsilon_n \to 0,$$

as $n \to \infty$. By (8), (9)

(10) $$G(x) = g(x) + \theta\left(\epsilon_n + \frac{A}{n}\right).$$

Observing that $|g(x)| \leqq A^2$, $|G(x)| \leqq A^2$ for all x, we have

$$\left|\frac{1}{T_n}\int_0^{T_n} |G(x)|^2\,dx - \frac{1}{T_n}\int_0^{T_n} |g(x)|^2\,dx\right| < 2A^2\left(\epsilon_n + \frac{A}{n}\right).$$

Hence, by (7), $$\lim \frac{1}{T_n}\int_0^{T_n} |g(x)|^2\,dx = 0,$$

i.e. $$M\{|g(x)|^2\} = 0.$$

By the theorem of 10°, § 3, we conclude that $|g(x)|^2 = 0$ for all x, and thus

$$g(0) = M\{|f(x)|^2\} = 0,$$

which is the Parseval equation. The application of the same theorem to the function $|f(x)|^2$ leads us to the conclusion that $f(x) = 0$ for all values of x. Thus there exists only one function $f(x)$ whose Fourier series is nought, and it is identically equal to nought.

7°. Uniqueness Theorem. *If two u.a.p. functions have the same Fourier series, then they are identical.*

The theorem follows from the fact that the difference of such two functions is a *u.a.p.* function with Fourier series nought.

8°. *Parseval equation for the general case.*

Let
$$f(x) \sim \sum_{n=1}^{\infty} A_n e^{i\Lambda_n x}$$
be any *u.a.p.* function with its Fourier series. We take again the function

(1)
$$g(x) = M_t\{f(x+t)\bar{f}(t)\}.$$
By an argument similar to one employed in 6° for $G(x)$ we see, on account of Problem of 3°, § 3, that the Fourier series of $g(x)$ is
$$g(x) \sim \sum_{n=1}^{\infty} |A_n|^2 e^{i\Lambda_n x}.$$
By the Bessel inequality (6°, § 3)
$$\sum_{n=1}^{\infty} |A_n|^2 \leq M\{|f(x)|^2\},$$
i.e. the series $\sum_{n=1}^{\infty} |A_n|^2$ is convergent. Then the series
$$\phi(x) = \sum_{n=1}^{\infty} |A_n|^2 e^{i\Lambda_n x}$$
is uniformly convergent. Thus by the corollary of 12°, § 1, $\phi(x)$ is a *u.a.p.* function and by the theorem of 8°, § 3, the Fourier series of $\phi(x)$ coincides with the series by which it is represented. Consequently the functions $g(x)$ and $\phi(x)$ have the same Fourier series. By the uniqueness theorem (7°)
$$g(x) = \phi(x),$$
i.e.
$$g(x) = \sum_{n=1}^{\infty} |A_n|^2 e^{i\Lambda_n x}.$$
Putting $x = 0$, we have
$$g(0) = \sum_{n=1}^{\infty} |A_n|^2.$$
By (1)
$$g(0) = M\{|f(t)|^2\},$$
and thus
$$M\{|f(t)|^2\} = \sum_{n=1}^{\infty} |A_n|^2,$$
which is the Parseval equation for the function $f(x)$.

§ 5. Polynomial approximation to *u.a.p.* functions.

1°. It has been proved that the limit of a uniformly convergent sequence of *u.a.p.* functions is a *u.a.p.* function (8°, § 1). Finite trigonometrical polynomials being *u.a.p.* functions we conclude that the limit of a uniformly convergent sequence of trigonometric polynomials is a *u.a.p.* function. The converse is also true: any *u.a.p.* function is the limit of a uniformly convergent sequence of trigonometrical polynomials. This is the main result of H. Bohr's second paper. For the proof of this theorem H. Bohr had to develop the theory of purely periodic functions of infinitely many variables.

S. Bochner arrived at the same result by extending in an elegant way the Fejér summation to the class of *u.a.p.* functions.

H. Weyl afterwards gave a new proof of this theorem as a direct corollary of the Parseval equation. We shall now give Weyl's proof, but later on we shall consider also Bochner's method. Weyl's method gives the error of the polynomial approximation. Bochner does not give the error, but the advantage of his method lies in the fact that it gives a definite algorithm for the polynomial approximation.

2°. Approximation Theorem. *Given a u.a.p. function*

$$f(x) \sim \sum_{n=1}^{\infty} A_n e^{i\Lambda_n x},$$

and a positive number ϵ, *there exists a trigonometric polynomial* $P(x)$, *whose exponents are Fourier exponents of* $f(x)$, *and which satisfies the inequality*

$$|f(x) - P(x)| < \epsilon$$

for all values of x.

We write $$f(x) - \sum_{n=1}^{p} A_n e^{i\Lambda_n x} = f_p(x).$$

By the Parseval equation

$$M\{|f_p(x)|^2\} = \sum_{n=p+1}^{\infty} |A_n|^2.$$

Given any $\eta > 0$, we can evidently find a p such that

$$M\{|f_p(x)|^2\} < \eta, \tag{1}$$

since the series $\sum_{n=1}^{\infty} |A_n|^2$ is convergent.

On the other hand, by (4) 2°, § 3, there exists $T_0 > 0$, such that

$$\left| \frac{1}{T}\int_0^T |f_p(x+s)|^2 dx - M\{|f_p(x)|^2\} \right| < \eta \tag{2}$$

for all $T > T_0$, and for all real s. Thus, by (1), (2),

$$\frac{1}{T}\int_0^T |f_p(x+s)|^2 dx < 2\eta. \tag{3}$$

Let now $l_{\epsilon/3}$ be an inclusion interval of $E\{\epsilon/3, f(x)\}$. Take a $T = N(l_{\epsilon/3}+1) > T_0$, where N is an integer, and in each of the intervals $\{k(l_{\epsilon/3}+1),\ k(l_{\epsilon/3}+1)+l_{\epsilon/3}\}$ $(k = 0, 1, \ldots, N-1)$ take a τ_k belonging to $E\{\epsilon/3, f(x)\}$. Taking then a δ $(0 < \delta < 1)$ such that

$$|f(x') - f(x'')| < \epsilon/3,$$

if only $|x' - x''| < \delta$, we define the function $e(x)$ in the interval $(0, T)$ by the equations

$e(x) = 1$ in all intervals $(\tau_k,\ \tau_k + \delta)$, $(k = 0, 1, \ldots, N-1)$

$e(x) = 0$ at all other points.

(The intervals $(\tau_k,\ \tau_k+\delta)$ do not overlap.)

By the Schwarz inequality

$$\left| \int_0^T f_p(x+s)\, e(x)\, dx \right|^2 \leqq \int_0^T |f_p(x+s)|^2 dx \int_0^T \{e(x)\}^2 dx. \tag{3.1}$$

Observing that

$$\int_0^T f_p(x+s)\, e(x)\, dx = \sum_{k=0}^{N-1} \int_{\tau_k}^{\tau_k+\delta} f_p(x+s)\, dx$$

$$= \sum_{k=0}^{N-1} \int_0^{\delta} f_p(x+\tau_k+s)\, dx,$$

and that

$$\int_0^T \{e(x)\}^2 dx = N\delta,$$

and taking into account (3), we conclude from (3.1)

$$\left| \sum_{k=0}^{N-1} \int_0^{\delta} f_p(x+\tau_k+s)\, dx \right| < \sqrt{2\eta T N\delta},$$

or $$\left| \frac{1}{N\delta} \sum_{k=0}^{N-1} \int_0^\delta f_p(x+\tau_k+s)\,dx \right| < \sqrt{\frac{2\eta\,(l_{\epsilon/3}+1)}{\delta}}.$$

Taking $\eta < \dfrac{\epsilon^2\delta}{18\,(l_{\epsilon/3}+1)}$, we obtain

(4) $$\left| \frac{1}{N\delta} \sum_{k=0}^{N-1} \int_0^\delta f_p(x+\tau_k+s)\,dx \right| < \frac{\epsilon}{3}.$$

Now

$$\frac{1}{N\delta}\int_0^\delta f_p(x+\tau_k+s)\,dx = \frac{1}{N\delta}\int_0^\delta f(x+\tau_k+s)\,dx - P_k(s),$$

where $$P_k(s) = \frac{1}{N\delta}\int_0^\delta \sum_{n=1}^{p} A_n e^{i\Lambda_n(x+\tau_k+s)}\,dx$$
$$= \frac{1}{N\delta} \sum_{n=1}^{p} e^{i\Lambda_n s} \int_0^\delta A_n e^{i\Lambda_n(x+\tau_k)}\,dx.$$

Thus $P_k(s)$ is a trigonometric polynomial with the exponents belonging to Fourier exponents of $f(x)$.

We now can write (4) in the form

(5) $$\left| \left\{ \frac{1}{N\delta} \sum_{k=0}^{N-1} \int_0^\delta f(x+\tau_k+s)\,dx \right\} - P(s) \right| < \frac{\epsilon}{3},$$

where $P(s) = \sum_{k=0}^{N-1} P_k(s)$.

Now the value of δ has been chosen in such a way that

$$|f(x+\tau_k+s) - f(\tau_k+s)| < \frac{\epsilon}{3}$$

for $0 \leqq x \leqq \delta$. Consequently

$$\left| \frac{1}{\delta}\int_0^\delta f(x+\tau_k+s)\,dx - f(\tau_k+s) \right| < \frac{\epsilon}{3};$$

combining this with

$$|f(\tau_k+s) - f(s)| \leqq \frac{\epsilon}{3},$$

we obtain $$\left| \frac{1}{\delta}\int_0^\delta f(x+\tau_k+s)\,dx - f(s) \right| < \frac{2\epsilon}{3}.$$

We can now replace (5) by

$$|f(s) - P(s)| < \epsilon,$$

which proves the theorem.

§ 6. Limit periodic functions.

1°. The approximation theorem of the last section enables us to investigate a class of *u.a.p.* functions—the class of limit periodic functions—which is the nearest class, from the point of view of structure, to the class of purely periodic functions.

DEFINITION. *A function $f(x)$ is called limit periodic if it is the limit of a uniformly convergent sequence $\{f_k(x)\}$, $(k=1, 2, \ldots)$ of continuous purely periodic functions.*

Thus limit periodic functions are *u.a.p.*

2°. THEOREM. *A u.a.p. function*

$$f(x) \sim \Sigma A_n e^{i\Lambda_n x},$$

for which the ratio of any pair of Fourier exponents is rational, is limit periodic.

We can obviously write in this case $\Lambda_n = r_n q$ $(n=1, 2, \ldots)$, where all r_n are rational. By the approximation theorem there exists a sequence of finite sums

$$s_k(x) = \Sigma b_n^{(k)} e^{ir_n qx}$$

uniformly convergent to $f(x)$, which proves the theorem, since the sums $s_k(x)$ are obviously purely periodic functions.

3°. CONVERSE THEOREM. *The Fourier series of any limit periodic function $f(x)$ can be represented in the form*

$$f(x) \sim \Sigma A_n e^{ir_n qx},$$

where all r_n are rational.

Let $f_k(x)$, $(k=1, 2, \ldots)$ be a sequence of continuous purely periodic functions, uniformly convergent to the function $f(x)$, and let

$$(1) \qquad f_k(x) \sim \sum_{\nu=-\infty}^{+\infty} a_\nu^{(k)} e^{i(2\pi/q_k)\nu x},$$

where q_k is the period of $f_k(x)$. The Fourier exponents of all the functions (1) can be written as a simple sequence $\{\Lambda_n\}$, $(n=1, 2, \ldots)$ and then all the series (1) can be written in the form

$$(2) \qquad f_k(x) \sim \Sigma A_n^{(k)} e^{i\Lambda_n x},$$

where $A_n^{(k)}$ can differ from nought only if Λ_n is a multiple of $\frac{2\pi}{q_k}$. We now write the Fourier series of $f(x)$

$$(3)\qquad f(x) \sim \Sigma A_n e^{i\Lambda_n x}.$$

By the theorem of 11°, § 3,

$$(4)\qquad A_n = \lim A_n^{(k)}, \qquad (n = 1, 2, \ldots)$$

as $k \to \infty$.

As the theorem is obvious when $f(x)$ is equal to a constant, we may assume $f(x)$ to be different from a constant. Then there exists n_0 such that $A_{n_0} \neq 0$, $\Lambda_{n_0} \neq 0$. Corresponding to this n_0 there exists k_0 such that

$$|f_k(x) - f(x)| < |A_{n_0}|$$

for all $k > k_0$. We have

$$|A_{n_0}^{(k)} - A_{n_0}| = |M[\{f_k(x) - f(x)\} e^{-i\Lambda_{n_0} x}]|$$
$$\leq M\{|f_k(x) - f(x)|\} < |A_{n_0}|$$

for $k > k_0$. Thus $A_{n_0}^{(k)} \neq 0$ for all $k > k_0$, and consequently Λ_{n_0} is a multiple of $\frac{2\pi}{q_k}$ for all $k > k_0$. We clearly have

$$(5)\qquad \frac{2\pi}{q_k} \nu = r_\nu^{(k)} \Lambda_{n_0}, \qquad (-\infty < \nu < +\infty,\ k > k_0)$$

where $r_\nu^{(k)}$ is rational. By the same argument we see that any Λ_n, to which corresponds $A_n \neq 0$, is a multiple of $\frac{2\pi}{q_k}$ for sufficiently large k, and consequently by (5) is a rational multiple of Λ_{n_0}. Thus we can write

$$\Lambda_n = r_n \Lambda_{n_0}, \qquad (r_n = \text{rational})$$

for all n for which $A_n \neq 0$. Writing $q = \Lambda_{n_0}$ we have the theorem.

Corollary. *If a sequence $\{f_k(x)\}$ of continuous purely periodic functions is uniformly convergent to a function which is not a constant, then there exists an integer k_0 such that the periods of all the functions $f_k(x)$ for $k > k_0$ are rational multiples of the same number.*

4°. By theorems of 2° and 3° we have proved the following:

THEOREM. *The class of all limit periodic functions is identical with the class of all u.a.p. functions all whose Fourier exponents are rational multiples of the same number.*

§ 7. Base of *u.a.p.* functions. Connection of *u.a.p.* functions with limit periodic functions of several variables.

1°. We shall now study the arithmetic nature of Fourier exponents of *u.a.p.* functions; this will lead us to important new results concerning *u.a.p.* functions.

DEFINITION 1. *A set α_i $(i=1, 2, \ldots)$ of real numbers is called linearly independent if for any n the only rational values of $r_1, r_2, \ldots, r_n$ satisfying the equation*

(1) $$r_1\alpha_1 + r_2\alpha_2 + \ldots + r_n\alpha_n = 0,$$

are $r_1 = r_2 = \ldots = r_n = 0$.

Let

(2) $$f(x) \sim \Sigma A_n e^{i\Lambda_n x}$$

be a *u.a.p.* function with its Fourier series.

DEFINITION 2. *A finite or enumerably infinite set α_i $(i=1, 2, \ldots)$ of linearly independent numbers is called a base of the function $f(x)$ (or of the Fourier exponents of $f(x)$) if every Λ_m can be represented as a finite linear form of α's with rational coefficients, i.e. if for any m we can write*

(3) $$\Lambda_m = r_1^{(m)}\alpha_1 + r_2^{(m)}\alpha_2 + \ldots + r_{n_m}^{(m)}\alpha_{n_m},$$

where all r's are rational.

Evidently every *u.a.p.* function has a base, and there may be many different bases of the same function, but for a fixed base a representation in the form (3) is always unique.

If a base consists of infinitely many terms it is called *an infinite base,* otherwise *a finite base.* If all r's in (3) are integral for all m the base is called *an integral base.*

The result of the preceding section can now be expressed in the form:

The class of all limit periodic functions is identical with the class of u.a.p. functions with one-term base.

Evidently a *u.a.p.* function with one-term integral base is purely periodic.

2°. DEFINITION 1. *If a sequence of continuous purely periodic functions* $F_k(x_1, x_2, \ldots, x_m)$ *converges uniformly to a function* $F(x_1, x_2, \ldots, x_m)$, *then this function is called a limit periodic function of m variables.*

If all the functions $F_k(x_1, x_2, \ldots, x_m)$ have common periods with respect to each variable, then clearly the function

$$F(x_1, x_2, \ldots, x_m)$$

is purely periodic.

Suppose we have a sequence of continuous purely periodic functions $F_k(x_1, x_2, \ldots, x_{m_k})$ such that $\overline{\lim}\, m_k = \infty$. Then we write for any k

$$\Phi_k(x_1, x_2, \ldots) = F_k(x_1, x_2, \ldots, x_{m_k}),$$

so that $\Phi_k(x_1, x_2, \ldots)$ is constant with respect to each of the variables $x_{m_k+1}, x_{m_k+2}, \ldots$. If the sequence $\Phi_k(x_1, x_2, \ldots)$ converges to a function $F(x_1, x_2, \ldots)$, then we say that the sequence $F_k(x_1, x_2, \ldots, x_{m_k})$ converges to the function $F(x_1, x_2, \ldots)$ of infinitely many variables.

DEFINITION 2. *If a sequence* $F_k(x_1, x_2, \ldots, x_{m_k})$ $(\overline{\lim}\, m_k = \infty)$ *of continuous purely periodic functions converges uniformly to a function* $F(x_1, x_2, \ldots)$, *then we call the function* $F(x_1, x_2, \ldots)$ *a limit periodic function of infinitely many variables.*

If all the functions $F_k(x_1, x_2, \ldots, x_{m_k})$ have common periods with respect to each of the variables $x_1, x_2, \ldots$, then clearly the function $F(x_1, x_2, \ldots)$ is purely periodic.

3°. We shall now quote a theorem on Diophantine approximations.

KRONECKER'S THEOREM. *If* $x_1^0, x_2^0, \ldots, x_m^0$ *are any real numbers and* $q_1^{-1}, q_2^{-1}, \ldots, q_m^{-1}$ *any real linearly independent numbers, then to any number* $\delta > 0$ *correspond a number* ξ *and m integers* $k_1, k_2, \ldots, k_m$ *such that the inequalities*

$$|\xi - x_i^0 - k_i q_i| < \delta, \qquad (i = 1, 2, \ldots, m)$$

are satisfied.

4°. Let $F(x_1, x_2, \ldots, x_m)$ be a continuous purely periodic function with periods $q_1, q_2, \ldots, q_m$ with respect to the variables $x_1, x_2, \ldots, x_m$. We assume $q_1^{-1}, q_2^{-1}, \ldots, q_m^{-1}$ to be linearly independent, and we introduce "a diagonal function" $f(x)$ of $F(x_1, x_2, \ldots, x_m)$ by the equation

$$f(x) = F(x, x, \ldots, x).$$

THEOREM. *The aggregate of all the values of the diagonal function $f(x)$ is everywhere dense in the aggregate of all the values of $F(x_1, x_2, \ldots, x_m)$.*

To prove the theorem we have to prove that, given an arbitrary point $(x_1^0, x_2^0, \ldots, x_m^0)$ and an arbitrary positive number ϵ, there exists a real number ξ such that

$$(1) \qquad |F(x_1^0, x_2^0, \ldots, x_m^0) - f(\xi)| < \epsilon.$$

The function $F(x_1, x_2, \ldots, x_m)$, being continuous and purely periodic, is also uniformly continuous. Consequently there exists a number $\delta > 0$ such that

$$(2) \qquad |F(x_1', x_2', \ldots, x_m') - F(x_1'', x_2'', \ldots, x_m'')| < \epsilon,$$

if only $|x_i' - x_i''| < \delta$ for all $i = 1, 2, \ldots, m$. By the preceding theorem we can define a number ξ and integers $k_1, k_2, \ldots, k_m$ to satisfy the inequalities

$$|\xi - x_i^0 - k_i q_i| < \delta.$$

By (2)

$$|F(x_1^0 + k_1 q_1, x_2^0 + k_2 q_2, \ldots, x_m^0 + k_m q_m) - F(\xi, \xi, \ldots, \xi)| < \epsilon,$$

which proves (1).

Corollary.

$$\underset{\substack{-\infty < x_1 < +\infty \\ \cdots\cdots\cdots \\ -\infty < x_m < +\infty}}{u.b.} |F(x_1, x_2, \ldots, x_m)| = \underset{-\infty < x < +\infty}{u.b.} |f(x)|.$$

5°. THEOREM. *Any u.a.p. function is the diagonal function of a limit periodic function of a finite or an infinite number of variables.*

Let
$$f(x) \sim \Sigma A_m e^{i\Lambda_m x}$$
$$\sim \Sigma A_m e^{i\left(r_1^{(m)}\alpha_1 + r_2^{(m)}\alpha_2 + \ldots + r_{n_m}^{(m)}\alpha_{n_m}\right)x}$$
be a *u.a.p.* function with a base
$$\alpha_1, \alpha_2, \ldots.$$
By the approximation theorem there exists a sequence
$$s_k(x) = \Sigma b_m^{(k)} e^{i\Lambda_m x}$$
$$= \Sigma b_m^{(k)} e^{i\left(r_1^{(m)}\alpha_1 + r_2^{(m)}\alpha_2 + \ldots + r_{n_m}^{(m)}\alpha_{n_m}\right)x}, \qquad (k = 1, 2, \ldots)$$
of finite trigonometric polynomials uniformly convergent to the function $f(x)$. Every $s_k(x)$ is the diagonal function of the purely periodic function
$$F_k(x_1, x_2, \ldots, x_{\nu_k}) = \Sigma b_m^{(k)} e^{i\left(r_1^{(m)}\alpha_1 x_1 + r_2^{(m)}\alpha_2 x_2 + \ldots + r_{n_m}^{(m)}\alpha_{n_m} x_{n_m}\right)},$$
whose periods $q_1, q_2, \ldots, q_{\nu_k}$ are integral multiples of the numbers
$$\frac{2\pi}{\alpha_1}, \frac{2\pi}{\alpha_2}, \ldots, \frac{2\pi}{\alpha_{\nu_k}}.$$

The reciprocals of these periods are evidently linearly independent. By the same argument the reciprocals of the periods of any difference
$$F_{k'}(x_1, x_2, \ldots, x_{\nu_{k'}}) - F_{k''}(x_1, x_2, \ldots, x_{\nu_{k''}})$$
are linearly independent. By the corollary of 4°
$$u.b. \left| F_{k'}(x_1, x_2, \ldots, x_{\nu_{k'}}) - F_{k''}(x_1, x_2, \ldots, x_{\nu_{k''}}) \right|$$
$$= u.b. \left| s_{k'}(x) - s_{k''}(x) \right|.$$
The sequence $\{s_k(x)\}$, being uniformly convergent, we see that the sequence $\{F_k(x_1, x_2, \ldots, x_{\nu_k})\}$ is also uniformly convergent. Let $F(x_1, x_2, \ldots)$ be its limit. It is a limit periodic function. Writing
$$f(x) = \lim s_k(x) = \lim F_k(x, x, \ldots, x),$$
we conclude that
$$f(x) = F(x, x, \ldots),$$
which proves the theorem.

Evidently if the function $f(x)$ has an integral base $\alpha_1, \alpha_2, \ldots$, then the function $F(x_1, x_2, \ldots)$ will be purely periodic, and if the base is finite, then $F(x_1, x_2, \ldots)$ is a limit periodic function of a finite number of variables.

§ 8. Summation of Fourier series of *u.a.p.* functions by partial sums.

1°. The tests of convergence of Fourier series of purely periodic functions, based on the behaviour of a function in the neighbourhood of a point or in an interval, have not been extended to the case of general *u.a.p.* functions.

These tests are intimately bound up with the nature of the Fourier series of purely periodic functions, and may be generalised only to some particular cases of *u.a.p.* functions whose Fourier series have analogous properties. This has been done by S. Bochner. Two cases can be indicated:

(*a*) the case in which the difference between any pair of Fourier exponents is larger than a fixed positive number (which obviously includes the case of purely periodic functions), and

(*b*) the case of limit periodic functions.

Generalisations to a more or less general class of *u.a.p.* functions seem to be very unlikely. Even the simplest case—the case of *u.a.p.* functions with an integral two-term base—shows completely the difficulty of the question. By the preceding section such a function $f(x)$ is the diagonal function of a purely periodic function of two variables $F(x_1, x_2)$, i.e. $f(x) = F(x, x)$. Convergence of the Fourier series of $f(x)$ follows of course from the convergence of the Fourier series of $F(x_1, x_2)$. But though the function $f(x)$ defines completely the function $F(x_1, x_2)$, the behaviour of the latter at a point or in a domain is not similar to that of $f(x)$. In fact even the existence of a bounded continuous derivative of $f(x)$ does not secure any kind of regularity of $F(x_1, x_2)$ which is known to be sufficient for the convergence of its Fourier series.

We shall now pass to the consideration of the two particular cases mentioned above. Observe that, as the Fourier series of a *u.a.p.* function has no established order of its terms, we have to specify in each case what partial sums are being considered.

2°. Writing as in 4°, § 3,

$$a(\lambda) = M\{f(x)e^{-i\lambda x}\},$$

and denoting

$$a(\lambda)\, e^{i\lambda x} + a(-\lambda)\, e^{-i\lambda x} = I(\lambda),$$

we can obviously represent the Fourier series of $f(x)$ in the form

$$f(x) \sim a(0) + \Sigma I(\lambda_\nu),$$

where all λ_ν are positive.

Lemma. *If $f(x) \sim a(0) + \Sigma I(\lambda_\nu)$ is a u.a.p. function, then*

$$S(x, \lambda) = \frac{1}{\pi} \int_{-\infty}^{+\infty} f(x+2t) \frac{\sin^2 \lambda t}{\lambda t^2}\, dt$$

is also a u.a.p. function of x with the expansion

$$(1) \qquad S(x, \lambda) \sim a(0) + \sum_{\lambda_\nu < \lambda} \left(1 - \frac{\lambda_\nu}{\lambda}\right) I(\lambda_\nu).$$

Observe first that for $\lambda > 0$

$$(2) \qquad \frac{1}{\pi} \int_{-\infty}^{+\infty} e^{2i\mu t} \frac{\sin^2 \lambda t}{\lambda t^2}\, dt = 1 - \frac{|\mu|}{\lambda} \quad \text{for } 0 \leqq |\mu| \leqq \lambda,$$

$$= 0 \qquad \text{for } \lambda \leqq |\mu|.$$

Given $\epsilon > 0$, let τ be a translation number of $f(x)$ belonging to ϵ. We have

$$(3) \qquad |S(x+\tau, \lambda) - S(x, \lambda)|$$

$$\leqq \frac{1}{\pi} \int_{-\infty}^{+\infty} |f(x+2t+\tau) - f(x+2t)| \frac{\sin^2 \lambda t}{\lambda t^2}\, dt$$

$$\leqq \epsilon\, \frac{1}{\pi} \int_{-\infty}^{+\infty} \frac{\sin^2 \lambda t}{\lambda t^2}\, dt = \epsilon.$$

Hence for any $\epsilon > 0$ the set $E\{\epsilon, f(x)\}$ is contained in $E\{\epsilon, S(x, \lambda)\}$, which proves that $S(x, \lambda)$ is *u.a.p.*

We now see that (1) follows immediately from (2) in the case when $f(x)$ is a trigonometric polynomial. In the general case let

$$p_k(x) \sim a_k(0) + \Sigma I_k(\lambda_\nu) \qquad (k = 1, 2, \ldots)$$

be a sequence of trigonometric polynomials uniformly convergent to $f(x)$. Hence by the theorem of 11°, § 3,

$$(3.1) \qquad a(0) = \lim a_k(0), \quad I(\lambda_\nu) = \lim I_k(\lambda_\nu),$$

as $k \to \infty$. We write

$$S_k(x, \lambda) = \frac{1}{\pi} \int_{-\infty}^{+\infty} p_k(x+2t) \frac{\sin^2 \lambda t}{\lambda t^2}\, dt,$$

so that

$$(4) \qquad S_k(x, \lambda) \sim a_k(0) + \sum_{\lambda_\nu < \lambda} \left(1 - \frac{\lambda_\nu}{\lambda}\right) I_k(\lambda_\nu).$$

We have

$$| S_k(x, \lambda) - S(x, \lambda) |$$
$$\leqq \frac{1}{\pi} \int_{-\infty}^{+\infty} | f(x + 2t) - p_k(x + 2t) | \frac{\sin^2 \lambda t}{\lambda t^2} dt$$
$$\leqq u.b. | f(x) - p_k(x) | \frac{1}{\pi} \int_{-\infty}^{+\infty} \frac{\sin^2 \lambda t}{\lambda t^2} dt = u.b. | f(x) - p_k(x) |,$$

for all x, which shows that the sequence $\{S_k(x, \lambda)\}$ converges uniformly to $S(x, \lambda)$.

Consequently the Fourier series of $S(x, \lambda)$ can be obtained from (4) by the passage to the limit

$$S(x, \lambda) \sim \lim a_k(0) + \Sigma \left(1 - \frac{\lambda_\nu}{\lambda}\right) \lim I_k(\lambda_\nu).$$

By (3.1) $\qquad S(x, \lambda) \sim a(0) + \Sigma \left(1 - \dfrac{\lambda_\nu}{\lambda}\right) I(\lambda_\nu),$

which proves the lemma.

3°. Consider now the case (a) of 1°. Without loss of generality we may assume that the difference between any pair of Fourier exponents of a given *u.a.p.* function is greater than 2. We write again the Fourier series of $f(x)$ in the form

$$(1) \qquad f(x) \sim a(0) + \sum_{\nu=1}^{\infty} I(\lambda_\nu)$$

(the series is of course assumed to contain an infinite number of terms). The sequence $\{\lambda_\nu\}$ is supposed to be increasing. Obviously $\lambda_\nu \to \infty$, as $\nu \to \infty$. Out of any pair of numbers λ_ν, $\lambda_{-\nu}$ only one need be a Fourier exponent of $f(x)$. Therefore if to two numbers λ_ν, $\lambda_{\nu+1}$ correspond exponents of the same sign, then $\lambda_{\nu+1} - \lambda_\nu > 2$, otherwise $\lambda_{\nu+1} - \lambda_\nu$ may take any positive value, as small as we please. But $\lambda_{\nu+2} - \lambda_\nu$ is always greater than 2, since at least one of the two sets

$$\lambda_\nu, \quad \lambda_{\nu+1}, \quad \lambda_{\nu+2},$$
$$-\lambda_\nu, \quad -\lambda_{\nu+1}, \quad -\lambda_{\nu+2},$$

contains two Fourier exponents of $f(x)$. Consequently out of any two consecutive intervals between the numbers $\lambda_1, \lambda_2, \lambda_3, \ldots$, at least one is greater than 1. In each such interval we take an interior interval $(\mu, \mu+1)$ of length 1.

We shall consider the summation of the series (1) *by partial sums of the form*

$$a(0)+\sum_{\nu=1}^{n} I(\lambda_\nu). \tag{2}$$

We shall in fact study the sums

$$S_\mu(x)=a(0)+\sum_{\lambda_\nu<\mu} I(\lambda_\nu), \tag{3}$$

for all μ, such that the interval $(\mu, \mu+1)$ does not contain any λ_ν. The summations by the sums (2) and by the sums (3) are equivalent, since to any sum (2) corresponds a sum (3) which differs from it by at most one term $I(\lambda_\nu)$ which tends to zero, as $\nu\to\infty$. By the preceding lemma

$$\begin{aligned}(\mu+1)\,S(x,\mu+1)-\mu\,S(x,\mu)&=(\mu+1)\,a(0)+\sum_{\lambda_\nu<\mu+1}(\mu+1-\lambda_\nu)\,I(\lambda_\nu)\\&\quad-\mu a(0)-\sum_{\lambda_\nu<\mu}(\mu-\lambda_\nu)\,I(\lambda_\nu)\\&=a(0)+\sum_{\lambda_\nu<\mu} I(\lambda_\nu)=s_\mu(x).\end{aligned}$$

Thus we have

$$\begin{aligned}s_\mu(x)&=\frac{1}{\pi}\int_{-\infty}^{+\infty} f(x+2t)\,\frac{\sin^2(\mu+1)\,t-\sin^2\mu t}{t^2}\,dt\\&=\frac{1}{\pi}\int_0^{\infty}\{f(x+2t)+f(x-2t)\}\,\frac{\sin(2\mu+1)\,t}{t}\,\frac{\sin t}{t}\,dt.\end{aligned}$$

Putting $f(x+2t)+f(x-2t)-2f(x)=\phi(t)$,

we write

$$\pi\,\{s_\mu(x)-f(x)\}=\int_0^{\infty}\phi(t)\,\frac{\sin t}{t}\,\frac{\sin(2\mu+1)\,t}{t}\,dt. \tag{4}$$

Since $f(x)$ is uniformly continuous it is easy to see that

$$\lim\int_\epsilon^{\infty}\phi(t)\,\frac{\sin t}{t}\,\frac{\sin(2\mu+1)\,t}{t}\,dt=0, \tag{5}$$

as $\mu\to\infty$, for any $\epsilon>0$, uniformly in x. Therefore from (4) and (5) we conclude that *the convergence of* $s_\mu(x)$ *to* $f(x)$, *as*

$\mu \to \infty$, depends only upon the behaviour of $f(x)$ in the neighbourhood of the point x (the Riemann-Lebesgue Theorem).

We now write

$$(6)\quad \left| \int_0^\epsilon \phi(t) \frac{\sin t}{t} \frac{\sin(2\mu+1)t}{t} dt - \int_0^\epsilon \phi(t) \frac{\sin(2\mu+1)t}{t} dt \right|$$

$$\leqq \int_0^\epsilon \left| \phi(t) \frac{\sin(2\mu+1)t}{t} \right| \frac{|t-\sin t|}{t} dt < \frac{1}{6} \int_0^\epsilon |\phi(t)|\, t\, dt$$

$$< \frac{\epsilon}{6} \int_0^\epsilon |\phi(t)|\, dt.$$

From (5) and (6) we conclude that given $\eta > 0$ there exists $\epsilon_0 > 0$ and a function $\mu(\epsilon)$ such that

$$(7)\quad \left| \int_0^\infty \phi(t) \frac{\sin t}{t} \frac{\sin(2\mu+1)t}{t} dt - \int_0^\epsilon \phi(t) \frac{\sin(2\mu+1)t}{t} dt \right| < \eta$$

for all positive $\epsilon < \epsilon_0$, all $\mu > \mu(\epsilon)$, and for all x. This, combined with (4), shows that all tests of convergence of purely periodic functions which are based on an analysis of

$$\int_0^\epsilon \phi(t) \frac{\sin \mu t}{t} dt$$

remain valid for any *u.a.p.* function of the type (*a*) of 1°. Such, for example, are the convergence tests of Dini, Dirichlet-Jordan, de la Vallée Poussin, and the most general test of Lebesgue and the test of Dini-Lipschitz for uniform convergence in partial intervals or in the whole range of x.

4°. Before passing to convergence in the case (*b*) of 1° (limit periodic functions of one variable) we have to study convergence properties of a certain type of sequences of *u.a.p.* functions.

Definition 1. *A set A of functions is said to be uniformly continuous if, given $\epsilon > 0$, there exists $\delta > 0$ such that for any function $f(x)$ of the set*

$$|f(x'') - f(x')| < \epsilon,$$

if only $$|x'' - x'| < \delta.$$

Definition 2. *A real number τ is called a translation number belonging to ϵ of a set A of functions, if for any function $f(x)$ of the set it is a translation number belonging to ϵ.*

The set of all translation numbers of the set A belonging to ϵ is denoted by $E\{\epsilon, A\}$.

DEFINITION 3. *A set A of functions is called a uniformly almost periodic set if the set $E\{\epsilon, A\}$ is relatively dense for all $\epsilon > 0$.*

DEFINITION 4. *A set A of functions is called a homogeneous set of u.a.p. functions if it is uniformly continuous and uniformly almost periodic.*

DEFINITION 5. *A sequence $\{f_n(x)\}$ is said to converge in mean if to any $\epsilon > 0$ corresponds a number $n(\epsilon)$ such that*

$$M\{|f_{n'}(x) - f_{n''}(x)|^2\} < \epsilon$$

for all $n' > n(\epsilon)$, $n'' > n(\epsilon)$.

5°. THEOREM. *If a homogeneous sequence $\{f_n(x)\}$ of u.a.p. functions converges in mean, then it also converges uniformly.*

We shall prove the following more general theorem.

If A is a homogeneous set of u.a.p. functions, then to any $\epsilon > 0$ corresponds $\delta > 0$ such that, if for a pair of functions of A

$$u.b.\ |f_1(x) - f_2(x)| > \epsilon,$$

then $$M\{|f_1(x) - f_2(x)|^2\} > \delta.$$

For let at some point x_0

$$|f_1(x_0) - f_2(x_0)| > \epsilon.$$

Taking an $h > 0$ such that, for any function of A,

$$|f(x') - f(x'')| < \epsilon/6$$

if only $|x' - x''| \leqq h$, we see that

$$|f_1(x) - f_2(x)| > 2\epsilon/3$$

in the interval $(x_0 - h,\ x_0 + h)$. Let $l_{\epsilon/6} > 2h$ be an inclusion interval of $E\{\epsilon/6, A\}$. Then any interval $\{(n-1)\,l_{\epsilon/6},\ nl_{\epsilon/6}\}$ contains at least one number of the form $x_0 + \tau$, where τ belongs to $E\{\epsilon/6, A\}$ and consequently one-half of the interval $(x_0 + \tau - h,\ x_0 + \tau + h)$. As in the latter interval

$$|f_1(x) - f_2(x)| > \epsilon/3,$$

we conclude that

$$\int_{(n-1)l_{\epsilon/6}}^{nl_{\epsilon/6}} |f_1(x) - f_2(x)|^2\,dx > \frac{\epsilon^2 h}{9},$$

and thus

$$M\{|f_1(x)-f_2(x)|^2\} = \lim_{n\to\infty} \frac{1}{nl_{\epsilon/6}} \int_0^{nl_{\epsilon/6}} |f_1(x)-f_2(x)|^2\,dx > \frac{\epsilon^2 h}{9l_{\epsilon/6}}.$$

Hence taking a $\delta < \dfrac{\epsilon^2 h}{9l_{\epsilon/6}}$ we prove the theorem.

6°. We shall now establish a process of generating purely periodic functions, which approximate to a given limit periodic function.

Theorem. *If $f(x)$ is a u.a.p. function, then*

(1) $$\lim_{\nu\to\infty} \frac{1}{\nu}\{f(x)+f(x+q)+f(x+2q)+\dots + f(x+\overline{\nu-1}\,q)\} = f^{(q)}(x)$$

exists uniformly in x and is a purely periodic function whose Fourier series consists of those of the terms of the Fourier series of $f(x)$ which have a period q.

The theorem is obvious in the case when $f(x)=e^{i\lambda x}$. Then it follows at once for the case when $f(x)$ is a finite polynomial $p(x)=\Sigma A_n e^{i\Lambda_n x}$. In this case the limit is the polynomial

$$p^{(q)}(x) = \Sigma_q A_n e^{i\Lambda_n x},$$

where the summation Σ_q is extended over those terms of $p(x)$ which have a period q, i.e. over those values of n for which $\dfrac{\Lambda_n q}{2\pi}$ is an integer.

Consider now the general case. Let

(2) $$f(x) \sim \Sigma A_n e^{i\Lambda_n x},$$

and let $$p_k(x) = \Sigma A_n^{(k)} e^{i\Lambda_n x} \qquad (k=1,2,\dots)$$

be a sequence of polynomials uniformly convergent to $f(x)$. We write as above

$$p_k^{(q)}(x) = \Sigma_q A_n^{(k)} e^{i\Lambda_n x}.$$

Now, given $\epsilon>0$, we can find k such that

$$|f(x)-p_k(x)| < \epsilon/2,$$

and ν_0 such that for $\nu \geqq \nu_0$

$$\left| p_k^{(q)}(x) - \frac{1}{\nu}\{p_k(x) + p_k(x+q) + \dots + p_k(x + \overline{\nu-1}\, q)\} \right| < \epsilon/2.$$

Then

$$\left| \frac{1}{\nu}\{f(x) + f(x+q) + \dots + f(x + \overline{\nu-1}\, q)\} - p_k^{(q)}(x) \right| < \epsilon$$

for all $\nu \geqq \nu_0$ and for all x, which shows that the limit (1) exists uniformly in x and that the sequence $p_k^{(q)}(x)$ $(k = 1, 2, \dots)$ converges uniformly to the limit (1), i.e. to $f^{(q)}(x)$.

Now by a double application of the theorem of 11°, § 3, we conclude that

$$f^{(q)}(x) \sim \Sigma_q A_n e^{i\Lambda_n x},$$

where the summation Σ_q is extended over those of the terms of the series (2) which have a period q. This completes the proof of the theorem.

7°. From the uniform convergence of (1) of 6° to its limit we conclude that given a *u.a.p.* function $f(x)$ the class of functions $f^{(q)}(x)$ for all real q is a *homogeneous set of functions.* We also conclude that if $f(x)$ has some further property, for example that of having a bounded derivative or satisfying a Lipschitz condition, then all the functions $f^{(q)}(x)$ have the same property (with the same constant).

8°. Now let $f(x)$ be a limit periodic function. We write its Fourier series in the form

(1) $$f(x) \sim \Sigma A_n e^{ir_n (2\pi/Q) x},$$

where all r_n are rational Put $q = \mu ! Q$ (μ integer). We shall have

(2) $$f^{(q)}(x) \sim \Sigma_q A_n e^{ir_n (2\pi/Q) x},$$

where the summation Σ_q is extended over all terms of the series (1) for which $r_n(\mu!)$ is an integer. We have

$$M\{|f(x) - f^{(q)}(x)|^2\} = \Sigma |A_n|^2 - \Sigma_q |A_n|^2.$$

Evidently the right-hand side of this equation tends to zero, as $\mu \to \infty$. *Thus the sequence of purely periodic functions* $f^{(\mu ! Q)}(x)$ $(\mu = 1, 2, \dots)$ *converges in mean to the function* $f(x)$, ***and consequently by the theorem of 5° converges uniformly to the same function.***

Now observing that a partial sum of $f^{(\mu\,!\,Q)}(x)$ is also a partial sum of $f(x)$, we define an obvious process of summation of $f(x)$ by partial sums. Let, for instance, $f(x)$ satisfy a Lipschitz condition

$$u.b.\,|f(x+\delta)-f(x)|<C\delta^{\rho}. \qquad (C>0,\ 0<\rho\leqq 1)$$

Then $f^{(\mu\,!\,Q)}(x)$ satisfies the same condition and consequently is summable by partial sums. Given $\epsilon>0$ we first define a function $f^{(\mu\,!\,Q)}(x)$ such that

$$u.b.\,|f(x)-f^{(\mu\,!\,Q)}(x)|<\epsilon/2,$$

and then a partial sum $s(x)$ of the Fourier series of $f^{(\mu\,!\,Q)}(x)$ such that

$$u.b.\,|f^{(\mu\,!\,Q)}(x)-s(x)|<\epsilon/2.$$

Then

$$u.b.\,|f(x)-s(x)|<\epsilon.$$

In this way we can construct a sequence of partial sums of the Fourier series of $f(x)$ uniformly convergent to $f(x)$.

§ 9. Bochner-Fejér summation of *u.a.p.* functions.

1°. We have already pointed out the difficulty of the problem of summation by partial sums of the Fourier series of *u.a.p.* functions, looked at from the point of view of diagonal functions of limit periodic functions of several variables. From the same point of view we may, however, expect summation by arithmetical means to be applicable to the general case of *u.a.p.* functions. The difference lies in the fact that, while on the one hand the conditions for summability by partial sums, such as the boundedness of the derivative, the Lipschitz conditions and so on, cannot be transplanted from the diagonal function of a function of several variables to the latter function, the continuity of a *u.a.p.* function does on the other hand establish the continuity of the corresponding limit periodic function of several variables, and this is a sufficient condition for the uniform convergence of the Fejér sums of the latter functions. Taking then the diagonal functions of these Fejér sums we shall obtain Fejér sums of our *u.a.p.* function. This is the idea of Bochner's generalisation of Fejér's summation to the case of *u.a.p.* functions.

2°. Fejér's sums for the case of a purely periodic function

$$f(x) \sim \sum_{\nu=-\infty}^{+\infty} A_\nu e^{i\nu\beta x},$$

are given by the formula

$$\sigma_n(x) = \sum_{|\nu|<n} \left(1 - \frac{|\nu|}{n}\right) A_\nu e^{i\nu\beta x}.$$

Since

$$A_\nu = M\{f(t)\, e^{-i\nu\beta t}\},$$

it follows that

$$A_\nu e^{i\nu\beta x} = M_t\{f(t)\, e^{-i\nu\beta(t-x)}\} = M_t\{f(t+x)\, e^{-i\nu\beta t}\},$$

whence

$$\sigma_n(x) = M_t\{f(x+t)\, K_n(\beta t)\},$$

where "the kernel" $K_n(\beta t)$ is defined by the equation

$$K_n(t) = \sum_{|\nu|<n} \left(1 - \frac{|\nu|}{n}\right) e^{-i\nu t} = \frac{1}{n}\left(\frac{\sin\frac{n}{2}t}{\sin\frac{t}{2}}\right)^2.$$

This kernel has two properties important for the summation: it is never negative and its mean value is equal to 1 (since it is obviously equal to the constant term of K_n).

Bochner replaced this simple kernel by a finite product of such kernels

$$K_{\binom{n_1,\, n_2,\, \dots,\, n_p}{\beta_1,\, \beta_2,\, \dots,\, \beta_p}}(t) = K_{n_1}(\beta_1 t)\, K_{n_2}(\beta_2 t) \dots K_{n_p}(\beta_p t)$$

$$= \sum_{\substack{|\nu_1|<n_1 \\ \cdots\cdots \\ |\nu_p|<n_p}} \left(1 - \frac{|\nu_1|}{n_1}\right)\left(1 - \frac{|\nu_2|}{n_2}\right) \dots \left(1 - \frac{|\nu_p|}{n_p}\right) e^{-i(\nu_1\beta_1 + \dots + \nu_p\beta_p)t},$$

where $\beta_1, \beta_2, \dots, \beta_p$ are certain real linearly independent numbers. This composite kernel has the same characteristic properties as the Fejér kernel—it is never negative and its mean value is equal to 1 (the constant term being 1 on account of the linear independence of the β's). We call this kernel the Bochner-Fejér kernel and we form "a Bochner-Fejér polynomial":

$$\sigma_{\binom{n_1,\, n_2,\, \dots,\, n_p}{\beta_1,\, \beta_2,\, \dots,\, \beta_p}}(x) = M_t\{f(x+t)\, K_{\binom{n_1,\, n_2,\, \dots,\, n_p}{\beta_1,\, \beta_2,\, \dots,\, \beta_p}}(t)\}$$

$$= \sum_{\substack{|\nu_1|<n_1 \\ \cdots\cdots \\ |\nu_p|<n_p}} \left(1 - \frac{|\nu_1|}{n_1}\right)\left(1 - \frac{|\nu_2|}{n_2}\right) \dots \left(1 - \frac{|\nu_p|}{n_p}\right) a(\nu_1\beta_1 + \nu_2\beta_2 + \dots + \nu_p\beta_p)$$

$$\times\, e^{i(\nu_1\beta_1 + \nu_2\beta_2 + \dots + \nu_p\beta_p)x},$$

where as usual $a(\lambda) = M\{f(t)e^{-i\lambda t}\}$.

Thus only those terms of a Bochner-Fejér polynomial differ from zero whose exponents are Fourier exponents of $f(x)$. When $\nu_1\beta_1 + \nu_2\beta_2 + \ldots + \nu_p\beta_p$ is a Fourier exponent of $f(x)$, we write

$$\nu_1\beta_1 + \nu_2\beta_2 + \ldots + \nu_p\beta_p = \Lambda_n$$

and we have

$$(1)\quad \sigma_{\binom{n_1,\, n_2,\, \ldots,\, n_p}{\beta_1,\, \beta_2,\, \ldots,\, \beta_p}}(x) = \Sigma\left(1 - \frac{|\nu_1|}{n_1}\right)\left(1 - \frac{|\nu_2|}{n_2}\right)\ldots\left(1 - \frac{|\nu_p|}{n_p}\right) A_n e^{i\Lambda_n x}.$$

We call the numbers $\beta_1, \beta_2, \ldots\ \beta_p$ "basic numbers," and the numbers $n_1, n_2, \ldots, n_p$ "indices" of the Bochner-Fejér kernel or of the polynomial.

Remark. Denoting by B the symbol $\binom{n_1,\, n_2,\, \ldots,\, n_p}{\beta_1,\, \beta_2,\, \ldots,\, \beta_p}$, we write (1) in the form

$$\sigma_B(x) = \Sigma d_n^{(B)} A_n e^{i\Lambda_n x},$$

where all $d_n^{(B)}$ satisfy the inequality

$$0 \leq d_n^{(B)} \leq 1,$$

and only a finite number of them are different from zero.

We observe that $d_n^{(B)}$ depend only on B (i.e. on basic numbers and on the indices of a Bochner-Fejér polynomial) and on Λ_n, but not on the values of the coefficients A_n, so that if we have an aggregate of *u.a.p.* functions

$$f_g(x) \sim \Sigma A_n^{(g)} e^{i\Lambda_n x},$$

with the same Fourier exponents but with different Fourier coefficients, then the Bochner-Fejér polynomials of all these functions corresponding to a given B have the same "multiples" $d_n^{(B)}$, i.e.

$$\sigma_{B\,|}^{f_g(x)}(x) = \Sigma d_n^{(B)} A_n^{(g)} e^{i\Lambda_n x},$$

where all $d_n^{(B)}$ are independent of g.

3°. Theorem. *A u.a.p. function $f(x)$ together with all its Bochner-Fejér polynomials form a homogeneous set of u.a.p. functions.*

For we have for any real number τ and for any Bochner-Fejér polynomial

$$|\sigma_{\binom{n_1, n_2, \ldots, n_p}{\beta_1, \beta_2, \ldots, \beta_p}}(x+\tau) - \sigma_{\binom{n_1, n_2, \ldots, n_p}{\beta_1, \beta_2, \ldots, \beta_p}}(x)|$$
$$= |M[\{f(x+t+\tau) - f(x+t)\} K_{\binom{n_1, n_2, \ldots, n_p}{\beta_1, \beta_2, \ldots, \beta_p}}(t)]|.$$

Now on account of the two characteristic properties of the kernel we conclude that

$$|\sigma_{\binom{n_1, n_2, \ldots, n_p}{\beta_1, \beta_2, \ldots, \beta_p}}(x+\tau) - \sigma_{\binom{n_1, n_2, \ldots, n_p}{\beta_1, \beta_2, \ldots, \beta_p}}(x)|$$
$$\leqq M\{|f(x+t+\tau) - f(x+t)| K_{\binom{n_1, n_2, \ldots, n_p}{\beta_1, \beta_2, \ldots, \beta_p}}(t)\}$$
$$\leqq M\{K_{\binom{n_1, n_2, \ldots, n_p}{\beta_1, \beta_2, \ldots, \beta_p}}(t)\} \underset{-\infty < x < +\infty}{u.b.} |f(x+\tau) - f(x)|$$
$$\leqq u.b. |f(x+\tau) - f(x)|,$$

which shows that the set of all Bochner-Fejér polynomials together with $f(x)$ is uniformly continuous and uniformly almost periodic, i.e. homogeneous.

4°. Our problem is to find a sequence of Bochner-Fejér polynomials uniformly convergent to the function $f(x)$. By the preceding theorem and by the theorem of 5°, § 8, this is equivalent to finding a sequence convergent in mean. Thus our problem is *given* $\epsilon > 0$ *to find a Bochner-Fejér polynomial*

$$\sigma(x) = \sigma_{\binom{n_1, n_2, \ldots, n_p}{\beta_1, \beta_2, \ldots, \beta_p}}(x),$$

such that $$M\{|f(x) - \sigma(x)|^2\} < \epsilon.$$

We write the Fourier series of $f(x)$

$$f(x) \sim \sum_{n=1}^{\infty} A_n e^{i\Lambda_n x},$$

and let $\alpha_1, \alpha_2, \ldots$ be a base of $f(x)$.

Define n_0 so that

(1) $$\sum_{n=n_0+1}^{\infty} |A_n|^2 < \epsilon/2.$$

Let p be the largest index of α's in the linear expressions of $\Lambda_1, \Lambda_2, \ldots, \Lambda_{n_0}$, so that we can write

$$\Lambda_n = r_1^{(n)} \alpha_1 + r_2^{(n)} \alpha_2 + \ldots + r_p^{(n)} \alpha_p, \quad (n = 1, 2, \ldots, n_0)$$

where all $r_i^{(n)}$ are rational. Let q be the common denominator of all the numbers $r_i^{(n)}$ $(i=1, 2, \ldots, p;\ n=1, 2, \ldots, n_0)$. We write

$$\Lambda_n = R_1^{(n)}\frac{\alpha_1}{q} + R_2^{(n)}\frac{\alpha_2}{q} + \ldots + R_p^{(n)}\frac{\alpha_p}{q},$$

where all $R_i^{(n)}$ are integers. Let R be the maximum of all $|R_i^{(n)}|$. Define numbers $\eta > 0$ and $N > 0$ by the conditions

$$(2) \qquad \eta^2 \sum_{n=1}^{n_0} |A_n|^2 < \epsilon/2,$$

$$(3) \qquad \left(1-\frac{R}{N}\right)^p > 1-\eta.$$

Take $\beta_i = \frac{\alpha_i}{q}$ $(i=1, 2, \ldots, p)$ and all $n_1, n_2, \ldots, n_p$ greater than N.

By (1), 2°,

$$(4) \quad \sigma(x) = \sigma_{\left(\substack{n_1,\, n_2,\, \ldots,\, n_p \\ \beta_1,\, \beta_2,\, \ldots,\, \beta_p}\right)}(x)$$

$$= \sum_{n=1}^{n_0}\left(1-\frac{|R_1^{(n)}|}{n_1}\right)\ldots\left(1-\frac{|R_p^{(n)}|}{n_p}\right)A_n e^{i\Lambda_n x} + \sum_{n=n_0+1}^{\infty} d_n A_n e^{i\Lambda_n x},$$

where d_n differs from zero only for a finite number of values of n and $0 \leqq d_n \leqq 1$ for all $n > n_0$. We have

$$M\{|f(x)-\sigma(x)|^2\} = \sum_{n=1}^{n_0}\left\{1-\left(1-\frac{|R_1^{(n)}|}{n_1}\right)\ldots\left(1-\frac{|R_p^{(n)}|}{n_p}\right)\right\}^2 |A_n|^2 + \sum_{n=n_0+1}^{\infty}(1-d_n)^2|A_n|^2.$$

By (1), (2) and (3)

$$M\{|f(x)-\sigma(x)|^2\} \leqq \eta^2 \sum_{n=1}^{n_0}|A_n|^2 + \sum_{n=n_0+1}^{\infty}|A_n|^2 < \epsilon.$$

We see that $\sigma(x)$ is a polynomial of the kind required and thus we have proved the

POLYNOMIAL APPROXIMATION THEOREM. *To any u.a.p. function corresponds a sequence of trigonometric polynomials—Bochner-Fejér polynomials—uniformly convergent to the function.*

Remark. By the above argument we have established the following result.

Given a u.a.p. function

$$f(x) \sim \Sigma A_n e^{i\Lambda_n x},$$

then to any positive integer n_0, *as large as we please and to any* $\eta > 0$ *as small as we please, corresponds a Bochner-Fejér polynomial*

$$\sigma_B(x) = \Sigma d_n^{(B)} A_n e^{i\Lambda_n x},$$

such that

$$d_n^{(B)} > 1 - \eta$$

for $n = 1, 2, \ldots, n_0$.

§ 10. Some particular cases of Fourier series of *u.a.p.* functions.

1°. We now shall apply the Bochner-Fejér summation to prove absolute convergence of the Fourier series in two particular cases: (*a*) that in which the Fourier exponents are linearly independent, and (*b*) that in which all Fourier coefficients are positive.

Take the case (*a*). Let $f(x)$ be a *u.a.p.* function, and let

$$(1) \qquad f(x) \sim \sum_{n=1}^{\infty} A_n e^{i\Lambda_n x},$$

where all Λ_n are linearly independent. Take a Bochner-Fejér sum

$$\sigma_{\nu,p}(x) = \sigma_{\binom{n_1,\, n_2,\, \ldots,\, n_p}{\Lambda_1,\, \Lambda_2,\, \ldots,\, \Lambda_p}}(x). \quad (n_1 = n_2 = \ldots = n_p = \nu)$$

As of all the values

$$\nu_1\Lambda_1 + \nu_2\Lambda_2 + \ldots + \nu_p\Lambda_p, \quad (\nu_1, \nu_2, \ldots, \nu_p \text{ integers})$$

only such are Fourier exponents for which one of the ν_k's is 1 and all other 0, we see that

$$(2) \qquad \sigma_{\nu,p}(x) = \left(1 - \frac{1}{\nu}\right) \sum_{n=1}^{p} A_n e^{i\Lambda_n x}.$$

We have

$$M\{|f(x) - \sigma_{\nu,p}(x)|^2\} = \frac{1}{\nu^2} \sum_{n=1}^{p} |A_n|^2 + \sum_{n=p+1}^{\infty} |A_n|^2.$$

Thus $\sigma_{\nu,p}(x)$ converges in mean to $f(x)$, and consequently converges uniformly to $f(x)$ as ν and p tend to infinity. Hence

$$\sum_{n=1}^{p} A_n e^{i\Lambda_n x} \to f(x),$$

as $p \to \infty$, i.e.

$$\Sigma A_n e^{i\Lambda_n x} = f(x).$$

But the order of terms of the series (1) has not been specified. Thus it converges for any order of its terms, and consequently *it converges absolutely.*

2°. We now take the case (*b*) of a *u.a.p.* function

$$f(x) \sim \sum_{n=1}^{\infty} A_n e^{i\Lambda_n x},$$

where all A_n are positive. In the same way as in 4°, § 9, we can find a Bochner-Fejér polynomial

$$(1) \qquad \sigma(x) = \sigma_{\binom{n_1, n_2, \ldots, n_p}{\beta_1, \beta_2, \ldots, \beta_p}}(x)$$

$$= \sum_{n=1}^{n_0} \left(1 - \frac{|R_1^{(n)}|}{n_1}\right) \ldots \left(1 - \frac{|R_p^{(n)}|}{n_p}\right) A_n e^{i\Lambda_n x}$$

$$+ \sum_{n=n_0+1}^{\infty} d_n A_n e^{i\Lambda_n x},$$

where n_0 is as large as we please and all

$$(2) \qquad \left(1 - \frac{|R_1^{(n)}|}{n_1}\right)\left(1 - \frac{|R_2^{(n)}|}{n_2}\right) \ldots \left(1 - \frac{|R_p^{(n)}|}{n_p}\right) > 1 - \eta,$$

$$(n = 1, 2, \ldots, n_0)$$

η being as small as we please. We may then assume that

$$(3) \qquad |f(x) - \sigma(x)| < 1.$$

By (1), (2), (3)

$$(1 - \eta) \sum_{n=1}^{n_0} A_n < \sigma(0) < f(0) + 1.$$

As n_0 is arbitrarily large and η arbitrarily small we conclude that the series $\sum_{n=1}^{\infty} A_n$ is convergent, and consequently that the series

$$\sum_{n=1}^{\infty} A_n e^{i\Lambda_n x}$$

is absolutely convergent.

§ 11. Arithmetical nature of translation numbers.

1°. We established certain properties of translation numbers in § 1. Now that the general theory of *u.a.p.* functions has been developed we can establish some new properties. We shall in fact give necessary conditions for a number to be a translation number, and also sufficient conditions.

We shall also investigate sets of integral translation numbers. This question has important applications to the problem of the generalisation of almost periodic functions.

2°. THEOREM. *Given a u.a.p. function*

$$f(x) \sim \sum_{n=1}^{\infty} A_n e^{i\Lambda_n x},$$

to any positive integer N and a positive number $\delta < \pi$ *corresponds a positive* ϵ *such that all numbers* τ *of the set* $E\{\epsilon, f(x)\}$ *satisfy the following Diophantine inequalities:*

$$|\Lambda_n \tau| < \delta \pmod{2\pi}^*. \qquad (n = 1, 2, \ldots, N)$$

Evidently the inequality $|\Lambda_n \tau| < \delta \pmod{2\pi}$ is equivalent to the ordinary inequality

$$(1) \qquad |e^{i\Lambda_n \tau} - 1| < |e^{i\delta} - 1| = \delta_1.$$

Writing $c_N = \min.\{|A_1|, |A_2|, \ldots, |A_N|\}$, we put $\epsilon = \frac{1}{2} c_N \delta_1$. Let τ be any number of the set $E\{\epsilon, f(x)\}$. We obviously have

$$|M[\{f(x+\tau) - f(x)\} e^{-i\Lambda_n x}]| \leqq M\{|f(x+\tau) - f(x)|\} \leqq \epsilon.$$

On the other hand

$$M[\{f(x+\tau) - f(x)\} e^{-i\Lambda_n x}]$$
$$= M\{f(x+\tau) e^{-i\Lambda_n (x+\tau)}\} e^{i\Lambda_n \tau} - M\{f(x) e^{-i\Lambda_n x}\} = A_n (e^{i\Lambda_n \tau} - 1).$$

Thus $$|A_n (e^{i\Lambda_n \tau} - 1)| \leqq \epsilon < c_N \delta_1,$$

consequently for $n = 1, 2, \ldots, N$

$$|e^{i\Lambda_n \tau} - 1| < \delta_1,$$

which proves the theorem.

3°. THEOREM. *Given a u.a.p. function*

$$f(x) \sim \sum_{n=1}^{\infty} A_n e^{i\Lambda_n x},$$

to any $\epsilon > 0$ *corresponds a positive integer N and a positive* $\delta < \pi$ *such that any number* τ *satisfying the N Diophantine inequalities*

$$|\Lambda_n \tau| < \delta \pmod{2\pi}, \qquad (n = 1, 2, \ldots, N)$$

belongs to $E\{\epsilon, f(x)\}$.

* The meaning of this inequality is that there exists an integer k satisfying the ordinary inequality

$$|\Lambda_n \tau - 2\pi k| < \delta.$$

Take a trigonometric polynomial $s(x)$, whose exponents are Fourier exponents of $f(x)$ and which satisfies the inequality

$$(1) \qquad |f(x) - s(x)| < \epsilon/3.$$

Let
$$s(x) = \sum_{n=1}^{N} B_n e^{i\Lambda_n x}.$$

Write $C = |B_1| + |B_2| + \ldots + |B_N|$, and take a positive $\delta_1 < \frac{\epsilon}{3C}$. Define the positive number $\delta < \pi$ by the equation

$$|e^{i\delta} - 1| = \delta_1.$$

Let now τ be any number satisfying the inequalities

$$|e^{i\Lambda_n \tau} - 1| < \delta_1, \qquad (n = 1, 2, \ldots, N)$$

or, what is the same thing, the inequalities

$$(2) \qquad |\Lambda_n \tau| < \delta \ (\mathrm{mod}\ 2\pi). \qquad (n = 1, 2, \ldots, N)$$

We have

$$|s(x+\tau) - s(x)| = \left| \sum_{n=1}^{N} B_n e^{i\Lambda_n x} (e^{i\Lambda_n \tau} - 1) \right|$$
$$\leq \sum_{n=1}^{N} |B_n| \, |e^{i\Lambda_n \tau} - 1| < \delta_1 C < \frac{\epsilon}{3}.$$

Thus any number τ satisfying the inequalities (2) is a translation number of $s(x)$ belonging to $\epsilon/3$. But any such number belongs to $E\{\epsilon, f(x)\}$, for by (1)

$$|f(x+\tau) - f(x)| \leq |f(x+\tau) - s(x+\tau)| + |s(x+\tau) - s(x)|$$
$$+ |s(x) - f(x)| < \epsilon/3 + \epsilon/3 + \epsilon/3 = \epsilon;$$

which proves the theorem.

4°. We now pass to the study of integral translation numbers of *u.a.p.* functions. Let $f(x)$ be a *u.a.p.* function and ϵ a positive number.

We denote by $\bar{E}\{\epsilon, f(x)\}$ the set of all integers of the set $E\{\epsilon, f(x)\}$.

THEOREM. *The set* $\bar{E}\{\epsilon, f(x)\}$ *is r.d.*

Take an $\epsilon_1 < \epsilon$. By the lemma of 9°, § 1, there exists a positive number $\delta < \frac{1}{2}$ such that all numbers, whose distances from the set $E\{\epsilon_1, f(x)\}$ are less than δ, belong to the set $E\{\epsilon, f(x)\}$.

Define now an $\epsilon_2 > 0$ so that all numbers of the set $E\{\epsilon_2, \sin 2\pi x\}$ differ from integers by less than δ. By the theorem of 11°, § 1, the set

$$I = E\{\epsilon_1, f(x)\} \,.\, E\{\epsilon_2, \sin 2\pi x\}$$

is *r.d.* All the numbers of I differ from integers by less than δ, since they belong to $E\{\epsilon_2, \sin 2\pi x\}$. Let $\bar{I}$ denote the set of the integers nearest to each number of I. Evidently $\bar{I}$ is *r.d.* On the other hand as I belongs to $E\{\epsilon_1, f(x)\}$ we see that the distance of each number of $\bar{I}$ from the set $E\{\epsilon_1, f(x)\}$ is less than δ, and consequently each number of $\bar{I}$ belongs to $E\{\epsilon, f(x)\}$, and obviously to $\bar{E}\{\epsilon, f(x)\}$. Thus $\bar{I}$ being *r.d.*, $\bar{E}\{\epsilon, f(x)\}$ is also *r.d.*

5°. We say that *the set* $\bar{E}\{\epsilon, f(x)\}$ *is a.p. with an error* $\leqq \eta$ if there exists a positive $\rho < \epsilon$ and a positive I_0 such that (a, b) being any interval of length $> I_0$ the points of $\bar{E}\{\epsilon, f(x)\} \,.\, (a, b)$* translated by any number of $\bar{E}\{\rho, f(x)\}$, go over on to points of $\bar{E}\{\epsilon, f(x)\}$ again with the exception of at most $\eta(b-a)$ of them.

If a set $\bar{E}\{\epsilon, f(x)\}$ is *a.p.* with an error which may be less than any given positive number, then we say that the set $\bar{E}\{\epsilon, f(x)\}$ is *almost periodic.*

For brevity's sake we shall write sometimes E_ϵ, $\bar{E}_\epsilon$ instead of $E\{\epsilon, f(x)\}$, $\bar{E}\{\epsilon, f(x)\}$.

We shall prove that

The set $\bar{E}_\epsilon$ *is a.p. for almost all values of* ϵ.

In the proof we may evidently consider only values of ϵ in the interval $0 < \epsilon < 1$.

6°. We have to investigate the "loss" of the set $\bar{E}_\epsilon$ on translation by a number of $\bar{E}_\rho$ $(\rho < \epsilon)$, i.e. to estimate the number of points of $\bar{E}_\epsilon$ in any interval which in their new position do not coincide with points of $\bar{E}_\epsilon$ in its original position.

We have first to observe some effects of translation on translation numbers.

* I.e. the points of $\bar{E}\{\epsilon, f(x)\}$ belonging to the interval (a, b).

(I) Obviously for any $\epsilon > 0$, $\rho > 0$ the set $\bar{E}_\epsilon$ translated by an arbitrary number τ_ρ of $\bar{E}_\rho$ is contained in the set $\bar{E}_{\epsilon+\rho}$.

(II) For any $\epsilon > \epsilon' > \rho \; (>0)$ the set $\bar{E}_\epsilon - \bar{E}_{\epsilon'}$ translated by a number τ_ρ of $\bar{E}_\rho$ is contained in the set $\bar{E}_{\epsilon+\rho} - \bar{E}_{\epsilon'-\rho}$.

7°. By (I) of the preceding section, all the numbers of $\bar{E}_{\epsilon-\rho} \; (\rho < \epsilon)$ translated by an integer τ_ρ of $\bar{E}_\rho$ go over on to points of $\bar{E}_\epsilon$, and thus the only points of $\bar{E}_\epsilon$ which can be lost by the translation τ_ρ are those of the set $\bar{E}_\epsilon - \bar{E}_{\epsilon-\rho}$; and we have to prove that for *almost all* values of ϵ the following is true:

The "mean density" of the set $\bar{E}_\epsilon - \bar{E}_{\epsilon-\rho}$ in a sufficiently long interval is small for small values of ρ.

Let E be a finite set of numbers. We denote by $N[E]$ the number of numbers of E. We have to consider

(1) $$N[(\bar{E}_\epsilon - \bar{E}_{\epsilon-\rho}) \times (a, b)]$$

for small ρ and large $b-a$. For convenience we let (a, b) represent the closed interval.

Let, for the moment, ϵ, $\rho \; (< \frac{1}{2}\epsilon)$ and $I_0 \; (>1)$ be taken to be fixed positive numbers. We denote by I_0 also the interval $(0, I_0)$. For the sake of brevity we write

$$N[(\bar{E}_{\epsilon+\rho} - \bar{E}_{\epsilon-2\rho}) \times I_0] = N_0(\epsilon, \rho, I_0).$$

Consider the interval $(\tau_\rho, \tau_\rho + I_0)$, where τ_ρ is an arbitrary number belonging to $\bar{E}_\rho$. As $-\tau_\rho$ is also a point of $\bar{E}_\rho$, a displacement $-\tau_\rho$ will, by (II), send all the integers of the set

$$(\bar{E}_\epsilon - \bar{E}_{\epsilon-\rho}) \times (\tau_\rho, \tau_\rho + I_0)$$

on to numbers of the set

$$(\bar{E}_{\epsilon+\rho} - \bar{E}_{\epsilon-2\rho}) \times I_0,$$

and consequently

(2) $$N[(\bar{E}_\epsilon - \bar{E}_{\epsilon-\rho}) \times (\tau_\rho, \tau_\rho + I_0)] \leqq N_0(\epsilon, \rho, I_0).$$

8°. Having estimated the number of points of $\bar{E}_\epsilon - \bar{E}_{\epsilon-\rho}$ in a special type of interval of length I_0, we shall now estimate the number of points of this set in any interval (a, b) of length greater than I_0. Let $\bar{L}_\rho \; (>1)$ denote an inclusion interval of $\bar{E}_\rho$. We can represent (a, b) as the sum of special intervals $(\tau_\rho, \tau_\rho + I_0)$ of the kind considered in the preceding paragraph with complementary intervals of length $< \bar{L}_\rho$; the last of the intervals $(\tau_\rho, \tau_\rho + I_0)$ may only partly belong to (a, b). For, let τ_ρ' be the first point of $\bar{E}_\rho$ belonging to (a, b). Then $\tau_\rho' - a < \bar{L}_\rho$. If $\tau_\rho' + I_0 \leqq b - \bar{L}_\rho$, then we denote by τ_ρ'' the first point of $\bar{E}_\rho$ to the right of $(\tau_\rho', \tau_\rho' + I_0)$, and take the interval $(\tau_\rho'', \tau_\rho'' + I_0)$, and so on. The number of intervals $(\tau_\rho, \tau_\rho + I_0)$ constructed in this way is evidently less than $\{(b-a)/I_0\} + 1$. It is clear that the number of complementary intervals is also less than this number. Using (2) and observing that the number of points of $\bar{E}_\epsilon - \bar{E}_{\epsilon-\rho}$ in any one complementary interval is $< \bar{L}_\rho + 1$, we have

$$(1)\quad N[(\bar{E}_\epsilon - \bar{E}_{\epsilon-\rho}) \times (a, b)] \leqq \left(\frac{b-a}{I_0} + 1\right) \{N_0(\epsilon, \rho, I_0) + (\bar{L}_\rho + 1)\}$$

$$< \frac{2(b-a)}{I_0} \{N_0(\epsilon, \rho, I_0) + 2\bar{L}_\rho\}.$$

9°. Thus, the estimation of the number (1) of 7° has been reduced to that of the number $N_0(\epsilon, \rho, I_0)$, i.e. to the discussion of the set

$$(\bar{E}_{\epsilon+\rho} - \bar{E}_{\epsilon-2\rho}) \times I_0.$$

We shall consider this set for fixed positive values of I_0 and $\rho < \frac{1}{3}$, and for a "variable" ϵ in the interval $2\rho < \epsilon < 1 - \rho$. Let k be a positive number, and denote by $G' = G'(k, \rho, I_0)$ the set of those of the values of ϵ in the interval $(2\rho, 1-\rho)$ for which

$$(1)\qquad N_0(\epsilon, \rho, I_0) > k\rho(I_0 + 1).$$

We can obviously choose in succession a finite set of numbers $\epsilon_1, \epsilon_2, \ldots, \epsilon_P$ from G' such that the corresponding intervals $(\epsilon_p - 2\rho, \epsilon_p + \rho)(p = 1, 2, \ldots, P)$ of length 3ρ do not overlap (or even abut), and that their total length $3\rho P$ satisfies the condition

$$(2)\qquad 3\rho P \geqq \tfrac{1}{2} m\, G'(k, \rho, I_0).$$

Consider the sum

$$\sum_{p=1}^{P} N[(\bar{E}_{\epsilon_p+\rho} - \bar{E}_{\epsilon_p-2\rho}) \times I_0].$$

Since the intervals $(\epsilon_p - 2\rho, \epsilon_p + \rho)$ do not overlap, we evidently have

$$I_0 + 1 \geqq \sum_{p=1}^{P} N[(\bar{E}_{\epsilon_p+\rho} - \bar{E}_{\epsilon_p-2\rho}) \times I_0],$$

and therefore, by (1) and (2),

$$I_0 + 1 \geqq P \,.\, k\rho\,(I_0+1) \geqq \frac{k}{6} mG'(k, \rho, I_0) \,.\, (I_0+1).$$

Thus $$mG'(k, \rho, I_0) \leqq \frac{6}{k},$$

i.e. mG' is small if only k is great, independently of ρ and I_0.

Writing $$G(k, \rho, I_0) = (2\rho, 1-\rho) - G'(k, \rho, I_0),$$

we have

$$\text{(3)} \qquad mG(k, \rho, I_0) \geqq 1 - 3\rho - \frac{6}{k}.$$

10°. By what has been indicated at the beginning of 7° we have, roughly speaking, that the error of almost periodicity of the set $\bar{E}_\epsilon$ is less than the mean density of $\bar{E}_\epsilon - \bar{E}_{\epsilon-\rho}$. We shall now prove the following theorems:

THEOREM. *Given positive numbers η and δ, we can find a certain set $G \subset (0, 1)$, of measure $> 1 - \delta$, such that for every ϵ in G the set $\bar{E}_\epsilon$ is a.p. with an error $\leqq \eta$.*

Putting

$$\text{(1)} \qquad k > \frac{12}{\delta}, \quad \rho < \min.\left(\frac{\eta}{8k}, \frac{\delta}{6}\right), \quad I_0 > \frac{8\bar{L}_\rho}{\eta},$$

we shall show that we can take $G(k, \rho, I_0)$ for G. For we have first, by (3) of 9° and (1),

$$mG(k, \rho, I_0) > 1 - \delta.$$

Now let ϵ be a number in $G(k, \rho, I_0)$. In virtue of the definition of $G(k, \rho, I_0)$ we have

$$N_0(\epsilon, \rho, I_0) \leqq k\rho\,(I_0 + 1),$$

and thus, by (1),

$$\text{(2)} \qquad N_0(\epsilon, \rho, I_0) < \frac{\eta}{8}(I_0 + 1) < \frac{\eta}{4} I_0.$$

Further

(3) $$\bar{L}_\rho < \frac{\eta}{8} I_0.$$

By (1) of 8°, (2) and (3), we get

$$\frac{1}{b-a} N[(\bar{E}_\epsilon - \bar{E}_{\epsilon-\rho}) \times (a, b)] < \eta,$$

which proves the theorem.

11°. Theorem. *For almost all values of* ϵ *in* $0 < \epsilon < 1$ *the set* $\bar{E}_\epsilon$ *is a.p.*

Take two sequences of numbers

$$\delta_1 > \delta_2 > \ldots, \quad \delta_n \to 0,$$
$$\eta_1 > \eta_2 > \ldots, \quad \eta_n \to 0.$$

Let G_i be the set G of the theorem of 10° corresponding to $\delta = \delta_i$, $\eta = \eta_i$. Denote by U the upper limit of the sequence*

$$G_1, G_2, \ldots.$$

By a well-known theorem $mU = 1$. Let ϵ be a point of U. Denote by

$$G_{n_1}, G_{n_2}, \ldots$$

the infinite sequence of sets to which ϵ belongs. Then the set $\bar{E}_\epsilon$ is *a.p.* with error less than or equal to each number of the sequence

$$\eta_{n_1}, \eta_{n_2}, \ldots,$$

i.e. the set $\bar{E}_\epsilon$ is *a.p.*, and thus our theorem is proved.

§ 12. *U.a.p.* functions of two variables.

1°. The theory of *u.a.p.* functions can be generalised to the case of functions of more than one variable. This has been done independently by Ph. Franklin and S. Bochner. Franklin's method is a mere reproduction of Bohr's arguments in terms of two variables. Bochner has developed the theory of *u.a.p.* functions of any finite or of an enumerably infinite number of variables, reducing the general case to the case of functions of one variable. We shall consider here only the case of *u.a.p.* functions of two variables, but the case of any finite number of variables can be treated in exactly the same way.

* I.e. the set of points which belong to an infinity of members of the sequence.

2°. Definition. *Given a function $f(x, y)$ and an $\epsilon > 0$, a vector $\tau(u, v)$ is said to be a translation vector belonging to ϵ if*

$$\underset{\substack{-\infty < x < +\infty \\ -\infty < y < +\infty}}{u.b.} |f(x+u, y+v) - f(x, y)| \leq \epsilon.$$

The set of all translation vectors of the function $f(x, y)$ belonging to $\epsilon > 0$ is denoted by $E\{\epsilon, f(x, y)\}$.

A plane set A of points is said to be relatively dense (r.d.), if there exists a number $l > 0$ such that any square of side l in the (x, y) plane contains at least one point of A.

A function $f(x, y)$ continuous in two variables, is called uniformly almost periodic (u.a.p.) if the set $E\{\epsilon, f(x, y)\}$ (or more exactly the set of ends of all the vectors of $E\{\epsilon, f(x, y)\}$) is r.d. for all $\epsilon > 0$.

We denote by l_ϵ a number such that any square of side l_ϵ contains the end of at least one vector of $E\{\epsilon, f(x, y)\}$.

Evidently the theorems of 4°, 5°, 6°, 7°, 8° of § 1, hold also for *u.a.p.* functions of two variables.

Sets of translation vectors have many properties similar to those of sets of translation numbers of functions of one variable. We mention, in particular, the following property.

If τ_1, τ_2 are respectively vectors of the sets

$$E\{\epsilon_1, f(x, y)\}, \quad E\{\epsilon_2, f(x, y)\},$$

then the vector $\tau_1 + \tau_2$ belongs to the set

$$E\{\epsilon_1 + \epsilon_2, f(x, y)\}.$$

Denote by the symbols $XE\{\epsilon, f(x, y)\}$, $YE\{\epsilon, f(x, y)\}$ respectively, the sets of all vectors of $E\{\epsilon, f(x, y)\}$ parallel to the X-axis and to the Y-axis.

Theorem. *If the sets $XE\{\epsilon, f(x, y)\}$, $YE\{\epsilon, f(x, y)\}$ are r.d. for any $\epsilon > 0$, then the function $f(x, y)$ is u.a.p.*

For the set of vectors (u, v), where u takes all values of $XE\{\epsilon, f(x, y)\}$ and v of $YE\{\epsilon, f(x, y)\}$, is *r.d.* for any $\epsilon > 0$. All these vectors belong to $E\{2\epsilon, f(x, y)\}$, which is thus *r.d.* for all $\epsilon > 0$. This proves the theorem.

3°. The converse of the preceding theorem is also true.

THEOREM. *If a function* $f(x, y)$ *is u.a.p., then the sets* $XE\{\epsilon, f(x, y)\}$, $YE\{\epsilon, f(x, y)\}$ *are r.d. for all* $\epsilon > 0$.

Take an $l_{\epsilon/3}$ and denote by S_n (n any integer) the square between the lines $y = 0$, $y = l_{\epsilon/3}$ and the lines $x = (n-1)\, l_{\epsilon/3}$, $x = n l_{\epsilon/3}$, and let $\tau_n(u_n, v_n)$ be a vector of $E\{\epsilon/3, f(x, y)\}$ whose end lies in S_n. The function $f(x, y)$, being uniformly continuous, let $\delta > 0$ be a number such that

$$|f(x'', y'') - f(x', y')| < \epsilon/3,$$

if only $|x'' - x'| + |y'' - y'| \leqq \delta$ (thus any vector of modulus $\leqq \delta$ belongs to $E\{\epsilon/3, f(x, y)\}$).

By an argument similar to one used in 10°, § 1, there exists an integer $n_0 > 0$ such that to any integer n corresponds an integer n' $(-n_0 \leqq n' \leqq +n_0)$, for which $|v_n - v_{n'}| < \delta$. We write now the following identity in vectors

$$(u_n - u_{n'}, 0) = (u_n - u_{n'}, v_n - v_{n'}) + (0, v_{n'} - v_n).$$

Observing that the vector $(u_n - u_{n'}, v_n - v_{n'}) = \tau_n - \tau_{n'}$ belongs to $E\{2\epsilon/3, f(x, y)\}$, and that by the definition of δ the vector $(0, v_{n'} - v_n)$ belongs to $E\{\epsilon/3, f(x, y)\}$, we conclude that the vector $(u_n - u_{n'}, 0)$ belongs to $E\{\epsilon, f(x, y)\}$, and being parallel to the X-axis belongs also to $XE\{\epsilon, f(x, y)\}$.

The set of vectors $(u_n - u_{n'}, 0)$ $(-\infty < n < +\infty)$ being *r.d.* on the X-axis we conclude that $XE\{\epsilon, f(x, y)\}$ is *r.d.* Similarly $YE\{\epsilon, f(x, y)\}$ is *r.d.*

Corollary. *A u.a.p. function of two variables is u.a.p. with respect to each of the variables.*

Remark. The converse of this corollary is not true: *a function* $f(x, y)$ *which is u.a.p. with respect to each variable need not be a u.a.p. function of two variables*, as the function $\cos xy$ shows.

4°. THEOREM. *If* $f_1(x, y)$, $f_2(x, y)$ *are u.a.p. functions, then the common numbers of the two sets* $XE\{\epsilon, f_1(x, y)\}$, $XE\{\epsilon, f_2(x, y)\}$ *form a r.d. set.*

The argument of 9°—11° of § 1 is applicable word for word to the sets $XE\{\epsilon, f_1(x, y)\}$, $XE\{\epsilon, f_2(x, y)\}$.

5°. THEOREM. *The sum and the product of two u.a.p. functions is u.a.p.*

In the same way as in 12°, 13°, § 1, the theorem follows from the theorem of 2° and from the preceding theorem.

6°. THEOREM. *If $f(x, y)$ is a u.a.p. function, then $M_y\{f(x, y)\}$ is a u.a.p. function of x.*

For let u be any number of $XE\{\epsilon, f(x, y)\}$. We have $|f(x+u, y)-f(x, y)| \leqq \epsilon$ for all x, y, and consequently

$$|M_y\{f(x+u, y)\} - M_y\{f(x, y)\}| \leqq M_y\{|f(x+u, y)-f(x, y)|\} \leqq \epsilon,$$

i.e. $E[\epsilon, M_y\{f(x, y)\}]$ contains the set $XE\{\epsilon, f(x, y)\}$, and consequently is *r.d.*, which proves the theorem.

7°. THEOREM. *For any u.a.p. function $f(x, y)$*

$$M_x[M_y\{f(x, y)\}] = \frac{1}{T_1 . T_2}\int_0^{T_1} dx \int_0^{T_2} f(x, y)\, dy + 2\theta\left(\epsilon + \frac{Al_\epsilon}{T_1} + \frac{Al_\epsilon}{T_2}\right),$$

where $A = \underset{\substack{-\infty < x < +\infty \\ -\infty < y < +\infty}}{u.b.} |f(x, y)|,$

ϵ, T_1, T_2 are any positive numbers and $l_\epsilon > 0$ is an inclusion interval of each of the sets $XE\{\epsilon, f(x, y)\}$, $YE\{\epsilon, f(x, y)\}$.

We observe that all numbers of $YE\{\epsilon, f(x, y)\}$ are translation numbers belonging to ϵ of $f(x, y)$ considered as a function of y only, and all numbers of $XE\{\epsilon, f(x, y)\}$ are translation numbers of $M_y\{f(x, y)\}$ belonging to ϵ. Thus any interval of length l_ϵ contains both a translation number of $f(x, y)$, considered as a function of y, and also a translation number of $M_y\{f(x, y)\}$.

Observing that

$$u.b. |M_y\{f(x, y)\}| \leqq A,$$

we shall have by (3) 2°, § 3,

$$(1) \quad M_y\{f(x, y)\} = \frac{1}{T_2}\int_0^{T_2} f(x, y)\, dy + \theta\left(\epsilon + \frac{2Al_\epsilon}{T_2}\right),$$

$$(2) \quad M_x[M_y\{f(x, y)\}] = \frac{1}{T_1}\int_0^{T_1} M_y\{f(x, y)\}\, dx + \theta\left(\epsilon + \frac{2Al_\epsilon}{T_1}\right).$$

Substituting the right-hand side of (1) for $M_y\{f(x, y)\}$ in the right-hand side of (2), we have

$$(3)\quad M_x[M_y\{f(x, y)\}]$$
$$= \frac{1}{T_1T_2}\int_0^{T_1} dx \int_0^{T_2} f(x, y)\,dy + 2\theta\left(\epsilon + \frac{Al_\epsilon}{T_1} + \frac{Al_\epsilon}{T_2}\right).$$

Corollary. *For any u.a.p. function* $f(x, y)$

$$(4)\qquad M_x[M_y\{f(x, y)\}] = M_y[M_x\{f(x, y)\}].$$

We denote the common value of these two expressions by

$$M_{xy}\{f(x, y)\}.$$

PROBLEM. Prove that

$$M_{xy}[M_{st}\{f(x+s, y+t)\,f(s, t)\,e^{-i(\lambda x+\mu y)}\}]$$
$$= M_{st}[M_{xy}\{f(x+s, y+t)\,\bar{f}(s, t)\,e^{-i(\lambda x+\mu y)}\}],$$

where $f(x, y)$ is a *u.a.p.* function of two variables, and λ, μ are real.

8°. Write $\qquad M_y\{f(x, y)\,e^{-i\mu y}\} = a(\mu, x),$

where μ is real. We know that for any fixed x, $a(\mu, x)$ can differ from nought for at most an enumerable set of values of μ. This set may of course depend upon the value of x. We shall now prove the following

THEOREM. *The set of all values of* μ *for which* $a(\mu, x)$ *differs from nought for at least one value of* x *is at most enumerably infinite.*

Observe first that the set of all functions $a(\mu, x)$ $(-\infty < \mu < +\infty)$ of x is uniformly continuous, since

$$|a(\mu, x+\delta) - a(\mu, x)| \leqq \underset{\substack{-\infty < x < +\infty \\ -\infty < y < +\infty}}{u.b.} |f(x+\delta, y) - f(x, y)|.$$

Assume now that the theorem is not true and that the set of values of μ, for which $a(\mu, x) \neq 0$ for at least one value of x, is more than enumerable. Then there exists an $a_0 > 0$ such that the part of the above set for which

$$(1)\qquad |a(\mu, x)| > a_0$$

is also more than enumerable. Define now a number δ_0 such that

(2) $$|a(\mu, x'') - a(\mu, x')| < \tfrac{1}{2} a_0,$$

for all μ if only $|x'' - x'| \leqq \delta_0$, which is possible on account of the uniform continuity of the set of functions $a(\mu, x)$.

It is easy to see that there exists a number x_0 such that the set of values of μ for which (1) is satisfied, for at least one value of x belonging to the interval $(x_0 - \delta_0, x_0 + \delta_0)$, is more than enumerable. For any μ of this set we have, by (2),

$$|a(\mu, x_0)| > \tfrac{1}{2} a_0,$$

and thus $a(\mu, x_0) \neq 0$ for more than an enumerable set of values of μ, which is impossible. Thus the theorem is proved.

Denote by $\mu_1, \mu_2, \ldots$, all values of μ for which $a(\mu, x)$ may differ from nought. Then, considering $f(x, y)$ as a *u.a.p.* function of y, we shall have

(3) $$f(x, y) \sim \sum_{m=1}^{\infty} a(\mu_m, x)\, e^{i\mu_m y}.$$

Substituting now in the right-hand side the Fourier series of all $a(\mu_m, x)$,

$$a(\mu_m, x) \sim \sum_{n=1}^{\infty} b_{n, m} e^{i\lambda_{n, m} x},$$

we obtain

(4) $$f(x, y) \sim \sum_{\substack{1 \leqq n < \infty \\ 1 \leqq m < \infty}} b_{n, m} e^{i(\lambda_{n, m} x + \mu_m y)},$$

and we call the double series on the right-hand side the Fourier series of $f(x, y)$ (as of a function of two variables).

Remark. Writing

$$c(\lambda, \mu) = M_{xy}\{f(x, y)\, e^{-i(\lambda x + \mu y)}\},$$

we see from (4), 7°, that we can represent the Fourier series of $f(x, y)$ in a more symmetrical form

(5) $$f(x, y) \sim \Sigma c(\lambda, \mu)\, e^{i(\lambda x + \mu y)},$$

where the summation is extended over all λ and μ for which $c(\lambda, \mu)$ differs from zero.

9°. Parseval Equation. *For any u.a.p. function*

(1) $$f(x, y) \sim \sum_{\substack{1 \leqq n < \infty \\ 1 \leqq m < \infty}} b_{n,m} e^{i(\lambda_{n,m} x + \mu_m y)},$$

the equation

(2) $$M_{xy} \{|f(x, y)|^2\} = \sum_{\substack{1 \leqq n < \infty \\ 1 \leqq m < \infty}} |b_{n,m}|^2$$

is satisfied.

Suppose first that all Fourier coefficients are nought, i.e. $b_{n,m} = 0$ for all n, m. Writing as before

(3) $$f(x, y) \sim \sum_{m=1}^{\infty} a(\mu_m, x) e^{i\mu_m y},$$

we see that the Fourier series of each function $a(\mu_m, x)$ is nought, and thus all $a(\mu_m, x) = 0$ identically. Consequently for any x the Fourier series of the *u.a.p.* function of y, $f(x, y)$ is nought, which proves that for any x, $f(x, y) = 0$ for all y, i.e. $f(x, y) = 0$ identically. Then

$$M_{xy} \{|f(x, y)|^2\} = 0,$$

which is the equation (2) for this particular case.

We have also proved that

If the Fourier series of a u.a.p. function is nought, then the function is identically equal to nought.

Passing now to the general case we first prove the Bessel inequality. By (3)

(4) $$M_y \{|f(x, y)|^2\} \geqq \Sigma' \, |a(\mu_m, x)|^2,$$

where the summation Σ' is extended over any finite number of values of m. Taking now the mean value of each side of (4) and applying the Bessel inequality to each term of the right-hand side, we conclude that

$$M_{xy} \{|f(x, y)|^2\} \geqq \Sigma'' \, |b_{n,m}|^2,$$

where Σ'' is extended over any finite number of terms, and the Bessel inequality

$$M_{xy} \{|f(x, y)|^2\} \geqq \sum_{\substack{1 \leqq n < \infty \\ 1 \leqq m < \infty}} |b_{n,m}|^2$$

follows. We introduce now the function

$$g(x, y) = M_{st} \{f(x + s, y + t) \bar{f}(s, t)\}.$$

In the same way as in 6°, § 4 (on account of Problem of 7°), we find the Fourier series of $g(x, y)$ in the form

$$g(x, y) \sim \Sigma |b_{n,m}|^2 e^{i(\lambda_{n,m}x+\mu_m y)}.$$

The series on the right-hand side being uniformly convergent, we conclude that the function represented by the sum of this series

$$\phi(x, y) = \Sigma |b_{n,m}|^2 e^{i(\lambda_{n,m}x+\mu_m y)}$$

is *u.a.p.* and has this series as its Fourier series. Then the Fourier series of the function

$$g(x, y) - \phi(x, y) = g(x, y) - \Sigma |b_{n,m}|^2 e^{i(\lambda_{n,m}x+\mu_m y)}$$

is nought, and consequently

$$g(x, y) - \Sigma |b_{n,m}|^2 e^{i(\lambda_{n,m}x+\mu_m y)} = 0$$

identically. Writing this equation for $x = y = 0$, and observing that

$$g(0, 0) = M_{st}\{|f(s, t)|^2\},$$

we obtain $$M_{xy}\{|f(x, y)|^2\} - \Sigma |b_{n,m}|^2 = 0,$$

which is the equation (2).

10°. Approximation Theorem. *Given a u.a.p. function*

$$f(x, y) \sim \Sigma b_{n,m} e^{i(\lambda_{n,m}x+\mu_m y)}$$

and a positive number ϵ, *there exists a trigonometrical polynomial* $P(x, y)$, *with exponents belonging to the Fourier exponents of* $f(x, y)$, *which satisfies the inequality*

$$|f(x, y) - P(x, y)| < \epsilon$$

for all values of x *and* y.

In other words:

Any u.a.p. function $f(x, y)$ *can be uniformly approximated to by trigonometric polynomials with exponents belonging to the Fourier exponents of* $f(x, y)$.

The proof is analogous to that of 2°, § 5.

CHAPTER II

GENERALISATION OF ALMOST PERIODIC FUNCTIONS

Introduction

We have seen that the class of *u.a.p.* functions may be considered from two different points of view. On the one hand it is the class of continuous functions possessing a certain structural property, which is a generalisation of pure periodicity, and on the other it is the class of limit functions of uniformly convergent sequences of trigonometric polynomials.

Corresponding to the two different points of view the generalisations of almost periodic functions went in two different directions.

On the one hand there were further structural generalisations of pure periodicity. The first generalisations were the very important ones given by W. Stepanoff, who succeeded in removing the continuity restrictions, and characterised the generalised almost periodicity not by values of the functions at each point but by mean values over integrals of fixed length. N. Wiener studied almost periodicity and gave a new proof of the fundamental theorem by means of the representation of functions by Fourier's integrals, and independently of Stepanoff he arrived at one of his (Stepanoff's) generalisations. H. Weyl also gave a new method in the theory of almost periodic functions based on integral equations. His method led him to a new structural generalisation of almost periodicity, which was wider than one of Stepanoff's types.

The second direction of generalisations was that adopted by the author. Corresponding to the definition of *u.a.p.* functions as limits of uniformly convergent sequences of trigonometrical polynomials, he enlarged the class of almost periodic functions, by considering the convergence of sequences of functions in a more general sense than uniform convergence, and by defining almost periodic functions as limits of such sequences of trigonometric polynomials. The purpose of this generalisation was to enlarge the class of almost periodic functions to the extent of existence of the Riesc-Fischer Theorem.

However, all these generalisations were not directed by the idea of a reciprocity between structural properties and the character of convergence of sequences of trigonometric polynomials, though important results were given by S. Bochner, H. Weyl and R. Schmidt.

Then H. Bohr and the author gave a systematic investigation of structural generalisations of almost periodicity, and they established a strict correspondence between various types of almost periodicity and the character of convergence of corresponding sequences of polynomials.

This question being of interest for the theory of almost periodic functions, acquires also its importance on account of the connection of almost periodic functions with general trigonometric series. The fact is that, like a *u.a.p.* function, any generalised *a.p.* function $f(x)$ has a Fourier series in the form of a general trigonometric series $\Sigma A_n e^{i\Lambda_n x}$ (all Λ_n real numbers) —and sequences of trigonometrical polynomials "convergent" to $f(x)$ converge formally to this series (i.e. the coefficients of the polynomials converge to those of the series).

Thus while studying various types of almost periodicity we study at the same time a large class of general trigonometric series (including for instance all series for which $\Sigma |A_n|^2$ is finite) with appropriate character of convergence.

§ 1. Auxiliary theorems and formulae.

1°. In this section we shall quote some theorems and formulae, which will be used later.

We introduced in Chapter I the notation $\overline{M}\{f(t)\}$, $\underline{M}\{f(t)\}$, $M\{f(t)\}$ for various mean values of a real function $f(t)$ of a continuous variable.

In the same way, if $f(i)$ is a real function defined for all integral values of i, we denote the various limits of the expression

$$\frac{1}{2n+1}\sum_{i=-n}^{+n} f(i),$$

as $n \to \infty$, by the symbols

$$\bar{M}\{f(i)\},\quad \underline{M}\{f(i)\},\quad M\{f(i)\}.$$

If $f(i)$ is defined only for positive integers, then we denote by these symbols the limits of the expression

$$\frac{1}{n}\sum_{i=1}^{n} f(i),$$

as $n \to \infty$.

2°. Hölder's Inequalities.

Let p and q be positive numbers satisfying the condition

$$\frac{1}{p}+\frac{1}{q}=1,$$

and $\phi(t)$, $\psi(t)$ two non-negative functions: then we have

$$(1)\qquad \int_a^b \phi(t)\,\psi(t)\,dt \leqq \left[\int_a^b \{\phi(t)\}^p\,dt\right]^{1/p}\left[\int_a^b \{\psi(t)\}^q\,dt\right]^{1/q}.$$

Similarly we have

$$(2)\qquad \sum_m^n \phi(i)\,\psi(i) \leqq \left[\sum_m^n \{\phi(i)\}^p\right]^{1/p}\left[\sum_m^n \{\psi(i)\}^q\right]^{1/q}.$$

From (1), (2) we conclude immediately that

$$(3)\qquad M\{\phi\,.\,\psi\} \leqq [M\{\phi^p\}]^{1/p}\,[M\{\psi^q\}]^{1/q},$$

or more generally that

$$(4)\qquad \underline{M}\{\phi\,.\,\psi\} \leqq [\underline{M}\{\phi^p\}]^{1/p}\,[\bar{M}\{\psi^q\}]^{1/q},$$

$$(5)\qquad \bar{M}\{\phi\,.\,\psi\} \leqq [\bar{M}\{\phi^p\}]^{1/p}\,[\bar{M}\{\psi^q\}]^{1/q}.$$

Formulae (3), (4) and (5) hold whether ϕ, ψ are functions of a continuous variable t or of an integral variable.

3°. Fatou's Theorem.

Let $f(t, n)$ be a non-negative function given for all t in a finite interval (a, b) and for all positive integral values of n. Then we have

$$(1)\qquad \int_a^b \underline{\lim}_{n\to\infty} f(t,n)\,dt \leqq \underline{\lim}_{n\to\infty} \int_a^b f(t,n)\,dt.$$

This formula also holds if n is a continuous variable. As an immediate corollary we have

$$(2)\qquad \int_a^b \underline{M}_x\{f(t,x)\}\,dt \leqq \underline{M}_x\left\{\int_a^b f(t,x)\,dt\right\}.$$

4°. **Lemma.** *Smoothing an integrable function.*

Let $f(t)$ be a function integrable (L) in a finite interval (a, b), and let

$$f_\delta(t) = \frac{1}{\delta}\int_t^{t+\delta} f(u)\,du. \qquad (a < t < b - \delta)$$

Then for any $\beta < b$

$$(1)\qquad \lim_{\delta\to 0}\int_a^\beta |f(t) - f_\delta(t)|\,dt = 0.$$

Remark. We observe that if $f(t)$ is periodic, then $f_\delta(t)$ is continuous and periodic with the same period.

5°. Some Inequalities.

(i) *If $f(t)$ is a non-negative function, then*

$$(1)\qquad \int_a^b dt\,\frac{1}{\delta}\int_t^{t+\delta} f(u)\,du \leqq \int_a^{b+\delta} f(t)\,dt.$$

(ii) *If $f(t)$ is a non-negative function and if $p' < p''$, then*

$$(2)\qquad \left[\frac{1}{b-a}\int_a^b \{f(t)\}^{p'}\,dt\right]^{1/p'} \leqq \left[\frac{1}{b-a}\int_a^b \{f(t)\}^{p''}\,dt\right]^{1/p''},$$

$$(3)\qquad [\bar{M}\{\{f(t)\}^{p'}\}]^{1/p'} \leqq [\bar{M}\{\{f(t)\}^{p''}\}]^{1/p''}.$$

(iii) *If $\phi(t)$ and $\psi(t)$ are non-negative and if $p \geqq 1$, then*

$$(4)\qquad \left[\int_a^b (\phi+\psi)^p\,dt\right]^{1/p} \leqq \left[\int_a^b \phi^p\,dt\right]^{1/p} + \left[\int_a^b \psi^p\,dt\right]^{1/p}.$$

§ 2. General closures and general almost periodicity.

1°. We now pass to our main problem, i.e. to the investigation of various classes of functions given in the whole interval $-\infty < x < +\infty$ which can be approximated in some way or other by finite trigonometric polynomials

$$(1)\qquad s(x) = \Sigma a_\nu e^{i\lambda_\nu x},$$

where the exponents λ_ν are any real numbers, and the coefficients a_ν any real or complex numbers. We denote the class of all polynomials (1) by A. We shall consider only those approximations which preserve the main characteristic properties of the functions $s(x)$ (those relating to oscillations).

Then we have to consider only approximations *which involve some sort of uniformity in the whole interval* $-\infty < x < +\infty$.

For the class of functions which can be approximated by a sequence $\{s_n(x)\}$ of polynomials (1), even uniformly in any finite interval, is too wide: this class contains in fact all continuous functions.

We shall talk of functions in terms of geometry. We call a class of functions a functional space, and any function of this class a point of the functional space. We first define the notion of the distance of two points. Corresponding to various definitions of the distance we define various "functional spaces."

2°. We introduce the following definitions of the distance between two points (functions) $f(x)$ and $\phi(x)$.

(i) We define the uniform distance $D_U[f(x), \phi(x)]$ by the equation

$$(1) \qquad D_U[f(x), \phi(x)] = \underset{-\infty < x < +\infty}{u.b.} |f(x) - \phi(x)|.$$

We define further the symbol $D_U[f(x)]$ by the equation

$$(2) \qquad D_U[f(x)] = D_U[f(x), 0] = \underset{-\infty < x < +\infty}{u.b.} |f(x)|.$$

(ii) We define S distance of the class p $(p \geqq 1)$ relating to the length l, $D_{S_l^p}[f(x), \phi(x)]$, by the equation

$$(3) \qquad D_{S_l^p}[f(x), \phi(x)] = \underset{-\infty < x < +\infty}{u.b.} \left[\frac{1}{l}\int_x^{x+l} |f(x) - \phi(x)|^p \, dx\right]^{1/p}.$$

We define the symbol $D_{S_l^p}[f(x)]$ by the equation

$$(4) \qquad D_{S_l^p}[f(x)] = D_{S_l^p}[f(x), 0] = \underset{-\infty < x < +\infty}{u.b.} \left[\frac{1}{l}\int_x^{x+l} |f(x)|^p \, dx\right]^{1/p}.$$

When any of the numbers p, l is equal to 1 we drop it in our notation. Thus we write D_{S_l}, D_{S^p}, D_S instead of $D_{S_l^1}$, $D_{S_1^p}$, $D_{S_1^1}$.

If $p'<p''$ we have on account of (2), 5°, § 1,

(5) $$D_{S_l^{p''}}[f(x), \phi(x)] \geqq D_{S_l^{p'}}[f(x), \phi(x)].$$

(iii) We define W distance of class $p (p \geqq 1)$, $D_{W^p}[f(x), \phi(x)]$, by the equation

(6) $$D_{W^p}[f(x), \phi(x)] = \lim D_{S_l^p}[f(x), \phi(x)],$$

as $l \to \infty$, and we write

(7) $$D_{W^p}[f(x)] = D_{W^p}[f(x), 0].$$

For the validity of this definition we have to prove the existence of the limit on the right-hand side of (6). Obviously it is enough to prove the existence for the case of $\phi(x) = 0$ and $p = 1$, i.e. to prove the existence of the limit

(8) $$\lim D_{S_l}[f(x)],$$

as $l \to \infty$.

If $D_{S_l}[f(x)]$ is infinite for one value of l then it is also infinite for all others, and thus in this case the limit (8) exists. Suppose now that $D_{S_l}[f(x)]$ is finite for all values of l. Let l_0, l be any two positive numbers and n the positive integer such that

(9) $$(n-1)\, l_0 < l \leqq n l_0.$$

We have

$$\frac{1}{l}\int_x^{x+l} |f(x)|\, dx \leqq \frac{n l_0}{l} \cdot \frac{1}{n l_0}\int_x^{x+n l_0} |f(x)|\, dx,$$

and thus

(10) $$D_{S_l}[f(x)] \leqq \frac{n l_0}{l} D_{S_{n l_0}}[f(x)] \leqq \frac{l + l_0}{l} D_{S_{n l_0}}[f(x)].$$

We have evidently

(11) $$D_{S_{n l_0}}[f(x)] \leqq D_{S_{l_0}}[f(x)].$$

By (10), (11)

(12) $$D_{S_l}[f(x)] \leqq \left(1 + \frac{l_0}{l}\right) D_{S_{l_0}}[f(x)],$$

from which we conclude that

(13) $$\overline{\lim_{l \to \infty}}\, D_{S_l}[f(x)] \leqq D_{S_{l_0}}[f(x)].$$

(13) being true for all values of l_0 we conclude that

(14) $$\overline{\lim_{l\to\infty}} D_{S_l}[f(x)] \leqq \lim_{l_0\to\infty} D_{S_{l_0}}[f(x)] = \lim_{l\to\infty} D_{S_l}[f(x)],$$

which proves the existence of the limit (8) and thus the existence of the limit on the right-hand side of (6).

In the same way as before we write D_W instead of D_{W^1}.

(iv) We define B distance of class p $(p \geqq 1)$,

$$D_{B^p}[f(x), \phi(x)],$$

by the equation

(15) $$D_{B^p}[f(x), \phi(x)] = [\bar{M}\{|f(x) - \phi(x)|^p\}]^{1/p}.$$

In the same way as before we write

(16) $$D_{B^p}[f(x)] = D_{B^p}[f(x), 0].$$

If the number p is equal to 1 we drop it in our notation.

Now we easily find

$$D_{S_l^p} \geqq D_{B^p},$$

and hence by definition

$$D_{W^p} \geqq D_{B^p}.$$

Thus by (13) we have

(17) $$D_U[f(x), \phi(x)] \geqq D_{S_l^p} \geqq D_{W^p} \geqq D_{B^p}. \qquad (p \geqq 1)$$

By (2), (3), 5°, §1,

(18) $D_{S_l^{p'}} \leqq D_{S_l^{p''}}$, $D_{W^{p'}} \leqq D_{W^{p''}}$, $D_{B^{p'}} \leqq D_{B^{p''}}$ for $p' < p''$.

These are the only distances which we shall consider in our general investigation. When we wish to speak of one of these distances without specifying a definite kind we shall write

$$D_G[f(x), \phi(x)].$$

It can be readily seen that the *Triangle Rule* holds in the general case, i.e. if $f(x)$, $\phi(x)$, $\psi(x)$ are any three functions, then

(19) $$D_G[f(x), \psi(x)] \leqq D_G[f(x), \phi(x)] + D_G[\phi(x), \psi(x)].$$

3°. If a function $f(x)$ and a sequence $\{f_n(x)\}$ of functions are such that

(1) $$D_G[f(x), f_n(x)] \to 0,$$

as $n \to \infty$, then we say that the function $f(x)$ is a G limit of the sequence $\{f_n(x)\}$.

Corresponding to the particular meanings of $D_G[f(x), f_n(x)]$, namely

$$D_U, \quad D_{S_l^p}, \quad D_{W^p}, \quad D_{B^p},$$

we write

$$f(x) = U \lim f_n(x), = S_l^p \lim f_n(x), = W^p \lim f_n(x), = B^p \lim f_n(x).$$

It is easy to see that if $S_l^p \lim f_n(x)$ exists, then $S^p \lim f_n(x)$ also exists and we have $S_l^p \lim f_n(x) = S^p \lim f_n(x)$.

Remark. We shall indicate the kind of uniqueness which lies in the definition of a limit function of a sequence $\{f_n(x)\}$ of functions. We conclude from (19) of 2° that if $f(x)$ is a G limit function of the sequence $\{f_n(x)\}$, then every function $\phi(x)$ which satisfies the condition

$$(2) \qquad D_G[f(x), \phi(x)] = 0,$$

is also a G limit function of the sequence $\{f_n(x)\}$, and no other function can be a G limit of this sequence. If

$$D_U[f(x), \phi(x)] = 0,$$

then

$$f(x) = \phi(x)$$

for all x.

If

$$D_{S^p}[f(x), \phi(x)] = 0,$$

then $\phi(x)$ may be any function which is equal to $f(x)$ at almost all points. In the cases when

$$D_{W^p}[f(x), \phi(x)] = 0, \quad \text{or} \quad D_{B^p}[f(x), \phi(x)] = 0,$$

the functions $f(x)$, $\phi(x)$ may differ at a set of points of finite and even of infinite measure.

Thus, *$U \lim f_n(x)$ is defined in a completely unique way; two determinations of $S^p \lim f_n(x)$ differ from one another only in a set of measure zero; but two determinations of $W^p \lim f_n(x)$ and a* fortiori *also of $B^p \lim f_n(x)$, may differ from one another at a set of positive and indeed infinite measure.*

4°. We call a function $f(x)$ a limit function of a set $\mathfrak{A}$ of functions if $f(x)$ is a limit function of a sequence $\{f_n(x)\}$ contained in $\mathfrak{A}$. The set $\mathfrak{A}$ with the set of all its limit functions is called *the closure of the set* $\mathfrak{A}$ and is denoted by

$$C_G(\mathfrak{A}).$$

Corresponding to various definitions of the distance we have the closures

(1) $C_U(\mathfrak{A}),\quad C_{S^p}(\mathfrak{A}),\quad C_{W^p}(\mathfrak{A}),\quad C_{B^p}(\mathfrak{A}).\qquad (p \geqq 1)$

The set $\mathfrak{A}$ is called a base of the closure $C_G(\mathfrak{A})$. We shall now prove the following

THEOREM ON UNIFORM CLOSURE OF THE BASE. *The closure of the set $\mathfrak{A}$ and the closure of the set $C_U(\mathfrak{A})$ are identical, or in symbols*

(2) $$C_G(\mathfrak{A}) = C_G[C_U(\mathfrak{A})].$$

(i) It is obvious that

(3) $$C_G(\mathfrak{A}) \subset C_G[C_U(\mathfrak{A})].$$

(ii) Let now $f(x)$ belong to $C_G[C_U(\mathfrak{A})]$. If it belongs at the same time to $C_U(\mathfrak{A})$, then it also belongs to $C_G(\mathfrak{A})$, as

$$C_G(\mathfrak{A}) \supset C_U(\mathfrak{A}).$$

If, however, $f(x)$ does not belong to $C_U(\mathfrak{A})$, then $C_U(\mathfrak{A})$ contains a sequence of points $\{\phi_n(x)\}$ such that

(4) $$D_G\{f(x), \phi_n(x)\} \to 0,$$

as $n \to \infty$. As $\phi_n(x)$ belongs to $C_U\{\mathfrak{A}\}$ we conclude that $\mathfrak{A}$ contains a point $f_n(x)$ (which may coincide with $\phi_n(x)$) such that

$$D_U\{\phi_n(x), f_n(x)\} < \frac{1}{n},$$

and consequently that

(5) $$D_G\{\phi_n(x), f_n(x)\} < \frac{1}{n}.$$

By the Triangle Rule

$$D_G\{f(x), f_n(x)\} \leqq D_G\{f(x), \phi_n(x)\} + D_G\{\phi_n(x), f_n(x)\},$$

and thus by (4), (5)

$$D_G\{f(x), f_n(x)\} \to 0,$$

as $n \to \infty$. As all $f_n(x)$ belong to $\mathfrak{A}$ we conclude that $f(x)$ belongs to $C_G(\mathfrak{A})$.

Thus in either case, whether $f(x)$ belongs to $C_U(\mathfrak{A})$ or not, it belongs to $C_G(\mathfrak{A})$. Consequently

(6) $$C_G(\mathfrak{A}) \supset C_G\{C_U(\mathfrak{A})\}.$$

By (3), (6) the theorem has been proved.

5°. At the beginning of this chapter we indicated the general nature of our investigation: we can now define its scope precisely by means of the symbols that have been introduced.

We shall study the closures

(1) $$C_U(A), \quad C_{S^p}(A), \quad C_{W^p}(A), \quad C_{B^p}(A),$$

where $p \geqq 1$ *and* A *is the class of all polynomials* (1), 1°, § 2.

We have

(2) $$C_U(A) \subset C_{S^p}(A) \subset C_{W^p}(A) \subset C_{B^p}(A), \qquad (p \geqq 1)$$

and if $p' < p''$

(3) $$C_{S^{p''}} \subset C_{S^{p'}}, \quad C_{W^{p''}} \subset C_{W^{p'}}, \quad C_{B^{p''}} \subset C_{B^{p'}}.$$

Our task falls into two parts:

PROBLEM I. *To characterise the closures* (1) *by structural properties of functions.*

PROBLEM II. *To find an algorithm for the construction of proper approximations to functions of various closures.*

The solution of these two problems for the general case of the closures

$$C_{S^p}(A), \quad C_{W^p}(A), \quad C_{B^p}(A), \qquad (p \geqq 1)$$

will be based on the solution for the special case of the closure $C_U(A)$.

We shall denote the class of all *u.a.p.* functions by the symbol $\{u.a.p.\}$.

The solution of Problem I for the case of the closure $C_U(A)$ follows from 1°, § 5, and from Theorem of 2°, § 5, Chapter I. With our new notation it can be formulated in the following way:

THEOREM $IC_U(A)$. *The closure* $C_U(A)$ *is identical with* $\{u.a.p.\}$, *i.e.*

(4) $$C_U(A) = \{u.a.p.\}.$$

Corollary. *For all closures which are considered in this chapter we have*

(5) $$C_G(A) = C_G[\{u.a.p.\}].$$

The proof follows from (2) 4°, (4).

6°. Our investigation of the general closures

(1) $C_{S^p}(A),\quad C_{W^p}(A),\quad C_{B^p}(A),$

will be based on Theorem $IC_U(A)$.

Each of the classes (1) will be characterised by some kind of *almost periodic* properties.

For this purpose we introduce the following definitions.

S_l^p almost periodic functions.

If for a given function $f(x)$ a real number τ satisfies the condition

(2) $$D_{S_l^p}[f(x+\tau), f(x)] \leqq \epsilon,$$

then we call the number τ *an S_l^p translation number belonging to* ϵ. Denote by $S_l^p E\{\epsilon, f(x)\}$ the set of all these numbers.

If the set $S_l^p E\{\epsilon, f(x)\}$ is relatively dense for all positive values of ϵ, then we say that the function $f(x)$ is S_l^p almost periodic (S_l^p a.p.).

It can be easily seen that *for any l an S_l^p a.p. function is also an S^p a.p. function.* Therefore we shall in future speak merely of S^p *a.p.* functions.

W^p almost periodic functions.

If a function $f(x)$ is such that to any $\epsilon > 0$ corresponds an $l = l(\epsilon)$ for which the set $S_l^p E\{\epsilon, f(x)\}$ is relatively dense, then we say that the function $f(x)$ is W^p almost periodic (W^p a.p.).

Thus the difference between S_l^p *a.p.* functions and W^p *a.p.* functions is that in the latter class l varies with ϵ.

It is easy to see that *if $\overline{\lim_{\epsilon \to 0}}\, l(\epsilon)$ is finite, then a W^p a.p. function is an S^p a.p. function.*

Remark. We shall always assume that S^p *a.p.* functions and W^p *a.p.* functions belong to the Lebesgue class L^p.

B^p almost periodic functions.

We shall first give a definition of a property of numerical sets. *A set E of real numbers is said to be satisfactorily uniform if* *there exists a positive number l such that the ratio of the maximum number of terms of E included in an interval of length l to the minimum number is less than* 2.

It is obvious that a satisfactorily uniform set is relatively dense.

We say that a function $f(x)$ of the class L^p is B^p almost periodic (B^p a.p.), if to any $\epsilon > 0$ corresponds a satisfactorily uniform set of numbers

$$(3) \qquad \ldots \tau_{-2} < \tau_{-1} < \tau_0 < \tau_1 < \tau_2 \ldots,$$

such that for each i

$$(4) \qquad \bar{M}_x\{|f(x+\tau_i)-f(x)|^p\} < \epsilon^p,$$

and that for every $c > 0$

$$(5) \qquad \bar{M}_x \bar{M}_i \frac{1}{c}\int_x^{x+c} |f(x+\tau_i)-f(x)|^p\, dx < \epsilon^p.$$

We call the numbers τ_i of (3) *B^p translation numbers of the function $f(x)$ belonging to ϵ.*

It may seem to be more natural to replace the condition (5) by the condition

$$(6) \qquad \bar{M}_x \bar{M}_i\{|f(x+\tau_i)-f(x)|^p\} < \epsilon^p.$$

We shall later on investigate also this kind of almost periodicity, but as in the conditions (5), (6) we use *upper* mean values, the smoothing process by which the condition (5) differs from the condition (6) appears to be of importance. We shall denote by the symbols $\{S^p$ *a.p.*$\}$, $\{W^p$ *a.p.*$\}$, $\{B^p$ *a.p.*$\}$ the classes of all S^p *a.p.* functions, W^p *a.p.* functions, B^p *a.p.* functions.

When $p=1$ we write *S a.p.*, *W a.p.*, *B a.p.* instead of S^1 *a.p.*, W^1 *a.p.*, B^1 *a.p.*

When we wish to speak of a function of one of these classes without specifying a definite one, we shall call it a *G a.p.* function.

Thus we have introduced three kinds of almost periodicity beside the uniform one. S^p almost periodicity is the nearest to the uniform one. It restricts the class L^p as uniform almost periodicity restricts the class of continuous functions. The typical property of imitation of values of functions, for values of argument increased by translation numbers, is substantially maintained. But the imitation at each point characterising *u.a.p.* functions is replaced by *integral imitation* of values over an interval of a fixed length. In other words, the uniformity of imitation belongs not to particular values of the argument but to intervals of a definite length. B^p almost periodicity is, as will be shown, the widest generalisation of the uniform one. The imitation due to this class of almost periodicity appears only as a general effect of the whole class of translation numbers and over the whole range of values of x. When we study this class of functions in connection with Fourier series we shall see that B^p almost periodicity is probably the generalisation of almost periodicity to its natural bounds.

W^p almost periodicity is intermediate between the S^p and B^p kinds.

§ 3. *S a.p.* functions.

1°. THEOREM $IC_S(A)$. *The closure $C_S(A)$ is identical with $\{S\ a.p.\}$, i.e.*

$$C_S(A) = \{S\ a.p.\}. \tag{1}$$

(i) We shall first prove that

$$C_S(A) \subset \{S\ a.p.\}. \tag{2}$$

Let $f(x)$ be any function of $C_S(A)$ and ϵ any positive number. In order to prove (2) we have only to prove that the set $SE\{\epsilon, f(x)\}$ is always relatively dense. Take a function $s(x)$ of A such that

$$D_S[f(x), s(x)] < \tfrac{1}{3}\epsilon. \tag{3}$$

Let τ be any number of the set $E\{\tfrac{1}{3}\epsilon, s(x)\}$. We shall have

$$\begin{aligned} D_S[f(x+\tau), f(x)] &\leqq D_S[f(x+\tau), s(x+\tau)] \\ &\quad + D_S[s(x+\tau), s(x)] + D_S[s(x), f(x)] \\ &\leqq 2D_S[s(x), f(x)] + D_U[s(x+\tau), s(x)] < \epsilon, \end{aligned} \tag{4}$$

which proves that

$$E\{\tfrac{1}{3}\epsilon, s(x)\} \subset SE\{\epsilon, f(x)\}. \tag{5}$$

The set $E\{\frac{1}{3}\epsilon, s(x)\}$ being relatively dense we conclude that so is the set $SE\{\epsilon, f(x)\}$, and thus (2) has been proved.

(ii) We shall now prove that

$$\{S\,a.p.\} \subset C_S(A). \tag{6}$$

Let $f(x)$ be $S\,a.p.$, and consider the functions

$$f_\delta(x) = \frac{1}{\delta}\int_x^{x+\delta} f(t)\,dt, \tag{7}$$

for $0<\delta<1$. Given $\epsilon>0$, let τ be any number of the set $SE\{\epsilon\delta, f(x)\}$. We have

$$(8)\quad |f_\delta(x+\tau)-f_\delta(x)| = \frac{1}{\delta}\left|\int_x^{x+\delta}[f(t+\tau)-f(t)]\,dt\right|$$
$$\leqq \frac{1}{\delta}\int_x^{x+1}|f(t+\tau)-f(t)|\,dt \leqq \epsilon,$$

whence

$$SE\{\epsilon\delta, f(x)\} \subset E\{\epsilon, f_\delta(x)\}, \tag{9}$$

which proves that the functions $f_\delta(x)$ are *u.a.p.* functions.

We shall now prove that

$$f(x) = S\lim f_\delta(x), \tag{10}$$

as $\delta \to 0$. Observe that for any x_0, and for any $\epsilon>0$ and $\tau \subset SE\{\epsilon, f(x)\}$, we have

$$(11)\quad \int_{x_0}^{x_0+1}|f_\delta(x+\tau)-f_\delta(x)|\,dx$$
$$\leqq \frac{1}{\delta}\int_{x_0}^{x_0+1}dx\int_x^{x+\delta}|f(\xi+\tau)-f(\xi)|\,d\xi$$
$$\leqq \frac{1}{\delta}\int_{x_0}^{x_0+1+\delta}|f(\xi+\tau)-f(\xi)|\,d\xi\int_{\xi-\delta}^{\xi}dx$$
$$\leqq \int_{x_0}^{x_0+2}|f(\xi+\tau)-f(\xi)|\,d\xi \leqq 2\epsilon,$$

whence

$$SE\{\epsilon, f(x)\} \subset SE\{2\epsilon, f_\delta(x)\}. \tag{12}$$

Given $\eta>0$, let $l = l_{\frac{1}{4}\eta}$ be an inclusion interval of

$$SE\{\tfrac{1}{4}\eta, f(x)\}$$

and consequently (on account of (12)) of $SE\{\frac{1}{2}\eta, f_\delta(x)\}$. Corresponding to any number x_0 we can define a number

$$\tau \subset SE\{\tfrac{1}{4}\eta, f(x)\} \subset SE\{\tfrac{1}{2}\eta, f_\delta(x)\},$$

such that the point $x_0 + \tau$ lies in the interval $(0, l)$. Then

$$(13) \quad \int_{x_0}^{x_0+1} |f(x) - f_\delta(x)|\, dx$$

$$\leqq \int_{x_0}^{x_0+1} |f(x) - f(x+\tau)|\, dx + \int_{x_0}^{x_0+1} |f(x+\tau) - f_\delta(x+\tau)|\, dx$$

$$+ \int_{x_0}^{x_0+1} |f_\delta(x+\tau) - f_\delta(x)|\, dx$$

$$\leqq \tfrac{1}{4}\eta + \int_{x_0+\tau}^{x_0+\tau+1} |f(x) - f_\delta(x)|\, dx + \tfrac{1}{2}\eta$$

$$\leqq \tfrac{3}{4}\eta + \int_{0}^{l+1} |f(x) - f_\delta(x)|\, dx.$$

By Lemma of 4°, § 1, there exists a number δ_0 such that

$$(14) \qquad \int_{0}^{l+1} |f(x) - f_\delta(x)|\, dx < \tfrac{1}{4}\eta$$

for all $\delta < \delta_0$. From (13), (14) we conclude that, given $\eta > 0$, there always exists a positive number δ_0 such that for all $\delta < \delta_0$ and for all x_0

$$\int_{x_0}^{x_0+1} |f(x) - f_\delta(x)|\, dx < \eta,$$

i.e.

$$D_S[f(x), f_\delta(x)] < \eta,$$

which proves (10). From (10) we conclude that

$$\{S\ a.p.\} \subset C_S[\{u.a.p.\}],$$

and (6) follows on account of (5) of 5°. The Theorem $IC_S(A)$ follows from (2) and (6).

2°. From the definition of *S a.p.* functions we can prove a theorem which will be of importance for the theory of analytic almost periodic functions.

Bochner's Theorem. *An S a.p. function $f(x)$, uniformly continuous in $(-\infty, +\infty)$, is u.a.p.*

For proving the theorem we have to prove that the set $E\{\epsilon, f(x)\}$ is *r.d.* for any $\epsilon > 0$. We shall prove this by proving that to any $\epsilon > 0$ corresponds $\delta > 0$ such that

$$(1) \qquad E\{\epsilon, f(x)\} \supset SE\{\delta, f(x)\}.$$

The function $f(x)$ being uniformly continuous, to any $\epsilon > 0$ corresponds an h $(0 < h < \frac{1}{2})$ such that

(2) $$|f(x') - f(x'')| < \tfrac{1}{4}\epsilon$$

if only $|x' - x''| \leqq h$.

Let now τ be any number of $SE\{\epsilon h, f(x)\}$. We shall prove that

(3) $$|f(x+\tau) - f(x)| \leqq \epsilon$$

for all x. For let otherwise x_0 be a number satisfying the inequality

(4) $$|f(x_0+\tau) - f(x_0)| > \epsilon.$$

By (2) $$|f(x+\tau) - f(x)| > \frac{\epsilon}{2}$$

for $x_0 - h \leqq x \leqq x_0 + h$. We have then

$$\int_{x_0-h}^{x_0-h+1} |f(x+\tau) - f(x)|\, dx > \int_{x_0-h}^{x_0+h} |f(x+\tau) - f(x)|\, dx > \epsilon h,$$

which is impossible, since τ is an S translation number of $f(x)$ belonging to ϵh. This proves (3) and consequently (1).

§ 4. *W a.p.* functions.

1°. Theorem $IC_W(A)$. *The closure* $C_W(A)$ *is identical with* $\{W\ a.p.\}$, *i.e.*

(1) $$C_W(A) = \{W\ a.p.\}.$$

(i) We shall first prove that

(2) $$C_W(A) \subset \{W\ a.p.\}.$$

Let $f(x)$ be any function of $C_W(A)$. In order to prove (2) we have only to show that to any positive ϵ corresponds an l such that the set $S_l E\{\epsilon, f(x)\}$ is relatively dense.

On account of the definition of $C_W(A)$ there exists a sequence $\{s_n(x)\}$ of functions of A such that

(3) $$D_W[f(x), s_n(x)] \to 0,$$

as $n \to \infty$. D_W being the limit of D_{S_l}, as $l \to \infty$, we can say that to the function $f(x)$ corresponds a sequence $\{s_n(x)\}$ of functions of A and a sequence $\{l_n\}$ of positive numbers such that

(4) $$D_{S_{l_n}}[f(x), s_n(x)] \to 0,$$

as $\rightarrow n\infty$. Then to any $\epsilon > 0$ corresponds an n such that

(5) $$D_{S_{l_n}}[f(x), s_n(x)] < \frac{\epsilon}{3}.$$

Now in the same way as in the case of Theorem $IC_S(A)$, we see that

(6) $$E\{\tfrac{1}{3}\epsilon, s_n(x)\} \subset S_{l_n} E\{\epsilon, f(x)\},$$

and consequently that the set $S_{l_n} E\{\epsilon, f(x)\}$ is relatively dense, which proves (2).

(ii) We shall now prove the converse, i.e.

(7) $$\{W\ a.p.\} \subset C_W(A).$$

The proof of this part of the theorem in the case of the closure $C_W(A)$ is considerably more difficult than in the case of the closure $C_S(A)$. We have first to prove two lemmas.

2°. **Lemma.** *W a.p. functions are "W-bounded," i.e. for any W a.p. function $f(x)$ $D_W[f(x)]$ is finite.*

Evidently it is enough to show that there exist two positive numbers L and Q such that

(1) $$D_{S_L}[f(x)] \leqq Q.$$

Define L by the condition that when $\epsilon = 1$ the set

(2) $$S_L E\{\epsilon, f(x)\}$$

is relatively dense. Let l_1 be an inclusion interval of (2). To any real x_0 corresponds a number τ of the set (2) such that the number $x_0 + \tau$ belongs to the interval $(0, l_1)$. We have then for any x_0

(3) $$\frac{1}{L}\int_{x_0}^{x_0+L} |f(x)|\,dx$$
$$\leqq \frac{1}{L}\int_{x_0}^{x_0+L} |f(x) - f(x+\tau)|\,dx + \frac{1}{L}\int_{x_0}^{x_0+L} |f(x+\tau)|\,dx$$
$$\leqq 1 + \frac{1}{L}\int_{x_0+\tau}^{x_0+\tau+L} |f(x)|\,dx \leqq 1 + \frac{1}{L}\int_0^{l_1+L} |f(x)|\,dx = Q.$$

which proves (1).

3°. **Lemma.** *W a.p. functions are "W-uniformly continuous," i.e. to any W a.p. function $f(x)$ and to any $\epsilon > 0$ there exist numbers $L > 0$ and $\delta_0 > 0$ such that*

(1) $$D_{S_L}[f(x+\delta), f(x)] < \epsilon$$

for all $|\delta| < \delta_0$.

Define a number L under the condition that the set

(2) $$S_L E\{\tfrac{1}{3}\epsilon, f(x)\}$$

is relatively dense, and let l be an inclusion interval of this set. To any x_0 corresponds a number τ of the set (2) such that the number $x_0 + \tau$ belongs to the interval $(0, l)$.

We have for any $\delta > 0$

(3) $$\begin{aligned}\frac{1}{L}\int_{x_0}^{x_0+L} &|f(x+\delta) - f(x)|\,dx \\ &\leq \frac{1}{L}\int_{x_0}^{x_0+L} |f(x+\delta) - f(x+\delta+\tau)|\,dx \\ &\qquad + \frac{1}{L}\int_{x_0}^{x_0+L} |f(x+\delta+\tau) - f(x+\tau)|\,dx \\ &\qquad + \frac{1}{L}\int_{x_0}^{x_0+L} |f(x+\tau) - f(x)|\,dx \\ &\leq \tfrac{1}{3}\epsilon + \frac{1}{L}\int_{x_0+\tau}^{x_0+L+\tau} |f(x+\delta) - f(x)|\,dx + \tfrac{1}{3}\epsilon \\ &\leq \tfrac{2}{3}\epsilon + \frac{1}{L}\int_0^{l+L} |f(x+\delta) - f(x)|\,dx.\end{aligned}$$

By a well-known Lebesgue theorem we can define $\delta_0 > 0$ so that for $|\delta| < \delta_0$

(4) $$\frac{1}{L}\int_0^{l+L} |f(x+\delta) - f(x)|\,dx < \frac{\epsilon}{3}.$$

By (3), (4) the lemma is proved.

4°. Now we shall proceed to the proof of (7) of 1°, or of the following equivalent statement:

(1) $$\{W\ a.p.\} \subset C_W[\{u.a.p.\}].$$

In order to prove (1) we have to prove that to any *W a.p.* function $f(x)$ and to any $\epsilon > 0$ corresponds a *u.a.p.* function $\phi(x)$ such that

(2) $$D_W[f(x), \phi(x)] < \epsilon.$$

We shall construct a *kernel* $K(t)$. We first choose the numbers L_1 and l so that the set

$$(3) \qquad S_{L_1} E\left\{\frac{\epsilon}{4}, f(x)\right\}$$

is relatively dense, and that l is its inclusion interval. Define now the numbers δ_0 and L_2 so that for any $|\delta| < \delta_0$

$$(4) \qquad D_{S_{L_2}}[f(x+\delta), f(x)] < \frac{\epsilon}{4}.$$

Now for any function $p(x)$ we have

$$D_{S_{L'}}[p(x)] \leqq 2D_{S_{L''}}[p(x)]$$

if $L' \geqq L''$, and hence when $L \geqq \max.(L_1, L_2)$, we have

$$(5) \qquad D_{S_L}[f(x+\delta), f(x)] < \frac{\epsilon}{2}$$

for any $|\delta| < \delta_0$, and

$$(6) \qquad D_{S_L}[f(x+\tau), f(x)] < \frac{\epsilon}{2}$$

for any τ of the set (3).

By (5), (6)

$$(7) \qquad D_{S_L}[f(x+\tau+\delta), f(x)] < \epsilon.$$

We construct the intervals I_n $(n = 0, \pm 1, \pm 2, \ldots)$ of length $2\delta_0$:

$$(8) \qquad \tau_n - \delta_0 < x < \tau_n + \delta_0,$$

so that τ_n belongs to the set (3) and lies between the numbers $n(l+2\delta_0) - \frac{1}{2}l$ and $n(l+2\delta_0) + \frac{1}{2}l$. The intervals I_n do not overlap because

$$(9) \qquad n(l+2\delta_0) + \tfrac{1}{2}l + \delta_0 = (n+1)(l+2\delta_0) - \tfrac{1}{2}l - \delta_0.$$

We now define the kernel $K(t)$ by the equations

$$K(t) = c = \frac{1}{2\delta_0}(l+2\delta_0) \text{ for } t \subset I_n \quad (n = 0, \pm 1, \ldots)$$

$$K(t) = 0 \text{ for all other values of } t.$$

Evidently

$$(10) \qquad \frac{1}{T}\int_{\gamma}^{\gamma+T} K(t)\,dt$$

tends to 1, as $T \to \infty$, uniformly in γ.

5°. We shall now prove that *there exists a sequence*

(1) $$1 < T_1 < T_2 < \ldots, \qquad (T_n \to \infty)$$

such that the mean value

$$\lim_{n\to\infty} \frac{1}{2T_n}\int_{-T_n}^{+T_n} f(x+t)\,K(t)\,dt$$

exists for all values of x in the whole interval $-\infty < x < +\infty$.

By Lemma 2° $D_W[f(x)]$ is finite. Consequently there exists a number $k > 0$ such that $D_{S_\lambda}[f(x)] < k$ for all $\lambda > 1$, whence

(2) $$\left|\frac{1}{2T}\int_{-T}^{+T} f(x+t)\,K(t)\,dt\right| < ck$$

for $T > \frac{1}{2}$ and for all x.

Take an enumerable set of numbers $x_1, x_2, \ldots$, which is everywhere dense in the whole interval $-\infty < x < +\infty$. By means of the "diagonal argument" we can construct a set

$$1 < T_1 < T_2 < T_3 < \ldots,$$

such that the limit

(3) $$\lim_{n\to\infty} \frac{1}{2T_n}\int_{-T_n}^{+T_n} f(x_m+t)\,K(t)\,dt$$

exists for every x_m. We shall now prove that the mean value

(4) $$\lim \frac{1}{2T_n}\int_{-T_n}^{+T_n} f(x+t)\,K(t)\,dt$$

exists for all values of x. Given η, there exists $\delta_1 = \delta_1(\eta) > 0$, such that

(5) $$D_W[f(t+\delta), f(t)] < \frac{\eta}{2c}$$

for all $|\delta| < \delta_1$ (by Lemma 3°).

Let x be any real number: take a number x_m so that $|x - x_m| < \delta_1$. We conclude on account of (5) and of the definition of D_W that for all sufficiently large n,

(6) $$\frac{1}{2T_n}\int_{-T_n}^{+T_n} |f(x+t) - f(x_m+t)|\,dt$$
$$< D_W[f(x+t), f(x_m+t)] + \frac{\eta}{2c} < \frac{\eta}{c},$$

whence

$$(7)\quad \left|\frac{1}{2T_n}\int_{-T_n}^{+T_n} f(x+t)\,K(t)\,dt - \frac{1}{2T_n}\int_{-T_n}^{+T_n} f(x_m+t)\,K(t)\,dt\right| \\ \leqq c\,\frac{1}{2T_n}\int_{-T_n}^{+T_n} |f(x+t)-f(x_m+t)|\,dt < \eta$$

for all sufficiently large n. η being arbitrary we conclude that the limit (4) exists with the limit (3).

6°. We write

$$(1)\qquad \phi(x) = \lim_{n\to\infty} \frac{1}{2T_n}\int_{-T_n}^{+T_n} f(x+t)\,K(t)\,dt.$$

We have

$$(2)\quad |\phi(x+\delta)-\phi(x)| \\ = \lim_{n\to\infty}\left|\frac{1}{2T_n}\int_{-T_n}^{+T_n}\{f(x+\delta+t)-f(x+t)\}\,K(t)\,dt\right| \\ \leqq \overline{\lim_{n\to\infty}}\; c\,\frac{1}{2T_n}\int_{-T_n}^{+T_n}|f(x+\delta+t)-f(x+t)|\,dt \\ \leqq c\,D_W[f(x+\delta), f(x)],$$

which proves (on account of Lemma 3°) that $\phi(x)$ *is continuous*.

Apply the above formula to the case of $\delta=\tau$, where τ is a W translation number of $f(x)$ belonging to $\dfrac{\eta}{c}>0$:

$$|\phi(x+\tau)-\phi(x)| \leqq c\,D_W[f(x+\tau), f(x)] \leqq \eta,$$

which proves that $\phi(x)$ is a *u.a.p.* function.

7°. Finally we prove that $\phi(x)$ satisfies (2) of 4° and in this way complete the theorem. By (10) of 4°

$$(1)\qquad f(x) = \lim_{T\to\infty}\frac{1}{2T}\int_{-T}^{+T} f(x)\,K(t)\,dt,$$

and thus

$$|\phi(x)-f(x)| = \lim_{n\to\infty}\left|\frac{1}{2T_n}\int_{-T_n}^{+T_n}[f(x+t)-f(x)]\,K(t)\,dt\right| \\ \leqq \lim_{n\to\infty}\frac{1}{2T_n}\int_{-T_n}^{+T_n}|f(x+t)-f(x)|\,K(t)\,dt,$$

whence

$$(2)\quad \frac{1}{L}\int_x^{x+L} |f(\xi)-\phi(\xi)|\,d\xi$$
$$\leq \frac{1}{L}\int_x^{x+L} d\xi \lim_{n\to\infty} \frac{1}{2T_n}\int_{-T_n}^{+T_n} |f(\xi+t)-f(\xi)|\,K(t)\,dt.$$

Applying Fatou's Theorem and then reversing the order of integration we have

$$\frac{1}{L}\int_x^{x+L} |f(\xi)-\phi(\xi)|\,d\xi$$
$$\leq \underline{\lim}\, \frac{1}{2T_n}\int_{-T_n}^{+T_n} K(t)\,dt\,\frac{1}{L}\int_x^{x+L} |f(\xi+t)-f(\xi)|\,d\xi$$
$$\leq \bar{M}_t\{D_{S_L}[f(x+t), f(x)]\,K(t)\}.$$

Assuming now that L has been chosen as in (5), (6), (7) of 4°, we have

$$D_{S_L}[f(x+t), f(x)] < \epsilon$$

for all values of t for which $K(t)$ differs from zero, whence

$$\frac{1}{L}\int_x^{x+L} |f(\xi)-\phi(\xi)|\,d\xi \leq \epsilon M\{K(t)\} = \epsilon,$$

which proves (2) of 4° and consequently (7) of 1°. Theorem $IC_W(A)$ follows from (2) and (7) of 1°.

Remark. We conclude from (10) of 4° and (1) of 6° that if $|f(x)| < Q$ for all x, then also $|\phi(x)| < Q$.

§ 5. S^p *a.p.* and W^p *a.p.* functions ($p > 1$).

1°. THEOREMS $IC_{S^p}(A)$ *and* $IC_{W^p}(A)$ ($p > 1$). *The closure* $C_{S^p}(A)$ *is identical with* $\{S^p\ a.p.\}$ *and the closure* $C_{W^p}(A)$ *is identical with* $\{W^p\ a.p.\}$, *i.e.*

$$(1)\qquad C_{S^p}(A) = \{S^p\ a.p.\},$$

$$(2)\qquad C_{W^p}(A) = \{W^p\ a.p.\}.$$

(i) We have first to prove that

$$(3)\qquad C_{S^p}(A) \subset (S^p\ a.p.),$$

$$(4)\qquad C_{W^p}(A) \subset (W^p\ a.p.).$$

Let $f(x)$ be a function of the closure $C_{W^p}(A)$. Corresponding to any $\epsilon > 0$ there exists a number $L > 0$ and a function $s(x)$ of A such that

(5) $$D_{S_L^p}[f(x), s(x)] < \frac{\epsilon}{3}.$$

Further we have for any

(6) $$\tau \subset E\left\{\frac{\epsilon}{3}, s(x)\right\},$$

(7) $$D_{S_L^p}[f(x+\tau), f(x)] \leqq D_{S_L^p}[f(x+\tau), s(x+\tau)] + D_{S_L^p}[s(x+\tau), s(x)] + D_{S_L^p}[s(x), f(x)] < \frac{\epsilon}{3} + D_U[s(x+\tau), s(x)] + \frac{\epsilon}{3} < \epsilon,$$

which shows that

(8) $$E\left\{\frac{\epsilon}{3}, s(x)\right\} \subset S_L^p E\{\epsilon, f(x)\}.$$

Thus the set $S_L^p E\{\epsilon, f(x)\}$ is relatively dense, which proves (4). If $f(x)$ is a function of the closure $C_{S^p}(A)$, then we can put $L=1$ in the formulae (5), (7), (8), and so obtain the result that $f(x)$ belongs to $\{S^p\ a.p.\}$: this proves (3).

(ii) We have now to prove the converse, viz.

(9) $$\{S^p\ a.p.\} \subset C_{S^p}(A),$$

(10) $$\{W^p\ a.p.\} \subset C_{W^p}(A).$$

2°. **Lemma.** *To any W^p a.p. function (S^p a.p. function) $f(x)$ and any $\epsilon > 0$ corresponds a bounded W^p a.p. function (S^p a.p. function) $g(x)$ such that*

(1) $$D_{W^p}[f(x), g(x)] < \epsilon. \qquad (D_{S^p}[f(x), g(x)] < \epsilon)$$

Let N be any positive number. We define the function $f_N(x)$ by the equations

(2) $$f_N(x) = f(x),$$

when $|f(x)| \leqq N$,

(3) $$f_N(x) = N\frac{f(x)}{|f(x)|},$$

when $|f(x)| > N$.

We have for any pair x_1, x_2 of real numbers

$$|f_N(x_1)-f_N(x_2)| \leq |f(x_1)-f(x_2)|,$$

from which we conclude that if $f(x)$ is a W^p *a.p.* function (S^p *a.p.* function) then so is $f_N(x)$.

By the definition of W^p *a.p.* functions, to any $\epsilon > 0$ there corresponds an $L > 0$ such that the set

$$S_L^p\, E\left\{\frac{\epsilon}{3}, f(x)\right\} \tag{4}$$

is relatively dense. Let $l > 0$ be its inclusion interval. Then to any real x_0 corresponds a number τ of the set (4) such that the number $x_0 + \tau$ belongs to the interval $(0, l)$. We have

$$\begin{aligned} &\left[\frac{1}{L}\int_{x_0}^{x_0+L} |f(x)-f_N(x)|^p\,dx\right]^{1/p} \\ &\leq \left[\frac{1}{L}\int_{x_0}^{x_0+L} |f(x)-f(x+\tau)|^p\,dx\right]^{1/p} \\ &\quad + \left[\frac{1}{L}\int_{x_0}^{x_0+L} |f(x+\tau)-f_N(x+\tau)|^p\,dx\right]^{1/p} \\ &\quad + \left[\frac{1}{L}\int_{x_0}^{x_0+L} |f_N(x+\tau)-f_N(x)|^p\,dx\right]^{1/p} \\ &\leq \frac{\epsilon}{3} + \left[\frac{1}{L}\int_0^{l+L} |f(x)-f_N(x)|^p\,dx\right]^{1/p} + \frac{\epsilon}{3}. \end{aligned} \tag{5}$$

Given the numbers ϵ, l, L, we can choose N so that

$$\left[\frac{1}{L}\int_0^{l+L} |f(x)-f_N(x)|^p\,dx\right]^{1/p} < \frac{\epsilon}{3}. \tag{6}$$

By (5), (6)

$$D_{S_L^p}[f(x), f_N(x)] < \epsilon. \tag{7}$$

If $f(x)$ is an S^p *a.p.* function, then we can put $L=1$ in all the above formulae. Thus we see that (1) will be satisfied by taking $g(x)=f_N(x)$.

3°. After the lemma has been proved the proof of both statements (9), (10) of 1° presents no difficulty. The proof being identical in the two cases we shall give it for the second case only. Given a W^p *a.p.* function $f(x)$ and a number $\epsilon > 0$, we define an $N > 0$ so that

(1) $$D_{W^p}[f(x), f_N(x)] < \frac{\epsilon}{2},$$

where $f_N(x)$ is defined by (2), (3) of 2° and is a W^p *a.p.* function, and therefore is also a W *a.p.* function. On account of Theorem $IC_W(A)$, and of the remark at the end of 7°, § 4, to any $\epsilon > 0$ there corresponds a *u.a.p.* function $\phi(x)$ and an $L > 0$ such that the conditions

(2) $$D_{S_L}[f_N(x), \phi(x)] < \left(\frac{\epsilon}{2}\right)^p (2N)^{1-p} \qquad (|\phi(x)| \leqq N)$$

are satisfied. We have

(3) $$\left\{\frac{1}{L}\int_{x_0}^{x_0+L} |f_N(x) - \phi(x)|^p \, dx\right\}^{1/p} \leqq (2N)^{1-(1/p)} \left\{\frac{1}{L}\int_{x_0}^{x_0+L} |f_N(x) - \phi(x)| \, dx\right\}^{1/p}.$$

By (2), (3)

(4) $$D_{S_L^p}[f_N(x), \phi(x)] < \frac{\epsilon}{2}.$$

By (1), (4)

(5) $$D_{W^p}[f(x), \phi(x)] < \epsilon.$$

The number $\epsilon > 0$ and the W^p *a.p.* function $f(x)$ being arbitrary in (5) we have proved (10) of 1°. In the same way can be proved (9) of 1°. By (3), (4), (9), (10) of 1° Theorems $IC_{S^p}(A)$ and $IC_{W^p}(A)$ have been proved.

§ 6. *B a.p.* functions.

1°. Before passing to the proof of the Theorem I for the class of *B a.p.* functions we have to prove a number of lemmas.

Given any *a.p.* set $\bar{E}_\epsilon$* of numbers τ_i, we define the function $K(t) = K(t, \delta)$ $(\delta < 1)$ by the conditions

$$K(t) = 1 \text{ for all intervals } \tau_i \leqq t \leqq \tau_i + \delta,$$
$$= 0 \text{ otherwise.}$$

* It is to be remembered that $\bar{E}_\epsilon$ is the set of integers of $E\{\epsilon, \psi(x)\}$, where $\psi(x)$ is a *u.a.p.* function.

Lemma. *The function $K(t)$ is W a.p.*

For, given $\eta > 0$, there exist positive numbers ρ and L such that the points of $\bar{E}_\epsilon \times (c, c+L)$ for any c translated by any number of $\bar{E}_\rho$ have a "relative loss" $\leqq \eta$. Thus for any τ belonging to $\bar{E}_\rho$

$$\frac{1}{L}\int_c^{c+L} |K(t+\tau) - K(t)|\, dt \leqq 2\eta\delta < 2\eta,$$

which proves the lemma, since $\bar{E}_\rho$ is relatively dense.

2°. **Lemma.** *The product $u(t)\, v(t)$ of a trigonometric polynomial $u(t)$ and a W a.p. function $v(t)$ is a W a.p. function.*

Let $D_U\{u(t)\} = M$. Given ϵ, we can find an $l > 0$ and a trigonometric polynomial $s(t)$ such that

$$D_{S_l}[v(t), s(t)] < \frac{\epsilon}{M},$$

since $v(t)$ belongs to $C_W(A)$. We obviously have

$$D_{S_l}[u(t)\, v(t), u(t)\, s(t)] \leqq M \,.\, D_{S_l}[v(t), s(t)] < \epsilon,$$

which proves that $u(t)\, v(t)$ is *W a.p.* since $u(t)\, s(t)$ is a trigonometric polynomial.

3°. **Lemma.** *If $f(t) \subset C_B(A)$, then also $f(t)\, K(t) \subset C_B(A)$.*

Given ϵ, there exists a trigonometric polynomial $\sigma(t)$ such that

$$D_B\{f(t), \sigma(t)\} < \frac{\epsilon}{2}.$$

Consequently

$$(1) \qquad D_B\{f(t)\, K(t), \sigma(t)\, K(t)\} < \frac{\epsilon}{2}.$$

On account of Lemma 2° $\sigma(t)\, K(t)$ is *W a.p.* Consequently there exists a polynomial $s(t)$ such that

$$(2) \qquad D_W\{\sigma(t)\, K(t), s(t)\} < \frac{\epsilon}{2}.$$

By (1), (2)

$$D_B\{f(t)\, K(t), s(t)\} < \epsilon,$$

which proves the lemma.

4°. **Lemma.** *If $f(t)$ belongs to the closure $C_B(A)$, then $M\{f(t)\}$ exists.*

Given $\epsilon > 0$, we can always write

$$f(t) = s(t) + \theta(t),$$

where $s(t)$ is a trigonometric polynomial and $\bar{M}\{|\theta(t)|\} < \frac{\epsilon}{4}$.

There exists $T_0 > 0$ such that

$$\frac{1}{2T}\int_{-T}^{+T} |\theta(t)|\, dt < \frac{\epsilon}{4},$$

and
$$\left|\frac{1}{2T}\int_{-T}^{+T} s(t)\, dt - M\{s(t)\}\right| < \frac{\epsilon}{4},$$

for all $T > T_0$. Consequently

$$\left|\frac{1}{2T}\int_{-T}^{+T} f(t)\, dt - M\{s(t)\}\right| < \frac{\epsilon}{2}$$

for all $T > T_0$. Thus for any pair of numbers T', T'' each of which is greater than T_0, we have

$$\left|\frac{1}{2T'}\int_{-T'}^{+T'} f(t)\, dt - \frac{1}{2T''}\int_{-T''}^{+T''} f(t)\, dt\right| < \epsilon,$$

which proves the lemma.

Corollary 1. *$M\{f(t)\}$ exists for any S a.p. and for any W a.p. function $f(t)$.*

Corollary 2. *If*

$$\{\tau_i\} \quad (i = \ldots, -2, -1, 0, +1, \ldots;\ \tau_0 = 0,\ \tau_i = -\tau_{-i})$$

is an a.p. set, then the limit

$$\lim_{i\to\infty} \frac{i}{\tau_i} = p$$

exists.

For
$$M\{K(t)\} = \lim \frac{(2i+1)\,\delta}{2\tau_i},$$

as $i \to \infty$, exists, since $K(t)$ is W *a.p.*

Remark. An *a.p.* set $\{\tau_i\}$ being satisfactorily uniform there exists a number b such that $\nu(b) < 2\mu(b)$, where $\mu(b)$, $\nu(b)$ are the minimum and the maximum number of numbers τ_i in any interval of length b. We obviously have

$$\frac{\mu(b)}{b} \leqq p \leqq \frac{\nu(b)}{b} \leqq 2p,$$

where p has the same meaning as in Cor. 2. Denoting by $n(t, T)$ the number of τ's in the interval $(t-T, t+T)$ we have for $T > b$

$$(1) \qquad \frac{n(t, T)}{2T} < \left(\frac{2T}{b} + 1\right)\frac{\nu(b)}{2T} < 3p.$$

5°. **Lemma.** *If $f(t)$ belongs to $C_B(A)$, then so does $|f(t)|$.*

Given $\epsilon > 0$, there exists a trigonometric polynomial $\sigma(t)$ such that

$$D_B\{f, \sigma\} < \frac{\epsilon}{2}.$$

Evidently
$$D_B\{|f|, |\sigma|\} < \frac{\epsilon}{2}.$$

As $|\sigma(t)|$ is *u.a.p.* there exists a trigonometric polynomial $s(t)$ such that

$$D_U\{|\sigma(t)|, s(t)\} < \frac{\epsilon}{2}.$$

Thus
$$D_B\{|f(t)|, s(t)\} < \epsilon,$$

which proves the lemma.

6°. **Lemma.** *If $f(t)$ belongs to $C_B(A)$ and if*

$$\{\tau_i\} \quad (-\infty < i < +\infty, \tau_0 = 0, \tau_i = -\tau_{-i})$$

is an arbitrary a.p. set (of integers), then

$$M_i\left\{\int_x^{x+\delta} |f(t+\tau_i) - f(t)|\, dt\right\}$$

exists.

Define a purely periodic function $p(t)$ with period 1 by the condition

$$p(t) = f(t),$$

for $x \leqq t < x + 1$. The function $p(t)$ obviously belongs to $C_B(A)$ and consequently $f(t) - p(t)$ also belongs to $C_B(A)$. On account of Lemma 5° the function $|f(t+x)-p(t+x)|$ (as a function of t) also belongs to $C_B(A)$.

On account of Lemmas 3° and 4° the mean value

$$M_t\{|f(t+x)-p(t+x)|K(t)\}$$

exists. But

$$\begin{aligned} M_t\{|f(t+x)-p(t+x)|K(t)\} &= \lim \frac{1}{2\tau_n}\int_{-\tau_n}^{\tau_n+\delta} |f(t+x)-p(t+x)|K(t)\,dt \\ &= \lim \frac{2n+1}{2\tau_n}\cdot\frac{1}{2n+1}\sum_{i=-n}^{+n}\int_{\tau_i}^{\tau_i+\delta}|f(t+x)-p(t+x)|\,dt \\ &= \lim \frac{2n+1}{2\tau_n}\cdot\frac{1}{2n+1}\sum_{i=-n}^{+n}\int_{x}^{x+\delta}|f(t+\tau_i)-f(t)|\,dt. \end{aligned}$$

By Lemma 4°, Cor. 2,

$$\lim \frac{2n+1}{2\tau_n},$$

as $n\to\infty$, exists and consequently the limit

$$\lim \frac{1}{2n+1}\sum_{i=-n}^{n}\int_{x}^{x+\delta}|f(t+\tau_i)-f(t)|\,dt$$

also exists, which proves the lemma.

7°. Theorem $IC_B(A)$. *The closure $C_B(A)$ is identical with the class of B a.p. functions, i.e.*

$$C_B(A)=\{B\ a.p.\}.$$

(i) We shall first prove that

$$C_B(A)\subset\{B\ a.p.\}.$$

Let $f(x)$ be a function of $C_B(A)$ and ϵ_0 any positive number. We put

$$f(x)=s(x)+\theta(x),$$

where $s(x)$ belongs to A and

$$\bar{M}\{|\theta(x)|\}<\epsilon_0.$$

Choose $\epsilon<\epsilon_0$ so that the set $\bar{E}\{\epsilon, s(x)\}$ is *a.p.*, and let its members be written τ_i. Then

$$(1)\quad \bar{M}_t\{|f(t)-f(t+\tau_i)|\}\leqq M_t\{|s(t)-s(t+\tau_i)|\} + \bar{M}_t\{|\theta(t)|\}+\bar{M}_t\{|\theta(t+\tau_i)|\}<3\epsilon_0.$$

Now by Lemma 6°

$$M_i\left\{\frac{1}{c}\int_x^{x+c}|f(t)-f(t+\tau_i)|\,dt\right\}$$

exists. By (1) 3°, § 1, and (1) 5°, § 1,

$$\frac{1}{2T}\int_{-T}^{+T}M_i\left\{\frac{1}{c}\int_x^{x+c}|f(t)-f(t+\tau_i)|\,dt\right\}dx$$
$$\leqq \bar{M}_i\frac{1}{2T}\int_{-T}^{+T}\left\{\frac{1}{c}\int_x^{x+c}|f(t)-f(t+\tau_i)|\,dt\right\}dx$$
$$\leqq M_i\frac{1}{2T}\int_{-T}^{T+c}|f(t)-f(t+\tau_i)|\,dt.$$

Hence for every $c>0$ we have

$$\bar{M}_x M_i\left\{\frac{1}{c}\int_x^{x+c}|f(t)-f(t+\tau_i)|\,dt\right\}$$
$$\leqq \overline{\lim_{T\to\infty}}\, M_i\frac{1}{2T}\int_{-T}^{+T}|f(t)-f(t+\tau_i)|\,dt.$$

In this relation we write

$$|f(t)-f(t+\tau_i)|<\epsilon+|\theta(t)|+|\theta(t+\tau_i)|,$$

and so obtain

$$(2)\qquad \bar{M}_x M_i\left\{\frac{1}{c}\int_x^{x+c}|f(t)-f(t+\tau_i)|\,dt\right\}$$
$$\leqq \epsilon+\epsilon_0+\overline{\lim_{T\to\infty}}\,\bar{M}_i\left\{\frac{1}{2T}\int_{-T}^{+T}|\theta(t+\tau_i)|\,dt\right\}.$$

Now

$$\frac{1}{2n+1}\sum_{i=-n}^{+n}\frac{1}{2T}\int_{-T}^{+T}|\theta(t+\tau_i)|\,dt$$
$$=\frac{1}{2T(2n+1)}\int_{\tau_{-n}-T}^{\tau_n+T}|\theta(t)|\,n(t,T)\,dt,$$

where $n(t, T)$ has the same meaning as in 4°.

By (1) 4°,

$$(3)\qquad \frac{1}{2n+1}\sum_{i=-n}^{+n}\frac{1}{2T}\int_{-T}^{+T}|\theta(t+\tau_i)|\,dt$$
$$<3p\frac{1}{2n+1}\int_{\tau_{-n}-T}^{\tau_n+T}|\theta(t)|\,dt,$$

and by Lemma 4°, Cor. 2,

$$(4) \qquad \overline{\lim_{n\to\infty}} \frac{1}{2n+1}\int_{\tau_{-n}-T}^{\tau_n+T} |\theta(t)|\,dt = \frac{1}{p}\overline{M}\{|\theta(t)|\}.$$

By (3), (4)

$$(5) \qquad \overline{\lim_{T\to\infty}}\, \overline{M}_i \frac{1}{2T}\int_{-T}^{+T} |\theta(t+\tau_i)|\,dt \leqq 3\overline{M}\{|\theta(t)|\} < 3\epsilon_0,$$

and so finally by (2), (5)

$$(6) \qquad \overline{M}_x\, M_i \left\{\frac{1}{c}\int_x^{x+c} |f(t)-f(t+\tau_i)|\,dt\right\} < 5\epsilon_0.$$

Since ϵ_0 is arbitrary, (1) and (6) show that $f(x)$ is *B a.p.*

8°. (ii) We have now to prove that $\{B\ a.p.\} \subset C_B(A)$. We commence with an important

Lemma. *If $f(t)$ is a B a.p function and*

$$f_\delta(t) = \frac{1}{\delta}\int_t^{t+\delta} f(u)\,du,$$

then

$$\overline{M}\{|f(t)-f_\delta(t)|\} \to 0,$$

as $\delta \to 0$.

The function $f(t)$ being *B a.p.*, to any $\epsilon > 0$ corresponds a satisfactorily uniform sequence $\{\tau_n\}$ such that the inequalities (4), (5) of 6°, § 2, hold with $p = 1$. Denote as before by $\mu(b)$, $\nu(b)$ respectively the minimum and maximum number of numbers τ_i in an interval of length b: we choose b (as we may) so large that

$$(1) \qquad \nu(b) < 2\mu(b).$$

The fact that the function f_δ approximates the function f in mean in any fixed interval arbitrarily closely is stated by Lemma 4° of § 1. Let η be any positive number less than b, and put $c = b + \eta$ in (5) of 6°, § 2. It follows that we can choose a so that

$$(2) \qquad \overline{M}_i \frac{1}{b+\eta}\int_a^{a+b+\eta} |f(t)-f(t+\tau_i)|\,dt < \epsilon.$$

We shall deduce from (2) that both f and f_δ "imitate" in mean over the whole line from $-\infty$ to $+\infty$, their values in the interval

$(a, \ a+b)$ with an approximation arbitrarily small with ϵ. Combining this result with Lemma 4° of § 1, we shall obtain the result desired. We have

$$\begin{aligned}\bar{M}_i \int_a^{a+b} |f_\delta(t+\tau_i) - f(t+\tau_i)|\, dt &\leqq \bar{M}_i \int_a^{a+b} |f_\delta(t+\tau_i) - f_\delta(t)|\, dt \\ &\quad + \bar{M}_i \int_a^{a+b} |f(t+\tau_i) - f(t)|\, dt \\ &\quad + \int_a^{a+b} |f_\delta(t) - f(t)|\, dt \\ &\leqq 2\bar{M}_i \int_a^{a+b+\delta} |f(t+\tau_i) - f(t)|\, dt \\ &\quad + \int_a^{a+b} |f_\delta(t) - f(t)|\, dt\end{aligned}$$

by (1) of 5°, § 1. If $\delta < \eta$ is so small that the last integral is less than $b\epsilon$, we at once obtain

$$\bar{M}_i \int_a^{a+b} |f_\delta(t+\tau_i) - f(t+\tau_i)|\, dt < b\epsilon + 2(b+\eta)\epsilon < 5b\epsilon.$$

Thus for n sufficiently large we have

$$\frac{1}{2n+1} \sum_{i=-n}^{n} \int_a^{a+b} |f_\delta(t+\tau_i) - f(t+\tau_i)|\, dt < 5b\epsilon.$$

Writing this in the form

$$\frac{1}{2n+1} \int_{a+\tau_{-n}}^{a+b+\tau_n} \lambda(t) |f_\delta(t) - f(t)| dt < 5b\epsilon, \tag{3}$$

we see that in the interval $(a+\tau_{-n}+b, \ a+\tau_n)$ the factor $\lambda(t)$ lies between $\mu(b)$ and $\nu(b)$, and that in the rest of the range of integration it lies between 0 and $\nu(b)$. Write

$$T_n = \text{min.}\,(a+\tau_n, \ -a-b-\tau_{-n});$$

for n sufficiently large both the terms in the bracket are positive. Then (3) gives

$$\frac{\mu(b)}{2n+1} \int_{-T_n}^{+T_n} |f_\delta(t) - f(t)| dt < 5b\epsilon.$$

Writing this formula for $n+1$, we have

$$\int_{-T_{n+1}}^{+T_{n+1}} |f_\delta(t)-f(t)|\,dt < \frac{5b\epsilon(2n+3)}{\mu(b)}.$$

Hence for $$T_n \leqq T \leqq T_{n+1},$$

$$\frac{1}{2T}\int_{-T}^{+T}|f_\delta(t)-f(t)|\,dt$$
$$< \frac{1}{2T_n}\int_{-T_{n+1}}^{+T_{n+1}}|f_\delta(t)-f(t)|\,dt < \frac{5b\epsilon(2n+3)}{2T_n\,\mu(b)}$$

and thus

$$(4)\quad \bar{M}_t\{|f_\delta(t)-f(t)|\} < \overline{\lim_{n\to\infty}}\,\frac{5b\epsilon(2n+3)}{2T_n\,\mu(b)} \leqq \frac{5\epsilon\,\nu(b)}{\mu(b)} \leqq 10\epsilon.$$

Thus the left-hand side is arbitrarily small with δ: this proves the lemma.

9°. We now suppose, as we may, $f(t)$ is real and positive, and define a function $\phi_\delta(t)$ by putting

$$\phi_\delta(t) = \bar{M}_i\,\frac{1}{\delta}\int_t^{t+\delta} f(u+\tau_i)\,du.$$

Then

$$|f_\delta(t)-\phi_\delta(t)| = \left|\frac{1}{\delta}\int_t^{t+\delta} f(u)\,du - \bar{M}_i\,\frac{1}{\delta}\int_t^{t+\delta} f(u+\tau_i)\,du\right|$$
$$\leqq \bar{M}_i\,\frac{1}{\delta}\int_t^{t+\delta} |f(u+\tau_i)-f(u)|\,du.$$

But by (5) of 6°, § 2,

$$\bar{M}_t\{|f_\delta(t)-\phi_\delta(t)|\} \leqq \epsilon,$$

in particular $\phi_\delta(t)$, is summable with the continuous function $f_\delta(t)$. By (4) of 8° we now have

$$(1)\qquad \bar{M}_t\{|f(t)-\phi_\delta(t)|\} \leqq 11\epsilon.$$

But if τ be any real number, we have

$$|\phi_\delta(t+\tau)-\phi_\delta(t)| \leqq \bar{M}_i\,\frac{1}{\delta}\int_{t+\tau_i}^{t+\delta+\tau_i} |f(u+\tau)-f(u)|\,du$$
$$\leqq \frac{1}{\delta}\,\overline{\lim_{n\to\infty}}\,\frac{1}{2n+1}\int_{t+\tau_{-n}}^{t+\tau_n+\delta} |f(u+\tau)-f(u)|\,du$$
$$\leqq \frac{1}{\delta}\,\bar{M}_u\{|f(u+\tau)-f(u)|\}\,\overline{\lim_{|n|\to\infty}}\,\frac{\tau_n}{n}.$$

If k be the value $\overline{\lim_{|n|\to\infty}} \frac{\tau_n}{n}$, then every B translation number of $f(t)$ belonging to $\frac{\eta\delta}{k}$ is a uniform translation number, and *a fortiori* an S translation number, of $\phi_\delta(t)$ belonging to η. It follows that $\phi_\delta(t)$ is an S *a.p.* function (we do not assert that it is a *u.a.p.* function because we have not proved it continuous). Thus we can find a polynomial $s(t)$ such that

$$D_S\{s(t) - \phi_\delta(t)\} \leqq \epsilon,$$

and *a fortiori* that

$$\bar{M}_t\{|s(t) - \phi_\delta(t)|\} \leqq \epsilon.$$

Combining this with (1) we obtain

$$\bar{M}\{|f - s|\} \leqq 12\epsilon,$$

and since ϵ is arbitrary, $f(t)$ belongs to $C_B(A)$.

§ 7. B^r *a.p.* functions.

1°. Theorem $IC_{B^r}(A)$. *The closure $C_{B^r}(A)$ is identical with the class of B^r a.p. functions, i.e. $C_{B^r}(A) = \{B^r\ a.p.\}$.*

Given a function $f(x)$ we define $f_N(x)$ by the equations

$$f_N(x) = f(x),$$

when

$$|f(x)| \leqq N;$$

$$f_N(x) = N\frac{f(x)}{|f(x)|},$$

when

$$|f(x)| > N;$$

and we write

$$f(x) = f_N(x) + R_N(x).$$

Lemma. *If $f(x) \subset C_{B^r}(A)$, then*

$$D_{B^r}(f - f_N) \to 0,$$

as $N \to \infty$.

Given ϵ we can find a polynomial $s(x)$ such that

$$D_{B^r}(f - s) \leqq \epsilon.$$

For any $N \geqq D_U(s)$ and for all t we have

$$|f(t)-f_N(t)| \leqq |f(t)-s(t)|,$$

and therefore

$$D_{B^r}(f-f_N) \leqq D_{B^r}(f-s) \leqq \epsilon,$$

which proves the lemma.

2°. Since $f(x)$ belongs to $C_{B^r}(A)$, it belongs also to $C_B(A)$, and so does $f_N(x)$. Now in proving that $C_B(A) \subset \{B\ a.p.\}$ we showed that, given a function f_N of $C_B(A)$, we can find corresponding to any $\eta > 0$ an *a.p.* sequence $\{\tau_i\}$ (where i runs from $-\infty$ to $+\infty$) such that

$$\bar{M}_t\{|f_N(t+\tau_i)-f_N(t)|\} \leqq \eta$$

for all i, and

$$\bar{M}_x \bar{M}_i \frac{1}{c}\int_x^{x+c} |f_N(t+\tau_i)-f_N(t)|\, dt \leqq \eta$$

for all $c > 0$.

We choose $\eta = \epsilon^r (2N)^{1-r}$ and find for all i

$$D_{B^r}\{f_N(t+\tau_i)-f_N(t)\} \leqq \epsilon,$$

(1) $$D_{B^r}\{f(t+\tau_i)-f(t)\} \leqq \epsilon + 2D_{B^r}\{R_n(t)\} \leqq 3\epsilon.$$

We also find for any $c > 0$

$$\left\{\bar{M}_x \bar{M}_i \frac{1}{c}\int_x^{x+c} |f(t+\tau_i)-f(t)|^r\, dt\right\}^{1/r}$$

$$\leqq \left\{\bar{M}_x \bar{M}_i \frac{1}{c}\int_x^{x+c} |R_N(t+\tau_i)|^r\, dt\right\}^{1/r}$$

$$+ \left\{\bar{M}_x \bar{M}_i \frac{1}{c}\int_x^{x+c} |f_N(t+\tau_i)-f_N(t)|^r\, dt\right\}^{1/r}$$

$$+ \left\{\bar{M}_x \bar{M}_i \frac{1}{c}\int_x^{x+c} |R_N(t)|^r\, dt\right\}^{1/r}$$

$$\leqq 2\epsilon + \left\{\bar{M}_x \bar{M}_i \frac{1}{c}\int_x^{x+c} |R_N(t+\tau_i)|^r\, dt\right\}^{1/r},$$

since it is easily seen that

$$\bar{M}_x\left\{\frac{1}{c}\int_x^{x+c} |R_N(t)|^r\, dt\right\} = \bar{M}_x\{|R_N(t)|^r\}.$$

Now $R_N(t)$ belongs to $C_{B^r}(A)$, and hence $|R_N(t)|^r$ belongs to $C_B(A)$.

As in the proof of Lemma 6° of § 6 it follows that

$$M_i \frac{1}{c}\int_x^{x+c} |R_N(t+\tau_i)|^r\,dt$$

exists, and hence by Fatou's Theorem

$$\frac{1}{2T}\int_{-T}^{+T} M_i\left\{\frac{1}{c}\int_x^{x+c} |R_N(t+\tau_i)|^r\,dt\right\}dx$$

$$\leqq \underline{M}_i\left\{\frac{1}{2T}\int_{-T}^{+T}\frac{dx}{c}\int_x^{x+c}|R_N(t+\tau_i)|^r\,dt\right\}$$

$$\leqq \underline{M}_i\frac{1}{2T}\int_{-T}^{T+c}|R_N(t+\tau_i)|^r\,dt$$

$$= \varliminf_{n\to\infty}\frac{1}{2n+1}\int_{\tau_{-n}-T}^{\tau_n+T+c}|R_N(t)|^r\frac{\lambda(t)}{2T}\,dt,$$

where $\lambda(t)$ is non-negative and does not exceed the number of numbers τ_i in the interval $(t-T-c, t+T)$. Choose b as in (1) 8°, § 6, so that $\nu(b) < 2\mu(b)$. Then

$$\lambda(t) < \left(\frac{2T+c}{b}+1\right)\nu(b),$$

and

$$\bar{M}_x\bar{M}_i\frac{1}{c}\int_x^{x+c}|R_N(t+\tau_i)|^r\,dt$$

$$\leqq \frac{\nu(b)}{b}\lim_{n\to\infty}\frac{\tau_n}{n}\,\underline{M}_x\{|R_N(x)|^r\} \leqq 2\underline{M}_x\{|R_N(x)|^r\},$$

the argument proceeding exactly as in Lemma 4° of § 6. We now have

$$\left[\bar{M}_x\bar{M}_i\left\{\frac{1}{c}\int_x^{x+c}|f(t+\tau_i)-f(t)|^r\,dt\right\}\right]^{1/r} \leqq (2+2^{1/r})\,\epsilon \leqq 4\epsilon.$$

Since ϵ is arbitrary these results combined with (1) show that $f(x)$ is B^r *a.p.*

3°. **Lemma.** *If $f(t)$ is B^r a.p., then*

$$D_{B^r}(f-f_N)\to 0,$$

as $N\to\infty$.

Given any $\epsilon > 0$ we can find a satisfactorily uniform sequence $\{\tau_i\}$ such that for every $b > 0$

$$\bar{M}_x\bar{M}_i\frac{1}{b}\int_x^{x+b}|f(t+\tau_i)-f(t)|^r\,dt < \epsilon^r.$$

As in Lemma 8° of § 6 we choose b so large that $\nu(b) < 2\mu(b)$: we can then find an a such that

$$\bar{M}_i \frac{1}{b} \int_a^{a+b} |f(t+\tau_i) - f(t)|^r \, dt < \epsilon^r.$$

Hence also

$$\bar{M}_i \frac{1}{b} \int_a^{a+b} |f_N(t+\tau_i) - f_N(t)|^r \, dt \leqq \epsilon^r$$

for every N.

Take now N so large that

$$\frac{1}{b} \int_a^{a+b} |f(t) - f_N(t)|^r \, dt < \epsilon^r.$$

It follows that

$$(1) \qquad \bar{M}_i \frac{1}{b} \int_a^{a+b} |f(t+\tau_i) - f_N(t+\tau_i)|^r \, dt < (3\epsilon)^r.$$

Now

$$\frac{1}{2n+1} \sum_{i=-n}^{n} \frac{1}{b} \int_a^{a+b} |f(t+\tau_i) - f_N(t+\tau_i)|^r \, dt$$
$$= \frac{1}{b(2n+1)} \int_{a+\tau_{-n}}^{a+b+\tau_n} |f(t) - f_N(t)|^r \lambda(t) \, dt,$$

where $\lambda(t) \geqq \mu(b)$ in the interval $(a+b+\tau_{-n},\ a+\tau_n)$. Hence

$$\bar{M}_i \frac{1}{b} \int_a^{a+b} |f(t+\tau_i) - f_N(t+\tau_i)|^r \, dt$$
$$\geqq \frac{\mu(b)}{b} \lim_{|n| \to \infty} \frac{\tau_n}{n} \bar{M}_t \{|f(t) - f_N(t)|^r\}$$
$$\geqq \tfrac{1}{2} \bar{M}_t \{|f(t) - f_N(t)|^r\},$$

and so by (1) $\quad \bar{M}_t \{|f(t) - f_N(t)|^r\} \leqq 2(3\epsilon)^r.$

Since this holds for all N sufficiently large, the lemma is proved.

4°. Now f_N being B^r *a.p.* is clearly also B *a.p.* and therefore belongs to $C_B(A)$. Being bounded it also belongs to $C_{B^r}(A)$. Thus we can find a polynomial $s(t)$ of A such that $D_{B^r}(f_N - s)$ is arbitrarily small: since, by Lemma 3°, $D_{B^r}(f - f_N)$ is arbitrarily small, so is $D_{B^r}(f - s)$ and thus f belongs to $C_{B^r}(A)$. Combining this result with the result of 2° we obtain the theorem.

5°. The definition of B *a.p.* functions was recently brought to its simplest form*, and is as follows.

A function $f(x)$ of class L is B *a.p.* if to any $\epsilon > 0$ corresponds a satisfactorily uniform set $\{\tau_i\}$ such that

$$\bar{M}_x \bar{M}_i \int_x^{x+1} |f(t+\tau_i) - f(t)| \, dt < \epsilon.$$

§ 8. Algorithm for polynomial approximation.

1°. In §§ 3–7 we have given a solution of Problem I of 5°, § 2. Let us now pass to Problem II, i.e. to the construction of an algorithm for the approximation by finite trigonometrical polynomials to functions of various types of almost periodicity.

The solution of Problem II for various types of *a.p.* functions will be based on that for the class of *u.a.p.* functions, which was given in § 9, Ch. I.

We shall show that generally for all types of *a.p.* functions, which have been considered in this book, a solution of Problem II can be given by Bochner's sequences.

We have first to prove:

THEOREM ON EXISTENCE OF FOURIER SERIES. *For all types of a.p. functions the Fourier series exists.*

According to the definition of a Fourier series, which remains the same for all types of *a.p.* functions, we have to show that:

(i) for any *a.p.* function $f(x)$ the mean value $M\{f(x)\, e^{-i\lambda x}\}$ exists for all real values of λ, and that

(ii) it may differ from nought for at most an enumerable set of values of λ.

As the classes $\{S^p \; a.p.\}$, $\{W^p \; a.p.\}$ $(p \geqq 1)$ and $\{B^p \; a.p.\}$ $(p > 1)$ are included in the class $\{B \; a.p.\}$ the proof given for the latter class will be a general proof.

The statement (i) is obvious, since for any real λ the function $f(x)\, e^{-i\lambda x}$ belongs to the class $\{B \; a.p.\}$ together with the function

* A. S. Besicovitch, "Analysis of conditions of almost periodicity," *Acta Math.* Vol. 58.

$f(x)$. On account of Theorem $IC_B(A)$, there exists a sequence $\{s_n(x)\}$ of finite trigonometrical polynomials such that

$$B \lim s_n(x) = f(x),$$

as $n \to \infty$, whence

$$(1) \qquad B \lim s_n(x)\, e^{-i\lambda x} = f(x)\, e^{-i\lambda x},$$

as $n \to \infty$.

It can easily be seen from (1) that $M\{f(x)\, e^{-i\lambda x}\}$ exists and that

$$\lim M\{s_n(x)\, e^{-i\lambda x}\} = M\{f(x)\, e^{-i\lambda x}\}.$$

For any fixed n the number $M\{s_n(x)\, e^{-i\lambda x}\}$ may differ from 0 only for a finite number of values of λ, namely the exponents of $s_n(x)$, from which we conclude that

$$\lim M\{s_n(x)\, e^{-i\lambda x}\},$$

as $n \to \infty$, may differ from 0 for at most an enumerable set of values of λ, which proves the statement (ii).

2°. THEOREM II. *If a function $f(x)$ belongs to the closure $C_G(A)$, then any Bochner sequence $\{\sigma^f_{B_n}(x)\}$ satisfies the condition*

$$(1) \qquad D_G[f(x), \sigma^f_{B_n}(x)] \to 0,$$

as $n \to \infty$.

We shall first prove the theorem jointly for the case of the closures $C_{S^p}(A)$, $C_{W^p}(A)$ $(p \geqq 1)$ and then for the case of the closure $C_{B^p}(A)$.

(i) We shall first prove the following:

AUXILIARY INEQUALITY. *If $\psi(x)$ is a function of the closure $C_{W^p}(A)$, then for any Bochner-Fejér polynomial $\sigma^\psi_B(x)$ and for any $L > 0$ we have*

$$(1) \qquad D_{S^p_L}[\sigma^\psi_B(x)] \leqq D_{S^p_L}[\psi(x)].$$

We write

$$(2) \qquad |\sigma^\psi_B(x)| \leqq M\{|\psi(x+t)|\, K_B(t)\}^*.$$

By Hölder's inequality

$$M\{|\psi(x+t)|\, K_B(t)\} \leqq [M\{|\psi(x+t)|^p K_B(t)\}]^{1/p}\, [M\{K_B(t)\}]^{(p-1)/p}$$
$$= [M\{|\psi(x+t)|^p K_B(t)\}]^{1/p},$$

* The notation of § 9, Ch. I.

and thus by (2)

$$|\sigma_B^{\psi(x)}(x)|^p \leqq M\{|\psi(x+t)|^p K_B(t)\},$$

whence

$$\{D_{S_l^p}[\sigma_B^{\psi(x)}(x)]\}^p \leqq M[\{D_{S_l^p}\{\psi(x)\}\}^p K_B(t)]$$
$$= \{D_{S_l^p}\{\psi(x)\}\}^p M\{K_B(t)\} = \{D_{S_l^p}\{\psi(x)\}\}^p,$$

which proves (1).

3°. Let now $f(x)$ be a function of $C_{W^p}(A)$, and let

(1) $$\sigma_{B_1}^f(x),\ \sigma_{B_2}^f(x),\ \ldots$$

be a Bochner sequence. We shall prove the theorem for the case of the closure $C_{W^p}(A)$ by showing that *given* ϵ *there exists a number* $L>0$ *and an integer* n_0 *such that*

(2) $$D_{S_L^p}[f(x),\ \sigma_{B_n}^f(x)] < \epsilon$$

for all $n > n_0$.

We know that to a given ϵ there corresponds a number L and a *u.a.p.* function $\phi(x)$ such that

(3) $$D_{S_L^p}[f(x),\ \phi(x)] < \frac{\epsilon}{3}.$$

We shall show that we can satisfy (2) by this value of L.

We form a base of $\phi(x)$ by taking all numbers of the base of $f(x)$ and by adding if necessary some other numbers. We form a Bochner sequence of $\phi(x)$,

(4) $$\sigma_{B_1'}^\phi(x),\ \sigma_{B_2'}^\phi(x),\ \ldots,$$

in such a way that for all n B_n' consists of all basic numbers contained in B_n with the same indices and possibly of numbers of the base of $\phi(x)$ which do not belong to the base of $f(x)$. Then it is easy to see that

$$\sigma_{B_n'}^f(x) = \sigma_{B_n}^f(x)$$

for all n.

Putting in (1) 2° $\psi(x)=\phi(x)-f(x)$, $B=B_n'$ and observing that

$$\sigma_{B_n'}^{\phi-f}(x) = \sigma_{B_n'}^\phi(x) - \sigma_{B_n'}^f(x),$$

we shall have on account of (3)

(5) $$D_{S_L^p}[\sigma_{B_n'}^\phi(x),\ \sigma_{B_n}^f(x)] < \frac{\epsilon}{3}.$$

The sequence (4) being a Bochner sequence and $\phi(x)$ being a *u.a.p.* function, we have

$$(6)\qquad u.b.\,|\phi(x)-\sigma^{\phi}_{B_{n'}}(x)|<\frac{\epsilon}{3}$$

for all n greater than a certain integer n_0, whence

$$(7)\qquad D_{S^p_L}[\phi(x),\ \sigma^{\phi}_{B_{n'}}(x)]<\frac{\epsilon}{3}.$$

By (3), (7), (5) the inequality (2) is proved, which shows that

$$(8)\qquad D_{W^p}[f(x),\ \sigma^{f}_{B_n}(x)]\to 0,$$

as $n\to\infty$.

In the case when the function $f(x)$ belongs to $C_{S^p}(A)$ we may put in the inequality (3) $L=1$ for any ϵ and thus we shall have the inequality (2) satisfied by $L=1$ for all values of ϵ. Consequently in this case

$$(9)\qquad D_{S^p}[f(x),\ \sigma^{f}_{B_n}(x)]\to 0,$$

as $n\to\infty$. Thus the Theorem II has been proved for the cases of closures $C_{S^p}(A)$, $C_{W^p}(A)$ $(p\geqq 1)$.

Remark. In the case when the function $f(x)$ belongs to C_{W^p} (but not to C_{S^p}) the inequality (2) is somewhat sharper than the limiting equation (8) which we had to prove. For it shows some feature of uniformity of the approximation to the function $f(x)$ by the functions of the sequence (1). We have really that for a given ϵ the inequality (2) is satisfied by the same value of L for all $n>n_0$ the fact which cannot be deduced from (8).

In the case of $p=2$ this property of approximation by trigonometrical polynomials was discovered by R. Schmidt.

4°. (ii) We pass now to the proof of the theorem in the case of the closure $C_{B^p}(A)$ $(p\geqq 1)$. As before we shall first prove the following:

AUXILIARY INEQUALITY. *If a function $\psi(x)$ belongs to $C_{B^p}(A)$, then for any Bochner-Fejér polynomial $\sigma^{\psi}_B(x)$ we have*

$$(1)\qquad D_{B^p}[\sigma^{\psi}_B(x)]\leqq D_{B^p}[\psi(x)].$$

We have
$$\sigma^{\psi}_B(x)=M\{\psi(x+t)\,K_B(t)\},$$
$$|\sigma^{\psi}_B(x)|\leqq M\{|\psi(x+t)|\,K_B(t)\}.$$

By Hölder's Theorem

$$|\sigma_B^\psi(x)|^p \leqq \underline{M}_t\{|\psi(x+t)|^p K_B(t)\},$$

and thus

$$(2) \qquad \{D_{B^p}[\sigma_B^\psi(x)]\}^p \leqq \overline{M}_x \underline{M}_t\{|\psi(x+t)|^p K_B(t)\} = \overline{M}_x \underline{M}_t\{|\psi(t)|^p K_B(t+x)\}.$$

To any $\eta > 0$ correspond values of L as large as we please and such that

$$(3) \quad \overline{M}_x \underline{M}_t\{|\psi(t)|^p K_B(t+x)\} < \frac{1}{L}\int_0^L \underline{M}_t\{|\psi(t)|^p K_B(t+x)\}\,dx + \eta.$$

By (2), (3) and by Fatou's Theorem

$$(4) \quad \{D_{B^p}[\sigma_B^\psi(x)]\}^p < \overline{M}_t\left\{|\psi(t)|^p \frac{1}{L}\int_0^L K_B(t+x)\,dx\right\} + \eta.$$

But for sufficiently large values of L

$$(5) \qquad \frac{1}{L}\int_0^L K_B(t+x)\,dx < M\{K_B(t)\} + \eta = 1 + \eta.$$

By (4), (5)

$$\{D_{B^p}[\sigma_B^\psi(x)]\}^p < (1+\eta)\, M_t\{|\psi(t)|^p\} + \eta.$$

η being arbitrary we have

$$\{D_{B^p}[\sigma_B^\psi(x)]\}^p \leqq M_t\{|\psi(t)|^p\},$$

which proves (1).

5°. Now we can arrive immediately to the proof of our theorem. We know that to any ϵ corresponds a *u.a.p.* function $\phi(x)$ such that

$$(1) \qquad D_{B^p}[f(x), \phi(x)] < \frac{\epsilon}{3}.$$

We define further a Bochner-Fejér polynomial $\sigma_B^\phi(x)$ such that

$$(2) \qquad u.b.\,|\phi(x) - \sigma_B^\phi(x)| < \frac{\epsilon}{3}.$$

Putting in (1) 4° $\quad \psi(x) = f(x) - \phi(x)$,

we have $\quad D_{B^p}[\sigma_B^\phi(x), \sigma_B^f(x)] \leqq D_{B^p}[f(x), \phi(x)],$

and by (1)

(3) $$D_{B^p}[\sigma_B^{\phi}(x), \sigma_B^{f}(x)] < \frac{\epsilon}{3}.$$

By (1), (2), (3)

$$D_{B^p}[f(x), \sigma_B^{f}(x)] < \epsilon,$$

which proves the theorem.

6°. UNIQUENESS THEOREM. *If two G a.p. functions $f(x)$, $g(x)$ have the same Fourier series, then*

$$D_G[f(x), g(x)] = 0.$$

Let $\sigma_{B_n}(x)$ $(n = 1, 2, \ldots)$ be a Bochner sequence of the common Fourier series of the functions $f(x)$, $g(x)$. By Theorem II

$$D_G\{\sigma_{B_n}(x), f(x)\} \to 0, \qquad D_G\{\sigma_{B_n}(x), g(x)\} \to 0,$$

as $n \to \infty$. Consequently

$$D_G\{f(x), g(x)\} = 0.$$

§ 9. Parseval Equation and Riesc-Fischer Theorem.

1°. We shall now prove the following:

THEOREM. *The Parseval equation holds for B^2 a.p. functions, and* a fortiori *for S^2 a.p. and W^2 a.p. functions.*

Let $$f(x) \sim \sum_{n=1}^{\infty} A_n e^{i\Lambda_n x}$$

be a B^2 *a.p.* function and

$$\sigma_{B_m}(x) = \sum_{n=1}^{\infty} d_n^{(m)} A_n e^{i\Lambda_n x}, \qquad (m = 1, 2, \ldots)$$

where $0 \leqq d_n^{(m)} \leqq 1$, and $d_n^{(m)} \underset{m \to +\infty}{\to} 1$ for all n, be a Bochner sequence of trigonometric polynomials. By Theorem II

$$D_{B^2}[f(x), \sigma_{B_m}(x)] \to 0,$$

as $m \to \infty$, from which we easily conclude that

$$M\{|f(x)|^2\} = \lim M\{|\sigma_{B_m}(x)|^2\},$$

as $m \to \infty$, i.e. that

$$M\{|f(x)|^2\} = \lim_{m \to \infty} \sum_{n=1}^{\infty} \{d_n^{(m)}\}^2 |A_n|^2 = \sum_{n=1}^{\infty} |A_n|^2,$$

which is the Parseval equation.

2°. We shall now prove:

RIESC-FISCHER THEOREM. *To any series*

(1) $$\Sigma A_n e^{i\Lambda_n x},$$

for which $\Sigma |A_n|^2$ *converges, corresponds a* B^2 *a.p. function having this series as its Fourier series.*

Writing $$s_j = \sum_{n=1}^{j} A_n e^{i\Lambda_n x}, \quad l_j = \sum_{i=1}^{j} |A_n|^2,$$

there exists, corresponding to an arbitrarily chosen sequence,

$$\epsilon_1 > \epsilon_2 > \ldots, \qquad (\epsilon_n \to 0)$$

a set of positive numbers (>1)

$$T_1, T_2, \ldots,$$

such that for every j and $k=0, 1, \ldots, j-1$, and for $T > T_j$ and for all x we have

(2) $$\left| \frac{1}{T} \int_x^{x+T} |s_j - s_k|^2 \, dx - (l_j - l_k) \right| < \epsilon_j. \quad (s_0 = l_0 = 0)$$

Since $$\frac{1}{x} \int_0^x |s_1(x)|^2 \, dx \to l_1,$$

as $x \to \infty$, and

$$\int_x^{x+\xi} |s_2|^2 \, dx \leqq \int_x^{x+T_2} |s_2|^2 \, dx < T_2 (l_2 + \epsilon_2) \text{ for } \xi \leqq T_2,$$

we can choose an $x_1 \geqq T_1$ so that for $\xi \leqq T_2$ the inequality

(3) $$\left| \frac{\int_0^{x_1} |s_1|^2 \, dx + \int_{x_1}^{x_1+\xi} |s_2|^2 \, dx}{x_1 + \xi} - l_1 \right| < \epsilon_1$$

is true.

For $\xi \geqq T_2$ we have

(4) $$\left| \frac{\int_0^{x_1} |s_1|^2 \, dx + \int_{x_1}^{x_1+\xi} |s_2|^2 \, dx}{x_1 + \xi} - \frac{x_1 l_1 + \xi l_2}{x_1 + \xi} \right| < \epsilon_1.$$

Since $$\frac{1}{x} \int_{x_1}^{x_1+x} |s_2 - s_k|^2 \, dx \to l_2 - l_k, \qquad (k=0, 1)$$

and $$\int_x^{x+\xi} |s_3 - s_k|^2 \, dx < T_3 (l_3 - l_k + \epsilon_3),$$

for $\xi \leqq T_3$, we can choose $x_2 \geqq T_2$ so that for $\xi \leqq T_3$ (and $k=0, 1$) the inequality

$$(5)\quad \left| \frac{\int_0^{x_1} |s_1 - s_k|^2 dx + \int_{x_1}^{x_1+x_2} |s_2 - s_k|^2 dx + \int_{x_1+x_2}^{x_1+x_2+\xi} |s_3 - s_k|^2 dx}{x_1 + x_2 + \xi} - (l_2 - l_k) \right| < \epsilon_2$$

is true. For $\xi > T_3$ we have [by using (5) for $\xi = 0$ and (2) for $j=3$]

$$(6)\quad \left| \frac{\int_0^{x_1} |s_1 - s_k|^2 dx + \int_{x_1}^{x_1+x_2} |s_2 - s_k|^2 dx + \int_{x_1+x_2}^{x_1+x_2+\xi} |s_3 - s_k|^2 dx}{x_1 + x_2 + \xi} - \frac{(x_1+x_2)(l_2 - l_k) + \xi(l_3 - l_k)}{x_1 + x_2 + \xi} \right| < \epsilon_2.$$

In the same way, since for $\xi \leqq T_4$,

$$\int_x^{x+\xi} |s_4 - s_k|^2 dx < T_4(l_4 - l_k + \epsilon_4), \qquad (k=0, 1, 2)$$

and

$$\frac{1}{x}\int_{x_1+x_2}^{x_1+x_2+x} |s_3 - s_k|^2 dx \underset{x\to\infty}{\to} l_3 - l_k,$$

we can choose $x_3 \geqq T_3$, so that for $\xi \leqq T_4$ the inequality

$$(7)\quad \left| \frac{\int_0^{x_1} |s_1 - s_k|^2 dx + \int_{x_1}^{x_1+x_2} |s_2 - s_k|^2 dx + \int_{x_1+x_2}^{x_1+x_2+x_3} |s_3 - s_k|^2 dx + \int_{x_1+x_2+x_3}^{x_1+x_2+x_3+\xi} |s_4 - s_k|^2 dx}{x_1 + x_2 + x_3 + \xi} - (l_3 - l_k) \right| < \epsilon_3$$

is true. For $\xi > T_4$ we have

$$(8)\quad \left| \frac{\int_0^{x_1} |s_1 - s_k|^2 dx + \int_{x_1}^{x_1+x_2} |s_2 - s_k|^2 dx + \int_{x_1+x_2}^{x_1+x_2+x_3} |s_3 - s_k|^2 dx + \int_{x_1+x_2+x_3}^{x_1+x_2+x_3+\xi} |s_4 - s_k|^2 dx}{x_1 + x_2 + x_3 + \xi} - \frac{(x_1+x_2+x_3)(l_3 - l_k) + \xi(l_4 - l_k)}{x_1 + x_2 + x_3 + \xi} \right| < \epsilon_3,$$

and so on.

We define now the function $f(x)$ in the following way:

$$f(x)=s_1(x) \text{ for } 0\leqq x< x_1,$$
$$=s_i(x) \text{ for } x_1+x_2+\ldots+x_{i-1}\leqq x< x_1+x_2+\ldots+x_i. \quad (i=2, 3, \ldots)$$

We shall show that

$$M\{|f(x)-s_k(x)|^2\}=l-l_k, \tag{9}$$

where
$$l=\sum_{n=1}^{\infty}|A_n|^2.$$

For $k=0$ we consider the integral

$$\frac{1}{x}\int_0^x |f(x)|^2\,dx.$$

		its value for	is included in
By	(2)	$T_1< x\leqq x_1$	$(l_1-\epsilon_1,\ l_1+\epsilon_1)$,
"	(3)	$x_1< x\leqq x_1+T_2$	$(l_1-\epsilon_1,\ l_1+\epsilon_1)$,
"	(4)	$x_1+T_2< x\leqq x_1+x_2$	$(l_1-\epsilon_1,\ l_2+\epsilon_1)$,
"	(5)	$x_1+x_2< x\leqq x_1+x_2+T_3$	$(l_2-\epsilon_2,\ l_2+\epsilon_2)$,
"	(6)	$x_1+x_2+T_3< x\leqq x_1+x_2+x_3$	$(l_2-\epsilon_2,\ l_3+\epsilon_2)$,

and so on. Since $l_j\to l$, $\epsilon_j\to 0$, as $j\to\infty$, we have

$$\frac{1}{x}\int_0^x |f(x)|^2\,dx \underset{x\to\infty}{\to} l.$$

In the same way we prove (9) for any $k>0$, which shows that $f(x)$ is a B^2 *a.p.* function with the Fourier series

$$\Sigma A_n e^{i\Lambda_n x}.$$

APPENDIX

$\bar{B}$ *a.p.* FUNCTIONS

When giving the definition of B *a.p.* functions, we mentioned a possible variation of conditions by which the functions have been defined. By this variation we obtain a new class of *a.p.* functions, defined as follows.

DEFINITION. *We call a function $f(x)$ a $\bar{B}$ a.p. function if*

$$\underline{M}\{|f(x)|\}$$

is finite, and if to any $\epsilon > 0$ corresponds a satisfactorily uniform set of numbers τ_i such that

$$(1) \qquad \bar{M}_x |f(x) - f(x+\tau_i)| < \epsilon$$

for all $-\infty < i < +\infty$, and

$$(2) \qquad \bar{M}_x \bar{M}_i |f(x) - f(x+\tau_i)| < \epsilon.$$

We call numbers τ_i *$\bar{B}$ translation numbers of $f(x)$ belonging to ϵ.*

The class of all $\bar{B}$ *a.p.* functions is denoted by $\{\bar{B}\ a.p.\}$. The conditions by which $\bar{B}$ *a.p.* functions are defined seem to be simpler and more natural than those by which B *a.p.* functions are defined, as the condition (2) does not involve the smoothing integration in the definition of B *a.p.* functions, but the class $\{B\ a.p.\}$ has the advantage of being identical with the closure $C_B(A)$. It will be proved that $\{\bar{B}\ a.p.\}$ is contained in $\{B\ a.p.\}$, and that they are very near each other, in fact from some point of view identical with each other. For though $\{B\ a.p.\}$ is not contained in $\{\bar{B}\ a.p.\}$, yet to every $\bar{B}$ *a.p.* function corresponds a B *a.p.* function with the same Fourier series. On account of this connection we consider the study of the class $\{\bar{B}\ a.p.\}$ as a study of $\{B\ a.p.\}$ from the point of view of *a.p.* properties given by (2).

Lemma 1. *If $A_1, A_2, \ldots$ form a set of finite real numbers such that $\bar{M}_i A_i > c$, then to any i' corresponds an $i'' > i'$, as large as we please, and such that*

$$A_{i'+1} + A_{i'+2} + \ldots + A_{i''} > (i'' - i')\,c.$$

The proof is obvious.

THEOREM 1. $\{\bar{B}\ a.p.\} \subset \{B\ a.p.\}$.

In order to prove Theorem 1 we first prove the following lemma.

Lemma 2. *If $f(x)$ is a $\bar{B}$ a.p. function and $\{\tau_i\}$ are $\bar{B}$ a.p. translation numbers $f(x)$, then*

$$(3) \qquad \bar{M}_i \int_0^1 |f(x) - f(x+\tau_i)|\,dx \leqq \int_0^1 \bar{M}_i |f(x) - f(x+\tau_i)|\,dx.$$

Lemma 2 is true when we mean by $\overline{M}_i$ in (3) the upper mean value corresponding either to all τ_i $(-\infty < i < +\infty)$ or only to τ_i with positive indices $(0 < i < +\infty)$. The proof in both cases is identical, but as the writing of formulae is slightly simpler for the second case we shall prove the lemma for this case.

Proof. Suppose that the lemma is not true and that

$$(4) \qquad \overline{M}_i \int_0^1 |f(x)-f(x+\tau_i)|\,dx = \int_0^1 M_i\,|f(x)-f(x+\tau_i)|\,dx + a,$$

where $a > 0$.

We shall first give the idea of the proof. On account of (4) we conclude that to any positive number ϵ corresponds an integer n, as large as we please, and such that

$$\int_0^1 \left[\frac{1}{n}\sum_{i=1}^{n} |f(x)-f(x+\tau_i)| - \overline{M}_i\{|f(x)-f(x+\tau_i)|\} - \epsilon\right] dx > a - 2\epsilon.$$

For sufficiently large values of n the integrand is negative in the whole range of integration except a set $E \subset (0, 1)$ of arbitrarily small measure. Thus

$$\int_E \left[\frac{1}{n}\sum_{i=1}^{n} |f(x)-f(x+\tau_i)| - M_i\{|f(x)-f(x+\tau_i)|\} - \epsilon\right] dx > a - 2\epsilon.$$

The functions

$$\overline{M}_i\{|f(x)-f(x+\tau_i)|\} \text{ and } \frac{1}{n}\sum_{i=1}^{n} |f(x)| = |f(x)|$$

being summable and independent of n we conclude that for sufficiently large values of n

$$\int_E \frac{1}{n}\sum_{i=1}^{n} |f(x+\tau_i)|\,dx > a - 3\epsilon.$$

The meaning of this inequality is that we can construct in each of the intervals (τ_i, τ_i+1) $(i=1, 2, \ldots, n)$ a set E_i congruent with E and such that

$$\frac{1}{n}\sum_{i=1}^{n} \int_{E_i} |f(x)|\,dx > a - 3\epsilon.$$

By choosing a suitable n we can take for E a set of arbitrarily small measure. It follows that we can construct in each of the intervals (τ_i, τ_i+1) $(i=1, 2, \ldots)$ a set E_i such that

$$M_i \int_{E_i} |f(x)|\,dx > a - 3\epsilon,$$

and that

$$mE_i \to 0,$$

as $i \to \infty$.

These sets naturally are no longer congruent. Let $\overline{E}=\sum_{i=1}^{\infty} E_i$, and let $\phi(x)$ be the characteristic function of $\overline{E}$. We have

$$(5) \qquad M\{\phi(x)\}=0, \quad \overline{M}\{\phi(x)\,|f(x)|\}>b$$

(we call the second of the above numbers *the upper mean value of* $|f(x)|$ *along the set* $\overline{E}$), where $b>0$ is some constant.

Now we take into account the almost-periodicity condition (2). On account of this condition the values of the function $|f(x)|$ on *almost* any interval are roughly speaking imitated throughout the whole range of values of x.

By (5) we conclude that we can find an interval (c, d) such that

$$\int_c^d \phi(x)\,|f(x)|\,dx=\int_{(c,\,d)\overline{E}} |f(x)|\,dx>b\,(d-c),$$

and that the mean density of $\overline{E}$ on (c, d) is as small as we please. On account of the above "imitation property" we can construct a set G of arbitrarily small density, imitation of the set $(c, d)\,\overline{E}$ in the whole range of values of x, on which the mean density of $|f(x)|$ is greater than b. We define in some way a sequence of non-overlapping sets

$$G_1, G_2, \ldots,$$

similar to G of decreasing mean density, on each of which the mean density of $|f(x)|$ is greater than a fixed constant, and thus we come to the conclusion that $\underline{M}_x\{|f(x)|\}$ is infinite, which is impossible on account of the definition. In this way we shall prove the lemma. We shall prove it in four stages.

1°. We first prove that there exists a set $\overline{E}$ of values of x such that if $\theta(x)$ is its characteristic function, then

$$(6) \qquad M\{\theta(x)\}=0 \text{ and } \overline{M}\{\theta(x)\,|f(x)|\}>\frac{a}{4b},$$

where $b>0$ is to be defined later.

Let

$$(7) \qquad 0<\epsilon<\frac{a}{4},$$

and let $\eta>0$ be such that, E being any set of points in the interval $(0, 1)$, we have

$$(8) \qquad \int_E |f(x)|\,dx<\epsilon,$$

if $mE<\eta$. We can evidently find a number n_0 such that the set E of all values of x in $(0, 1)$ for which the inequality

$$(9) \qquad \frac{1}{n}\sum_{i=1}^{n} |f(x)-f(x+\tau_i)|>\overline{M}_i\,|f(x)-f(x+\tau_i)|+\epsilon$$

is satisfied for at least one value $n \geqq n_0$, is of measure less than η. We have then for any $n \geqq n_0$

$$(10)\quad \int_{(0,1)-E} \frac{1}{n}\sum_{i=1}^{n} |f(x)-f(x+\tau_i)|\,dx \leqq \int_{(0,1)-E} M_i |f(x)-f(x+\tau_i)|\,dx+\epsilon$$

$$\leqq \int_0^1 \overline{M}_i |f(x)-f(x+\tau_i)|\,dx+\epsilon,$$

or

$$(11)\quad \frac{1}{n}\sum_{i=1}^{n} \int_{(0,1)-E} |f(x)-f(x+\tau_i)|\,dx \leqq \int_0^1 \overline{M}_i |f(x)-f(x+\tau_i)|\,dx+\epsilon,$$

and consequently

$$(12)\quad \overline{M}_i \int_{(0,1)-E} |f(x)-f(x+\tau_i)|\,dx \leqq \int_0^1 \overline{M}_i |f(x)-f(x+\tau_i)|\,dx+\epsilon.$$

We have

$$(13)\quad \overline{M}_i \int_0^1 |f(x)-f(x+\tau_i)|\,dx \leqq \overline{M}_i \int_{(0,1)-E} |f(x)-f(x+\tau_i)|\,dx + \overline{M}_i \int_E |f(x)-f(x+\tau_i)|\,dx.$$

By (4), (12), (13)

$$(14)\quad M_i \int_E |f(x)-f(x+\tau_i)|\,dx \geqq a-\epsilon,$$

and consequently

$$(15)\quad \int_E |f(x)|\,dx + \overline{M}_i \int_E |f(x+\tau_i)|\,dx \geqq a-\epsilon.$$

By (7), (8), (15)

$$(16)\quad M_i \int_E |f(x+\tau_i)|\,dx > \frac{a}{2}.$$

Denote by k_j the number of all τ_i satisfying the inequality

$$(17)\quad (j-1)\,b \leqq \tau_i < jb,$$

and suppose that b is so great that the ratio of the greatest of k_j to the smallest is < 2, which is possible, since the sequence of numbers τ_i is satisfactorily uniform. Thus there exists an integer k such that

$$(18)\quad k \leqq k_j < 2k$$

for all j. We take now those numbers τ_i which satisfy (17) for an odd j and denote them in order of their greatness by

$$\tau_1', \tau_2', \ldots.$$

We denote the other τ_i by

$$\tau_1'', \tau_2'', \ldots.$$

Then at least one of the two inequalities

$$(19)\quad M_i \int_E |f(x+\tau_i')|\,dx > \frac{a}{2}, \quad \overline{M}_i \int_E |f(x+\tau_i'')|\,dx > \frac{a}{2}$$

is satisfied. Suppose that it is the first one. Put in (17) $j=2l-1$ and denote by t_l that one (or one of those) of the numbers τ_i of (17) for which the integral

$$\int_E |f(x+\tau_i)|\,dx \tag{19.1}$$

has the maximum value. We shall have by virtue of (18)

$$2k\int_E |f(x+t_l)|\,dx \geqq \sum_{(2l-2\,b\leqq\tau'_i<(2l-1)\,b}\int_E |f(x+\tau'_i)|\,dx, \tag{20}$$

$$\frac{\sum_{i=1}^{n}\int_E |f(x+t_i)|\,dx}{n} \geqq \frac{\sum_{0\leqq\tau'_i<2nb}\int_E |f(x+\tau'_i)|\,dx}{2kn} \tag{21}$$

$$\geqq \frac{1}{2}\,\frac{\sum_{0\leqq\tau'_i<2nb}\int_E |f(x+\tau'_i)|\,dx}{k_1+k_3+\ldots+k_{2n-1}}.$$

But $k_1+k_3+\ldots+k_{2n-1}$ is the index of the largest τ_i' which is $< 2nb$. Then we conclude from (21)

$$\overline{M}_i\int_E |f(x+t_i)|\,dx \geqq \tfrac{1}{2}\overline{M}_i\int_E |f(x+\tau_i')|\,dx > \tfrac{1}{4}a. \tag{22}$$

Thus corresponding to any $\eta > 0$ we have a set $E \subset (0, 1)$ of measure $< \eta$, for which (22) is satisfied. Let us give to η a sequence of values

$$\eta_1 > \eta_2 > \ldots, \qquad (\eta_n \to 0) \tag{22.1}$$

and let us denote the corresponding sets E by

$$E_1,\ E_2,\ \ldots.$$

Denote by $t_i^{(j)}$ the value of t_i corresponding to $E = E_j$. We have for all j

$$2\,(i-1)\,b \leqq t_i^{(j)} < 2ib, \tag{23}$$

and

$$\overline{M}_i\int_{E_j} |f(x+t_i^{(j)})|\,dx > \tfrac{1}{4}a. \tag{24}$$

From (24) we conclude on account of Lemma 1 that we can choose numbers $i_1 < i_2 < i_3 < \ldots$ such that

$$\frac{1}{i_1}\sum_{i=1}^{i_1}\int_{E_1} |f(x+t_i^{(1)})|\,dx > \tfrac{1}{4}a, \tag{25}$$

$$\frac{1}{i_2-i_1-1}\sum_{i=i_1+2}^{i_2}\int_{E_2} |f(x+t_i^{(2)})|\,dx > \tfrac{1}{4}a,$$

$$\frac{1}{i_3-i_2-1}\sum_{i=i_2+2}^{i_3}\int_{E_3} |f(x+t_i^{(3)})|\,dx > \tfrac{1}{4}a,$$

....

and that

$$i_n - i_{n-1} \to \infty, \text{ as } n \to \infty. \tag{26}$$

The difference between any two consecutive numbers of the sequence

(27) $$t_1^{(1)},\ t_2^{(1)},\ \ldots,\ t_{i_1}^{(1)},\ t_{i_1+2}^{(2)},\ t_{i_1+3}^{(2)},\ \ldots,\ t_{i_2}^{(2)},\ t_{i_2+2}^{(3)},\ \ldots,$$

is always greater than b. Denoting by $[E+u]$ the set of the numbers of E each increased by the number u, and observing that all the sets E_j are included in the interval $(0, 1)$ we see that no two sets of the sequence

(28) $$[E_1+t_1^{(1)}],\ [E_1+t_2^{(1)}],\ \ldots,\ [E_1+t_{i_1}^{(1)}],\ [E_2+t_{i_1+2}^{(2)}],\ \ldots,$$

have points in common. Denote by $\overline{E}$ the sum of all sets of (28) and by $\theta(x)$ its characteristic function. Remembering that $mE_j < \eta_j$ we conclude on account of (22.1) that

$$M_x\{\theta(x)\}=0.$$

We conclude further on account of (25), (26), (23) that

(29) $$\overline{M}_x\{\theta(x)\,|f(x)|\} \geqq \frac{a}{8b}.$$

Definition. *If F is a set of points and $\theta(x)$ its characteristic function, then we call the numbers*

$$\overline{M}\{\theta(x)\},\ \ \underline{M}\{\theta(x)\},\ \ M\{\theta(x)\},$$

the upper density of F, the lower density, and simply density, and we denote them by

$$\overline{D}(F),\ \ \underline{D}(F),\ \ D(F).$$

As we said before we call the number (29) *the upper mean value of $|f(x)|$ on the set $\overline{E}$.* In a similar way is defined the lower mean value on the set $\overline{E}$.

2°. We now proceed to construct a certain class of sets of arbitrarily small density on which the upper mean value of $|f(x)|$ is greater than some fixed number. Let d be an arbitrarily small positive number. Take ϵ_1

(30) $$0<\epsilon_1<\frac{a}{96b},$$

and let σ_i be $\overline{B}$ translation numbers of $f(x)$ belonging to $\frac{1}{4}\epsilon_1$, so that

(31) $$\overline{M}_x\overline{M}_i\,|f(x)-f(x+\sigma_i)|<\epsilon_1$$

(where $\overline{M}_x$ and $\overline{M}_i$ are taken only over positive values of x and i). We choose a number $c>0$ satisfying the following conditions

(32) (i) $$\frac{m[\overline{E}(0,c)]}{2c}<d,$$

(33) (ii) $$\frac{1}{c}\int_0^c \overline{M}_i\{|f(x)-f(x+\sigma_i)|\}\,dx<\epsilon_1,$$

(34) (iii) $$\frac{1}{c}\int_0^c \theta(x)\,|f(x)|\,dx>\frac{a}{8b}-\epsilon,$$

(iv) the ratio of the maximum number of numbers σ_i lying on a segment of length c, to the minimum number is < 2.

Let $\epsilon_2 > 0$ be such that

$$(35)\qquad \int_{E'} \theta(x)\,|f(x)|\,dx < \epsilon$$

for any set $E' \subset (0, c)$ of measure less than ϵ_2. We can find an integer n'_0 such that the set E' of all values of x of the interval $(0, c)$ for which the inequality

$$(36)\qquad \frac{1}{n}\sum_{i=1}^{n} |f(x)-f(x+\sigma_i)| \geqq \overline{M}_i\,|f(x)-f(x+\sigma_i)| + \epsilon_1$$

is satisfied for at least one $n \geqq n'_0$ has a measure $< \epsilon_2$. We have then

$$(37)\qquad \frac{1}{n}\sum_{i=1}^{n}\int_{(0,\,c)-E'} |f(x)-f(x+\sigma_i)|\,dx < \int_{(0,\,c)-E'} \overline{M}_i\,|f(x)-f(x+\sigma_i)|\,dx + \epsilon_1 c.$$

By (33), (37)

$$(38)\qquad \overline{M}_i\,\frac{1}{c}\int_{(0,\,c)-E'} |f(x)-f(x+\sigma_i)|\,dx < 2\epsilon_1,$$

and *a fortiori*

$$(39)\qquad M_i\,\frac{1}{c}\int_{\overline{E}(0,\,c)-E'} |f(x)-f(x+\sigma_i)|\,dx < 2\epsilon_1.$$

In a way analogous to one used in 1° from (17) to (22) for definition of numbers t_l we can find a set of numbers

$$s_1,\ s_2,\ \ldots,$$

such that

$$(40)\qquad 2ic \leqq s_i < 2(i+1)\,c, \quad s_{i+1}-s_i > c$$

for $i = 1, 2, 3, \ldots$; and that

$$(41)\qquad M_i\,\frac{1}{c}\int_{\overline{E}(0,\,c)-E'} |f(x)-f(x+s_i)|\,dx < 4\epsilon_1,$$

(s_l is that one of σ_i which renders the integral

$$\int_{\overline{E}(0,\,c)-E'} |f(x)-f(x+\sigma_i)|\,dx$$

minimum (and not maximum as in (19.1)) when i varies in some interval).

Observing that

$$(42)\qquad \underline{M}_i\,|B_i| \geqq \underline{M}_i\,|A_i| - \overline{M}_i\,|A_i - B_i|,$$

and putting

$$A_i = \frac{1}{c}\int_{E(0,\,c)-E'} |f(x)|\,dx, \qquad B_i = \frac{1}{c}\int_{E(0,\,c)-E'} |f(x+s_i)|\,dx,$$

we shall have

$$\underline{M}_i \frac{1}{c} \int_{\overline{E}(0, c)-E'} |f(x+s_i)| \, dx$$

$$\geqq \frac{1}{c} \int_{\overline{E}(0, c)-E'} |f(x)| \, dx - \overline{M}_i \left| \frac{1}{c} \int_{\overline{E}(0, c)-E'} \{|f(x)| - |f(x+s_i)|\} \, dx \right|,$$

and *a fortiori*

$$(43) \quad \underline{M}_i \frac{1}{c} \int_{\overline{E}(0, c)-E'} |f(x+s_i)| \, dx$$

$$\geqq \frac{1}{c} \int_{\overline{E}(0, c)} |f(x)| \, dx - \frac{1}{c} \int |f(x)| \, dx$$

$$- \overline{M}_i \frac{1}{c} \int_{E(0, c)-E'} |f(x) - f(x+s_i)| \, dx.$$

By (34), (35), (41), (30)

$$(44) \qquad \underline{M}_i \frac{1}{c} \int_{\overline{E}(0, c)} |f(x+s_i)| \, dx > \frac{a}{8b} - 6\epsilon_1 > \frac{a}{16b}.$$

The sets

$$(45) \qquad [\overline{E}(0, c) + s_i] \qquad (i=1, 2, 3, \ldots)$$

are non-overlapping. Denoting by G the sum of all sets (45) and by $\phi(x)$ the characteristic function of G we shall have

$$(46) \qquad M\{\phi(x)\} = \frac{m\{\overline{E}(0, c)\}}{2c} < d,$$

and also on account of (44)

$$(47) \qquad \underline{M}_x\{\phi(x)|f(x)|\} > \frac{a}{32b}.$$

Thus *corresponding to any number* $d > 0$ *we can construct a* ("*segmentwise periodic*") *set* G *of density* $< d$ *on which the lower mean value of* $|f(x)|$ *is* $> \frac{a}{32b}$.

Remark. Let H be any subset of G. Define the function $f_1(x)$ by putting

$$f_1(x) = f(x - s_i), \quad x \subset (s_i, s_i + c) H, \qquad (i=1, 2, 3, \ldots)$$

$$f_1(x) = f(x) \text{ for all other values of } x.$$

We evidently have for any x in the interval $(0, c)$

$$(48) \qquad |f_1(x) - f_1(x+s_i)| \leqq |f(x) - f(x+s_i)|,$$

and consequently the inequality (41) remains true if we put in it $f_1(x)$ instead of $f(x)$. But then (47) also remains true. Thus we have

$$(49) \qquad \underline{M}_x\{\phi(x)|f_1(x)|\} > \frac{a}{32b}.$$

3°. We shall now show that corresponding to any $\epsilon > 0$ there exists a number δ such that the lower mean value of $|f(x)|$ on the set $G-H$ is $> \frac{a}{32b} - \epsilon$, if H is any subset of G subject to the only condition that $\overline{D}H < \delta$. Given $\epsilon > 0$, let δ be a number such that for any set $U \subset (0, c)$

$$\int_U |f(x)|\, dx < 2c\epsilon, \tag{50}$$

if only $mU < 2\delta c$. Let $H \subset G$ be a set such that $\overline{D}(H) < \delta$. Define now a function $f_2(x)$ in the following way:

$$\begin{aligned} f_2(x) &= f(x - s_i), \quad s_i \leqq x < s_i + c, \qquad (i = 1, 2, 3, \ldots) \\ &= 0 \ \text{ for all other values of } x. \end{aligned}$$

At all points of H we have

$$f_2(x) = f_1(x), \tag{51}$$

where $f_1(x)$ is the function defined in the above remark. Let n_0'' be an integer such that for all $n \geqq n_0''$

$$m\{H(0, s_n + c)\} < 2nc\delta. \tag{52}$$

Consider the integral

$$\int_{H(0,\, s_n+c)} |f_2(x)|\, dx,$$

the function $|f_2(x)|$ has the same positive values on n intervals (s_i, s_i+c) $i = 1, 2, \ldots, n$ (the values of $|f(x)|$ in $(0, c)$) and is zero for other values of x in $(0, s_n+c)$; therefore the above integral is less than n times the maximum of the integral

$$\int_U |f(x)|\, dx,$$

for any set U in $(0, c)$ of measure $\leqq \frac{1}{n} m[H(0, s_n + c)] < 2c\delta$, and thus on account of (50)

$$\frac{1}{s_n + c} \int_{H(0,\, s_n+c)} |f_2(x)|\, dx < \frac{2nc\delta}{s_n + c}. \tag{53}$$

Denote by $\psi(x)$ the characteristic function of H. By (53), (51), (40)

$$\overline{M}_x\{\psi(x)|f_1(x)|\} \leqq \epsilon. \tag{54}$$

By (49)

$$\underline{M}_x[\{\phi(x) - \psi(x)\}|f_1(x)|] > \frac{a}{32b} - \epsilon. \tag{55}$$

But at the points of $G - H$

$$f_1(x) = f(x).$$

Therefore

$$\underline{M}_x[\{\phi(x) - \psi(x)\}|f(x)|] > \frac{a}{32b} - \epsilon > \frac{a}{64b}, \tag{56}$$

if $\epsilon < \frac{a}{64b}$.

Thus corresponding to a set G there exists a number δ such that the lower mean value of $|f(x)|$ on any set $G-H$ is greater than $a/64b$ if only H is a subset of G of upper density less than δ.

4°. Let G_1 be one of the above sets and δ_1 the corresponding value of δ. We take a set G_2 of density $d_2 < \frac{\delta_1}{2}$ and denote by δ_2 the value of δ corresponding to the set $G = G_2$. We construct further a set G_3 of density $d_3 < \frac{\delta_2}{2}$ and so on. Consider now $\underline{M}_x\{|f(x)|\}$. Evidently it is greater than or equal to the lower mean value of $|f(x)|$ on the set

(57) $$G_1 + G_2 + \ldots + G_s,$$

for any s. But this set consists of the s non-overlapping sets

(57.1) $$\begin{cases} G_1 - G_1(G_2 + G_3 + \ldots + G_s), \\ G_2 - G_2(G_3 + G_4 + \ldots + G_s), \\ \ldots\ldots\ldots\ldots\ldots\ldots\ldots\ldots, \\ G_{s-1} - G_{s-1}\cdot G_s, \\ G_s. \end{cases}$$

Observing that

(58) $$\begin{aligned} \overline{D}G_i(G_{i+1} + G_{i+2} + \ldots + G_s) &\leqq \overline{D}(G_{i+1} + G_{i+2} + \ldots + G_s) \\ &\leqq d_{i+1} + d_{i+2} + \ldots + d_s < \frac{\delta_i}{2} + \frac{\delta_{i+1}}{2} + \ldots + \frac{\delta_{s-1}}{2} \\ &< \frac{\delta_i}{2} + \frac{\delta_i}{4} + \ldots < \delta_i, \end{aligned}$$

we conclude that the lower mean value of $|f(x)|$ on any of the sets (57.1) is greater than $a/64b$, and thus the lower mean value on the set (57) is greater than $sa/64b$, and consequently

$$\underline{M}_x\{|f(x)|\} > s\frac{a}{64b}.$$

s being arbitrary we have

(59) $$\underline{M}_x\{|f(x)|\} = \infty,$$

which is impossible since $f(x)$ is a $\overline{B}$ *a.p.* function. Thus Lemma 2 is proved.

Evidently we may replace in (3) the limits of integration 0, 1 by any two numbers $\alpha < \beta$, so that the lemma should be formulated as follows:

Lemma 2. *If $f(x)$ is a $\overline{B}$ a.p. function, then for any α, $\beta > \alpha$*

(60) $$\overline{M}_i \int_\alpha^\beta |f(x) - f(x+\tau_i)|\,dx \leqq \int_\alpha^\beta \overline{M}_i\{|f(x) - f(x+\tau_i)|\}\,dx.$$

Proof of Theorem 1. Let $f(x)$ be a $\overline{B}$ *a.p.* function. Then to any $\epsilon > 0$ corresponds a satisfactorily uniform set of numbers τ_i such that

(61) $$M_x|f(x) - f(x+\tau_i)| < \epsilon$$

for all i, and

(62) $$M_x M_i\{|f(x) - f(x+\tau_i)|\} < \epsilon.$$

Remembering that if $\theta(x) \geqq 0$, then

(63) $$\int_a^b dx \frac{1}{c} \int_x^{x+c} \theta(t)\,dt \leqq \int_a^{b+c} \theta(x)\,dx,$$

we conclude that

(64) $$\int_{-a}^{+a} \frac{dx}{c} \int_x^{x+c} \overline{M}_i |f(x)-f(x+\tau_i)|\,dx \leqq \int_{-a}^{a+c} M_i |f(x)-f(x+\tau_i)|\,dx.$$

Applying Lemma 2 to the left-hand side, we obtain

(65) $$\frac{1}{2a} \int_{-a}^{+a} dx \left[\overline{M}_i \frac{1}{c} \int_x^{x+c} |f(x)-f(x+\tau_i)|\,dx \right] \leqq \frac{1}{2a} \int_{-a}^{a+c} \overline{M}_i\,|f(x)-f(x+\tau_i)|\,dx,$$

and passing to the limit we have

$$M_x \overline{M}_i \frac{1}{c} \int_x^{x+c} |f(x)-f(x+\tau_i)|\,dx \leqq M_x M_i |f(x)-f(x+\tau_i)|.$$

By (62)

(66) $$\overline{M}_x \overline{M}_i \frac{1}{c} \int_x^{x+c} |f(x)-f(x+\tau_i)|\,dx < \epsilon$$

for all positive values of c.

The existence of the inequalities (61) and (66) proves Theorem 1.

THEOREM 2 (converse theorem). *To any B a.p. function corresponds a $\overline{B}$ a.p. function differing from the first function only by a function the mean value of whose modulus is zero.*

Let $f(x)$ be a B *a.p.* function. We consider the set of functions

$$f(x)+\phi(x)$$

for a given function $f(x)$ and for all functions $\phi(x)$ which satisfy the condition

$$M\{|\phi(x)|\}=0.$$

We call this set a *B a.p. functional class* (*B a.p.f.c.*). All functions of a (*B a.p.f.c.*) are B *a.p.* functions. Two such classes are either identical or have no function in common. All functions of a (*B a.p.f.c.*) have the same Fourier series. Our theorem may be formulated as follows.

THEOREM 2. *Any (B a.p.f.c.) contains a $\overline{B}$ a.p. function.*

Thus on account of this theorem we shall conclude that with respect to Fourier series the classes of B *a.p.* functions and of $\overline{B}$ *a.p.* functions are identical. We shall give the main idea of the proof without entering into every detail. The proof will be based on the following lemmas.

Let $\psi(x)$ be a *u.a.p.* function and $\overline{E}$ an *a.p.* set of translation numbers τ_i of some function (not necessarily of $\psi(x)$). We denote by the symbol

$$M_i\{\psi(x+\tau_i), (\alpha, \beta)\}$$

the mean value of numbers $\psi(x+\tau_i)$ corresponding to all τ_i satisfying the condition

$$\alpha \leqq x+\tau_i \leqq \beta.$$

Lemma 1. *$M_i\{\psi(x+\tau_i)\}$ exists.*

Lemma 2. *The difference*

$$M_i\{\psi(x+\tau_i), (\alpha, \beta)\} - M_i\{\psi(x+\tau_i)\} = \epsilon(x, \alpha, \beta)$$

tends to zero, as $\beta-\alpha \to +\infty$ uniformly in x and α.

Lemma 3. *To any B a.p. function $f_1(x)$ and to any sequence $\{\epsilon_n\}$ of positive numbers corresponds a series of u.a.p. functions*

$$\phi_1(x)+\phi_2(x)+\phi_3(x)+\ldots,$$

such that

$$M_x\{|f_1(x)-\phi_1(x)-\phi_2(x)-\ldots-\phi_n(x)|\}<\epsilon_n, \tag{67}$$

$$M_x\{|\phi_n(x)|\}<\epsilon_n. \quad (n>1) \tag{68}$$

Lemma 1 has been proved in the preceding part of this chapter.

Lemma 3 is quite obvious. The proof of Lemma 2 is similar to those relating to the existence of mean values connected with *a.p.* sets.

Passing now to the sketch of the proof of Theorem 2, let $f_1(x)$ be a B *a.p.* function and

$$\phi_1(x)+\phi_2(x)+\ldots \tag{69}$$

a series of Lemma 3 corresponding to $f_1(x)$. We assume that *the series $\Sigma\epsilon_n$ is convergent.* We take a sequence of rapidly increasing numbers

$$l_0=0<l_1<l_2<\ldots. \quad (l_n\to\infty) \tag{70}$$

We define a function $f(x)$ by the equations

$$f(x)=\phi_1(x)+\phi_2(x)+\ldots+\phi_n(x) \tag{71}$$

for x belonging to the intervals

$$l_{n-1}\leqq x<l_n, \quad -l_n<x\leqq -l_{n-1}.$$

Let $\{\epsilon_n'\}$ be another set of positive numbers ($\epsilon_n'\to 0$, as $n\to\infty$). We study the behaviour of the expression

$$\Phi_n(T)=\frac{1}{2T}\int_{-T}^{+T}|f(x)-\phi_1(x)-\ldots-\phi_n(x)|\,dx. \tag{72}$$

It can be shown that if the numbers of (70) increase rapidly enough, then for values of T belonging to the interval

$$l_N\leqq T\leqq l_{N+1}, \quad (N\geqq n+1)$$

$$|\Phi_n(T)-M\{|\phi_{n+1}(x)+\ldots+\phi_N(x)+\theta\phi_{N+1}(x)|\}|<\epsilon'_{N+1}, \tag{73}$$

where $|\theta|\leqq 1$*. Hence

$$\overline{M}_x\{|f(x)-\phi_1(x)-\ldots-\phi_n(x)|\}\leqq \sum_{i=n+1}^{\infty} M_x\{|\phi_i(x)|\} < \sum_{i=n+1}^{\infty}\epsilon_n. \tag{74}$$

By (67), (74)

$$M_x\{|f_1(x)-f(x)|\}=0.$$

* The proof is similar to that of 2°, § 9.

Thus $f(x)$ is a B a.p. function of the same functional class as $f_1(x)$.

We study now the behaviour of the expression

(75) $$\Psi(x, T) = M_i\{|f(x) - f(x+\tau_i)|, (-T, +T)\}.$$

In a way similar to that which had to be employed for the proof of (73), and on account of Lemmas 1 and 2, it can be shown that, if the numbers of (70) increase rapidly enough, then for values of T in the interval (l_n, l_{n+1}),

(76) $$|\Psi(x, T) - M_i\{|f(x) - \phi_1(x+\tau_i) - \dots - \phi_n(x+\tau_i)|, (-T, +T)\}| < \epsilon'_{n+1} + M_i\{|\phi_{n+1}(x+\tau_i)|\}.$$

We write (76) for $l_N \leqq T \leqq l_{N+1}$, $(N > n+1)$
and we conclude that

(77) $$|\Psi(x, T) - M_i\{|f(x) - \phi_1(x+\tau_i) - \dots - \phi_n(x+\tau_i)|, (-T, +T)\}| < \epsilon'_{N+1} + M_i\{|\phi_{n+1}(x+\tau_i) + \dots + \phi_N(x+\tau_i)|, (-T, +T)\} + M_i\{|\phi_{N+1}(x+\tau_i)|\}.$$

A certain rapidity of increase of the numbers of (70) can secure the inequality

(78) $$M_i\{|\phi_{n+1}(x+\tau_i) + \dots + \phi_N(x+\tau_i)|, (-T, +T)\} < 2M_i\{|\phi_{n+1}(x+\tau_i)|\} + \dots + 2M_i\{|\phi_N(x+\tau_i)|\},$$

for any n, N and $T \subset (l_N, l_{N+1})$.

Thus

(79) $$|\Psi(x, T) - M_i\{|f(x) - \phi_1(x+\tau_i) - \dots - \phi_n(x+\tau_i)|, (-T, +T)\}| < \epsilon'_{N+1} + 2M_i\{|\phi_{n+1}(x+\tau_i)|\} + \dots + 2M_i\{|\phi_{N+1}(x+\tau_i)|\}.$$

Suppose that for a given value of x the series

(80) $$M_i\{|\phi_1(x+\tau_i)|\} + M_i\{|\phi_2(x+\tau_i)|\} + \dots$$

converges. Then, as the second term of the left-hand side expression of (79) tends to a limit, as $T \to \infty$, it is not difficult to conclude that $\Psi(x, T)$ *tends to a limit, as $T \to \infty$.*

Take now an interval $(d, d+1)$ of values of x. Consider the question of convergence of the series (80). We have

(81) $$\int_d^{d+1} M_i\{|\phi_n(x+\tau_i)|\}\, dx \leqq \underline{M}_i \int_d^{d+1} |\phi_n(x+\tau_i)|\, dx < LM_x\{|\phi_n(x)|\} < L\epsilon_n,$$

where L denotes the maximum distance between two consecutive τ_i. Denoting by $s_j(x)$ the sum of the first j terms of (80) we conclude on account of (81)

(82) $$\int_d^{d+1} s_j(x)\, dx < L[M_x\{|\phi_1(x)|\} + \epsilon_2 + \epsilon_3 + \dots]$$

for any j.

The series $\Sigma\epsilon_n$ being convergent we conclude that the series (80) converges for almost all values of x, and consequently the limit of $\Psi(x, T)$, as $T \to \infty$, exists for almost all values of T, i.e.

$$(83) \qquad M_i\{|f(x)-f(x+\tau_i)|\}$$

exists for almost all values of x.

In Chapter II we have proved that if $f(x)$ is a B *a.p.* function, then to any $\epsilon > 0$ corresponds an *a.p.* set of numbers τ_i such that the condition

$$(84) \qquad M_x \overline{M}_i \frac{1}{c} \int_x^{x+c} |f(x)-f(x+\tau_i)|\, dx < \epsilon$$

for all $c > 0$ is satisfied.

On account of the existence of mean value (83) we can apply Fatou's Theorem to the inner mean value of (84). We have

$$(85) \quad \frac{1}{c} \int_x^{x+c} M_i |f(x)-f(x+\tau_i)|\, dx \leqq \overline{M}_i \frac{1}{c} \int_x^{x+c} |f(x)-f(x+\tau_i)|\, dx.$$

By (84) $\qquad \overline{M}_x \frac{1}{c} \int_x^{x+c} M_i |f(x)-f(x+\tau_i)|\, dx < \epsilon,$

and consequently*

$$(86) \qquad M_x M_i |f(x)-f(x+\tau_i)| < \epsilon_1,$$

which proves that the function $f(x)$ is $\overline{B}$ *a.p.* Thus Theorem 2 has been proved.

Example of a B a.p. function which is not $\overline{B}$ a.p.

Let a, b, l be positive numbers such that $m = \dfrac{l}{a+b}$ is an integer. We define the function ϕ in the following way:

$$(1) \quad \phi(x, l, a, b, c) = c, \quad k(a+b) \leqq x < k(a+b)+a, \quad (k = 0, 1, \ldots, m-1)$$
$$= 0 \quad \text{for all other values of } x.$$

Define now the function:

$$(2) \qquad f(x) = \sum_{n=1}^{\infty} \phi(x - 2^n, l_n, a_n, b_n, c_n),$$

where

$$(3) \quad l_n = [\sqrt{n}] \text{ (integral part of } \sqrt{n}), \quad \frac{1}{a_n+b_n} = 2^{2^n}, \quad \frac{a_n}{a_n+b_n} = \frac{1}{n}, \quad c = 2^n \sqrt[4]{n}.$$

We have $\qquad M_x\{f(x)\} = 0,$

and thus $f(x)$ is a B *a.p.* function.

Let now

$$(4) \qquad 0 < \tau_1 < \tau_2 < \ldots$$

be an arbitrary "satisfactorily uniform" (and consequently relatively dense) sequence of numbers†.

* If $p(x) \geqq 0$ then $\overline{M}_x \left\{\frac{1}{c} \int_x^{x+c} p(x)\, dx\right\} = \overline{M}_x \{p(x)\}$.

† The meaning of terms "satisfactorily uniform," "relatively dense," for one-sided sequences like (4) is clear. Obviously when (6) has been proved for any one-sided *s.u.* set, it is also proved for any two-sided *s.u.* set of numbers τ_i.

Then there exists n'_0 such that for all $n \geqq n'_0$

(5) $$nk \leqq \tau_n < 2nk,$$

where k is some positive number. We shall prove that

(6) $$\int_d^{d+1} \overline{M}_i |f(x) - f(x+\tau_i)| \, dx = \infty$$

for any value of d.

Let l be a positive number such that any interval of length l contains at least one of the numbers (4).

Let d have a fixed value, and let A be an arbitrarily large positive number. Choose $n_0 \geqq n'_0$ such that

(7) (i) $$\max_{d \leqq x \leqq d+1} |f(x)| + A < \sqrt[4]{n_0},$$

(8) (ii) $$l_{n_0} = [\sqrt{n_0}] > l + 1.$$

Then each interval $(2^n, 2^n + l_n)$ for $n \geqq n_0$ contains at least one of the intervals $(\tau_i + d, \tau_i + d + 1)$; denote such an interval (or one of them, if there is more than one) by

$$(\tau_{i_n} + d, \tau_{i_n} + d + 1).$$

Let $n_1 \geqq n_0$ and $n_1 > 2$. Consider the value of the functions

(9) $$f(x + \tau_{i_n}),$$

for $n = n_1, n_1 + 1, \ldots, 8n_1 - 1$, in the interval $(d, d+1)$. In the interval $(d, d+1)$ the function $f(x + \tau_{i_n})$ takes the same values as the function

$$\phi(x, l_n, a_n, b_n, c_n)$$

does in a certain interval of length 1 belonging to $(0, l_n)$, and thus $f(x + \tau_{i_n})$ is equal either to 0 or to $2^n \sqrt[4]{n}$. Denote by $E^{(1)}$ the set of values of x in the interval $(d, d+1)$ for which at least one of the functions (9) differs from zero. We shall prove that

(10) $$\lambda = mE^{(1)} \geqq \tfrac{1}{2}.$$

Let E_n denote the set of values of x in $(d, d+1)$ for which $f(x + \tau_{i_n}) \neq 0$. Then

(11) $$E^{(1)} = E_{n_1} + E_{n_1+1} + \ldots + E_{8n_1-1}.$$

We have $$mE_n = \frac{1}{n}.$$

E_n consists either of 2^{2^n} equal intervals or of $2^{2^n} + 1$ intervals of which all interior intervals are equal to one another and the sum of the two extreme intervals is equal to the length of an interior interval. Define now

(12) $$m[E_{n+1} \times (E_{n_1} + E_{n_1+1} + \ldots + E_n)].$$

The set

(13) $$E_{n_1} + E_{n_1+1} + \ldots + E_n$$

is a set of non-overlapping intervals, whose number is less than or equal to

(14) $$2^{2^{n_1}} + 2^{2^{n_1+1}} + \ldots + 2^{2^n} < 2 \cdot 2^{2^n}.$$

Now if δ is any interval, then denoting its length also by δ it is easy to see that

$$(15)\qquad m[E_{n+1}\times\delta]\leqq\frac{\delta a_{n+1}}{a_{n+1}+b_{n+1}}+a_{n+1}.$$

Therefore

$$(16)\quad m[E_{n+1}\times(E_{n_1}+E_{n_1+1}+\ldots+E_n)]$$

$$<\frac{[m(E_{n_1}+E_{n_1+1}+\ldots+E_n)]\,a_{n+1}}{a_{n+1}+b_{n+1}}+2\,.\,2^{2^n}a_{n+1},$$

and by (11)
$$<\frac{\lambda a_{n+1}}{a_{n+1}+b_{n+1}}+\frac{2\,.\,2^{2^n}}{(n+1)\,2^{2^{n+1}}}<\frac{\lambda}{n+1}+\frac{1}{2^{2^n}}.$$

We have

$$(17)\quad m[E_{n_1}+E_{n_1+1}+\ldots+E_n+E_{n+1}]$$

$$=m[E_{n_1}+E_{n_1+1}+\ldots+E_n]+mE_{n+1}-m[E_{n+1}(E_{n_1}+E_{n_1+1}+\ldots+E_n)]$$

$$>m[E_{n_1}+E_{n_1+1}+\ldots+E_n]+\frac{1-\lambda}{n+1}-\frac{1}{2^{2^n}}$$

$$>(1-\lambda)\left(\frac{1}{n_1}+\frac{1}{n_1+1}+\ldots+\frac{1}{n}+\frac{1}{n+1}\right)-\frac{1}{2^{2^{n_1}}}-\frac{1}{2^{2^{n_1+1}}}-\ldots-\frac{1}{2^{2^n}}$$

$$>(1-\lambda)\left(\frac{1}{n_1}+\frac{1}{n_1+1}+\ldots+\frac{1}{n+1}\right)-\frac{2}{2^{2^{n_1}}}.$$

Putting in (17) $n+1=8n_1-1$, we shall have (observing that

$$\frac{1}{n_1}+\frac{1}{n_1+1}+\ldots+\frac{1}{8n_1-1}>2)$$

$$(18)\qquad \lambda>2(1-\lambda)-\tfrac{1}{2},$$

which shows that $\lambda>\frac{1}{2}$.

Now let x be any point of E_n for $n\geqq n_0$. We have

$$f(x+\tau_{i_n})=2^n\sqrt[4]{n}>2^n\sqrt[4]{n_0},$$

$$|f(x)-f(x+\tau_{i_n})|\geqq 2^n\sqrt[4]{n_0}-\underset{d\leqq x\leqq d+1}{\text{Max.}}|f(x)|\geqq 2^n\{\sqrt[4]{n_0}-\underset{d\leqq x\leqq d+1}{\text{Max.}}|f(x)|\}$$

and by (7)

$$(19)\qquad |f(x)-f(x+\tau_{i_n})|>2^nA,$$

and *a fortiori*

$$\sum_{i=1}^{i_n}|f(x)-f(x+\tau_i)|>2^nA,$$

whence
$$\frac{\sum_{i=1}^{i_n}|f(x)-f(x+\tau_i)|}{i_n}>\frac{2^nk}{i_nk}A.$$

By (5)

$$(20)\quad \frac{\sum_{i=1}^{i_n}|f(x)-f(x+\tau_i)|}{i_n}>\frac{2^nk}{\tau_{i_n}}A>\frac{2^nk}{2^n+[\sqrt{n}]}A>\frac{2^nk}{2\,.\,2^n}A=\frac{k}{2}A.$$

Denote by $M(x, n', n'')$ the maximum of

$$\frac{\sum_{i=1}^{i=n} |f(x)-f(x+\tau_i)|}{n}$$

as n varies from $i_{n'}$ to $i_{n''-1}$. We conclude from (20) that

$$M(x, n_1, 8n_1) > \frac{k}{2} A \tag{21}$$

for all values of x belonging to $E^{(1)}$.

We take now a sequence of integers

$$n_1, n_2, n_3, \ldots,$$

such that $\qquad n_2 \geqq 8n_1, \quad n_3 \geqq 8n_2, \ \ldots.$

Write

$$E^{(j)} = E_{n_j} + E_{n_j+1} + \ldots + E_{8n_j-1}. \qquad (j=1, 2, 3, \ldots) \tag{22}$$

At any point x of $E^{(j)}$

$$M(x, n_j, 8n_j) > \frac{k}{2} A. \tag{23}$$

Let E be the upper limit of the sequence of sets

$$E^{(1)}, E^{(2)}, \ldots, \tag{24}$$

i.e. the set of points each of which belongs to an infinite number of sets of (24). Then

$$mE \geqq \tfrac{1}{2}. \tag{25}$$

Let x be a point of E, and let

$$E^{(j_1)}, \ E^{(j_2)}, \ \ldots$$

be the sets which contain x; then for any $s=1, 2, 3, \ldots,$

$$M(x, n_{j_s}, 8n_{j_s}) > \frac{k}{2} A,$$

i.e.
$$\frac{\sum_{i=1}^{i=n} |f(x)-f(x+\tau_i)|}{n} > \frac{k}{2} A$$

for at least one n in any interval $i_{n_{j_s}} \leqq n \leqq i_{8n_{j_s}-1}$, which proves that

$$\overline{M}_i \{|f(x)-f(x+\tau_i)|\} \geqq \frac{k}{2} A. \tag{26}$$

By (25) and (26)

$$\int_d^{d+1} \overline{M}_i \{|f(x)-f(x+\tau_i)|\} \, dx \geqq \frac{k}{4} A. \tag{27}$$

A being arbitrary we have

$$\int_d^{d+1} \overline{M}_i \{|f(x)-f(x+\tau_i)|\} \, dx = \infty, \tag{28}$$

and thus $\qquad M_x \overline{M}_i \{|f(x)-f(x+\tau_i)|\} = \infty$

for any satisfactorily uniform set of numbers $\tau_1, \tau_2, \ldots,$ which proves that $f(x)$ is not a $\overline{B}$ *a.p.* function.

CHAPTER III

ANALYTIC ALMOST PERIODIC FUNCTIONS

§ 1. Some auxiliary theorems in the theory of analytic functions.

1°. NOTATION. We denote by (a, b) the open interval $a < x < b$, by $[a, b]$ the closed interval $a \leqq x \leqq b$, by $\langle a, b\rangle$ any interval (a_1, b_1) where $a < a_1 < b_1 < b$, so that if we say that a property holds in "the interval" $\langle a, b\rangle$, we mean that it holds in any interval (a_1, b_1) where $a < a_1 < b_1 < b$. We use also combinations of these notations, so that $(a, b]$ denotes the interval $a < x \leqq b$, $[a, b\rangle$ any interval $[a, b_1)$ where $a < b_1 < b$, and so on.

We write the complex variable z or s in the form $z = s = \sigma + it$. The set of all the values of z for which σ is equal to a fixed value σ_0 is called "the line σ_0". The set of all the values of z for which σ belongs to an interval (a, b) is called "the strip (a, b)." We shall also speak of strips $[a, b]$, $\langle a, b\rangle$, $(a, b\rangle$ and so on.

2°. In this section we shall establish the Montel "selection principle." We first have to prove a number of lemmas.

Lemma 1. *Given a sequence $\{f_n(z)\}$ $(n = 1, 2, \ldots)$ of functions uniformly bounded in a domain D, then corresponding to any enumerably infinite set a_k $(k = 1, 2, \ldots)$ of points of this domain there exists a subsequence of the sequence $\{f_n(z)\}$ which is convergent at all these points.*

For, the sequence $\{f_n(a_1)\}$ $(n = 1, 2, \ldots)$ of constant numbers being bounded there exists a convergent subsequence $\{f_{n_k^{(1)}}(a_1)\}$ (Weierstrass' theorem).

By the same argument the sequence $\{f_{n_k^{(1)}}(a_2)\}$ contains a convergent subsequence $\{f_{n_k^{(2)}}(a_2)\}$, also the sequence $\{f_{n_k^{(2)}}(a_3)\}$ a convergent subsequence $\{f_{n_k^{(3)}}(a_3)\}$, and so on. Take now the sequence

$$(1) \qquad f_{n_1^{(1)}}(z), \quad f_{n_2^{(2)}}(z), \quad f_{n_3^{(3)}}(z), \quad \ldots$$

It converges at any point a_k, since for any k the sequence

$$f_{n_k^{(k)}}(a_k),\quad f_{n_{k+1}^{(k+1)}}(a_k),\quad f_{n_{k+2}^{(k+2)}}(a_k),\ \ldots$$

is a subsequence of the sequence

$$\{f_{n_i^{(k)}}(a_k)\},\qquad (i=1,2,\ldots)$$

and the lemma is proved.

Lemma 2. *A uniformly continuous sequence of functions $\{f_n(z)\}$, convergent at a set of points everywhere dense in a bounded domain D, converges uniformly in this domain.*

For, given $\epsilon>0$ there exists $\delta=\delta\left(\frac{\epsilon}{3}\right)>0$, such that for any n

$$(1)\qquad |f_n(z')-f_n(z'')|<\tfrac{1}{3}\epsilon$$

if

$$|z'-z''|<\delta.$$

Divide the domain D into partial domains $\Delta_1, \Delta_2, \ldots, \Delta_k$, each of diameter $<\delta$, and let $a_1, a_2, \ldots, a_k$ be points of these domains at which the sequence converges. There exists an integer n_0 such that for any $i=1, 2, \ldots, k$,

$$(2)\qquad |f_{n'}(a_i)-f_{n''}(a_i)|<\tfrac{1}{3}\epsilon$$

if

$$n'>n_0,\quad n''>n_0.$$

Take now any point z_0 of D. Suppose it belongs to Δ_i. We write

$$(3)\quad |f_{n'}(z_0)-f_{n''}(z_0)|\leqq|f_{n'}(z_0)-f_{n'}(a_i)| + |f_{n'}(a_i)-f_{n''}(a_i)|+|f_{n''}(a_i)-f_{n''}(z_0)|.$$

By (1)

$$|f_{n'}(z_0)-f_{n'}(a_i)|<\tfrac{1}{3}\epsilon,\quad |f_{n''}(a_i)-f_{n''}(z_0)|<\tfrac{1}{3}\epsilon,$$

since $|z_0-a_i|<\delta$. Thus by (2) and (3)

$$|f_{n'}(z_0)-f_{n''}(z_0)|<\epsilon$$

if

$$n'>n_0,\quad n''>n_0,$$

which proves the lemma.

Lemma 3. *A set of analytic functions uniformly bounded in a domain D is uniformly continuous in any domain D' interior to D.*

Let $\delta > 0$ be the distance between the boundaries of the domains D and D', and M the upper bound of the moduli of all the functions of the set. Take any pair z', z'' of points of D' such that $|z' - z''| < \delta/2$. We shall have for any function $f(z)$ of the set

$$f(z') - f(z'') = \frac{1}{2\pi i}\int_{c(z',\,\delta)} f(z)\left(\frac{1}{z - z'} - \frac{1}{z - z''}\right) dz,$$

where $c(z', \delta)$ is the circle of radius δ with centre z'. We conclude that

$$(4)\quad |f(z') - f(z'')| \leq \frac{1}{2\pi} M \frac{|z' - z''|\, 2\pi\delta}{\frac{1}{2}\delta^2} = \frac{2M}{\delta}|z' - z''|,$$

which proves the lemma.

Lemma 4. *Given a sequence of analytic functions $\{f_n(z)\}$ uniformly bounded in a domain D and given an interior domain D', there exists a subsequence uniformly convergent in D'.*

Take an enumerably infinite set of points a_k $(k = 1, 2, \ldots)$ everywhere dense in the domain D'. By Lemma 1 there exists a subsequence $\{f_{n_k}(z)\}$ convergent at all these points. By Lemma 3 the whole sequence $\{f_n(z)\}$ is uniformly continuous in the domain D'; *a fortiori* so is the subsequence $\{f_{n_k}(z)\}$. Consequently, by Lemma 2, this subsequence is uniformly convergent, and the lemma is proved.

Montel's Theorem. *Given a sequence $\{f_n(z)\}$ of analytic functions uniformly bounded in a domain D, there exists a subsequence uniformly convergent in every interior domain.*

Let D_i $(i = 1, 2, 3, \ldots)$ be the domain of all points of D whose distance from the boundary is $> \frac{1}{i}$. By Lemma 4 the sequence $\{f_n(z)\}$ has a subsequence $\{f_{n_k^{(1)}}(z)\}$ uniformly convergent in D_1.

Applying the same lemma, we deduce successively that the sequence $\{f_{n_k^{(1)}}(z)\}$ has a subsequence $\{f_{n_k^{(2)}}(z)\}$ uniformly convergent in D_2, the sequence $\{f_{n_k^{(2)}}(z)\}$ has a subsequence $\{f_{n_k^{(3)}}(z)\}$ uniformly convergent in D_3, and so on. Take now the sequence

$$f_{n_1^{(1)}}(z), \quad f_{n_2^{(2)}}(z), \quad f_{n_3^{(3)}}(z), \quad \ldots\ldots,$$

It is obviously uniformly convergent in any domain D_i and consequently in any domain interior to D, and thus the theorem is proved.

3°. **Lemma.** *A domain D consists of two domains D_1 and D_2 having a linear segment AB as a common boundary. A function $f(z)$ is analytic at all interior points of D_1 and of D_2 and is continuous at all points of AB. Then it is also analytic at all interior points of AB.*

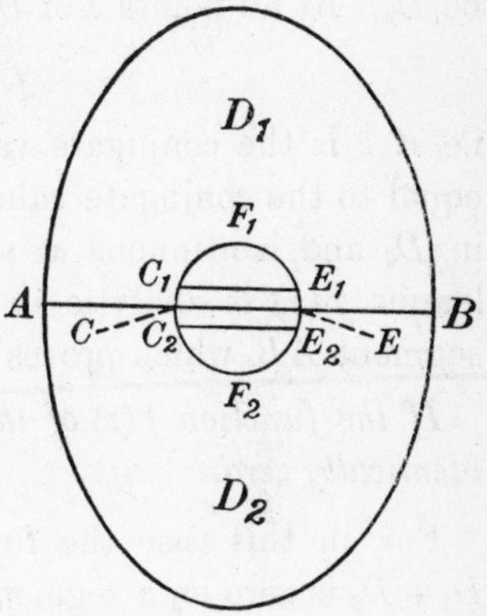

Take a circle CF_1EF_2 interior to the domain D and crossing the segment AB. We draw chords C_1E_1, C_2E_2 parallel to AB. Define a function

$$\phi(z) = \frac{1}{2\pi i}\int_{CF_2EF_1} \frac{f(s)\,ds}{s-z}$$

which is obviously analytic inside the circle. We write

$$\phi(z) = \frac{1}{2\pi i}\int_{E_1F_1C_1E_1} \frac{f(s)\,ds}{s-z} + \frac{1}{2\pi i}\int_{E_1C_1C_2E_2E_1} \frac{f(s)\,ds}{s-z} + \frac{1}{2\pi i}\int_{E_2C_2F_2E_2} \frac{f(s)\,ds}{s-z}.$$

In this formula let z be an interior point of CEF_1C. We take C_1E_1 so near CE that the point z is inside $C_1E_1F_1C_1$. Then the first integral in this formula is equal to $f(z)$ and the third one to zero. Let now C_1E_1 and C_2E_2 tend to coincide with CE, then the second integral will tend to zero and thus $\phi(z) = f(z)$ at all points of the circle above CE. By the same argument $\phi(z)=f(z)$ at all points of the circle below CE, and on account of the continuity of both the functions $\phi(z)=f(z)$ on CE. Thus $f(z)$ is analytic at all interior points of the segment CE. The lemma now follows immediately.

THEOREM. SCHWARZ'S REFLECTION PRINCIPLE. *If a function $f(z)$ is analytic inside a domain D_1, above the real axis and bounded from below by a segment AB of the real axis, and is continuous and real at all points of AB, then it can be analytically continued beyond the segment AB.*

Take the reflection of the domain D_1 in the real axis. Let it be D_2. At all points z of D_2 we define $f(z)$ by the equation

$$f(z)=f(\bar{z}),$$

i.e. if $\bar{z}$ is the conjugate value of z then we define $f(z)$ to be equal to the conjugate value of $f(\bar{z})$. Evidently $f(z)$ is analytic in D_2 and continuous at all points of AB. By the preceding lemma $f(z)$ is analytic in the domain D_1+D_2, including the segment AB, which proves the theorem.

If the function $f(z)$ of this theorem is zero on AB, then it is identically zero.

For, in this case the function $f(z)$ analytic in the domain D_1+D_2 is zero on a segment AB inside this domain.

Evidently it is not essential for the segment AB to lie on the real axis. We have therefore the following

Corollary. *If a function $f(z)$ is analytic in a domain, a part of whose boundary is a segment AB, and if it is continuous and equal to zero at all points of AB, then it is identically zero in the domain.*

4°. ROUCHÉ'S THEOREM. *If functions $f(z)$ and $\phi(z)$ are analytic in and on a regular contour C, and if $|\phi(z)|<|f(z)|$ at all points of C, then the functions $f(z)$ and $f(z)+\phi(z)$ have the same number of zeros inside C.*

For the number of zeros of $f(z)$ is known to be equal to the variation of $\frac{1}{2\pi i}\operatorname{Log} f(z)$, as z describes the contour C in the positive direction. The difference between the number of zeros of $f(z)+\phi(z)$ and the number of zeros of $f(z)$ is the variation of $\frac{1}{2\pi i}\operatorname{Log}\left\{1+\frac{\phi(z)}{f(z)}\right\}$, as z describes C. The real part of $1+\frac{\phi(z)}{f(z)}$ at all points of C is positive. Therefore if we define the amplitude of $1+\frac{\phi(z)}{f(z)}$ at a starting-point of C to be in the interval $\left(-\frac{\pi}{2}, +\frac{\pi}{2}\right)$, then it will remain in this interval when z describes the whole of C, and thus we shall arrive at the starting-point with the original value of the amplitude, i.e. the variation of $\frac{1}{2\pi i}\operatorname{Log}\left\{1+\frac{\phi(z)}{f(z)}\right\}$ on the contour C is zero, which proves the theorem.

5°. SCHWARZ'S LEMMA. *If*

(1) $w=\phi(z)$ *is analytic inside the circle* $|z|=1$,

(2) $|\phi(z)|<1$ *inside the same circle,*

(3) $\phi(0)=0$,

then

$$|w| \leqq |z|$$

inside the same circle.

For on any circle $|z|=r<1$

$$\left|\frac{\phi(z)}{z}\right|<\frac{1}{r},$$

which inequality holds true also inside the circle, since $\frac{\phi(z)}{z}$ is analytic. Thus for any $|z|<1$ we have

$$\left|\frac{\phi(z)}{z}\right|<\frac{1}{r}$$

for all $r>|z|$ and <1, whence

$$\left|\frac{\phi(z)}{z}\right|\leqq 1,$$

i.e. $|w|\leqq|z|$, which proves the lemma.

Corollary. *If*

(1) $w' = \psi(z')$ *is analytic in the half-plane* $Rz' > 0$,

(2) $Rw' > 0$ *for* $Rz' > 0$,

(3) $w' = 1$ *at* $z' = 1$,

then

$$(1) \qquad \left|\frac{w'-1}{w'+1}\right| \leqq \left|\frac{z'-1}{z'+1}\right|$$

for $Rz' > 0$.

For, putting

$$z = \frac{z'-1}{z'+1}, \quad w = \frac{w'-1}{w'+1},$$

we define a function $w = \phi(z)$ satisfying the conditions of the lemma and consequently $|w| \leqq |z|$ for $|z| < 1$, which is equivalent to (1).

6°. Theorem. *If a function* $f(s)$ *is*

(*a*) *analytic in a strip* (a, b),

(*b*) *S-bounded in the same strip, i.e. there exists a finite number* $K > 0$ *such that* $\int_s^{s+i} |f(s)|\, dt < K$ *at all points of the strip,*

then $f(s)$ *is bounded in* $\langle a, b \rangle$.

Take any strip (a_1, b_1), $(a < a_1 < b_1 < b)$ and write

$$\delta = \min. (a_1 - a,\ b - b_1,\ \tfrac{1}{2}).$$

Let $s_0 = \sigma_0 + it_0$ be any point of the strip (a_1, b_1), and $c(s_0, r)$ be the circle $|s - s_0| = r$. We have for any $r \leqq \delta$

$$2\pi r\, |f(s_0)| \leqq \int_{c(s_0, r)} |f(s)|\, |ds|.$$

Integrating from $r = 0$ to $r = \delta$, we have

$$\begin{aligned} \pi\delta^2 |f(s_0)| &\leqq \int_0^\delta dr \int_{c(s_0, r)} |f(s)|\, |ds| \\ &\leqq \int_{\sigma_0-\delta}^{\sigma_0+\delta} d\sigma \int_{\sigma+(t_0-\frac{1}{2})i}^{\sigma+(t_0+\frac{1}{2})i} |f(s)|\, |ds| \\ &\leqq 2\delta K. \end{aligned}$$

Thus at all points s_0 of the strip (a_1, b_1)

$$|f(s_0)| \leqq \frac{2}{\pi\delta} K,$$

which proves the theorem.

7°. THE PHRAGMÉN-LINDELÖF THEOREM. *If a function $\phi(s)$, analytic and bounded in a strip $[a, b]$, satisfies the condition*

$$|\phi(s)| \leqq K$$

on the boundary lines of the strip, then it satisfies the same condition at all points of the strip.

Consider the product $\phi(s) e^{cs^2}$ $(c > 0)$ in a rectangle $\sigma = a$, $\sigma = b$, $t = T$, $t = -T$. For large values of T $|\phi(s) e^{cs^2}|$ is small on the last two sides of the rectangle, and therefore T can be taken so that the upper bound of $|\phi(s) e^{cs^2}|$ on each of these sides is less than $K\, u.b. |e^{cs^2}|$, where $u.b. |e^{cs^2}|$ is the upper bound of $|e^{cs^2}|$ on the two lines $\sigma = a$, $\sigma = b$, i.e. max. (e^{ca^2}, e^{cb^2}). Thus at any point s inside the rectangle

(1) $$|\phi(s) e^{cs^2}| \leqq K\, u.b. |e^{cs^2}|.$$

As T can be taken as large as we please, we see that (1) is true at all points of the strip. Let now c in (1) tend to zero. We shall have at any point s of the strip

$$|\phi(s)| \leqq K,$$

which proves the theorem.

7.1°. THEOREM. *If a sequence of exponential polynomials*

$$\phi_k(s) = \sum_{n=1}^{N_k} a_{n,k} e^{\lambda_{n,k} s}, \qquad (k = 1, 2, \ldots)$$

where all the $\lambda_{n,k}$ are real, converges uniformly on two lines $\sigma = \alpha$, $\sigma = \beta$, then it converges uniformly in the strip $[\alpha, \beta]$.

For, given $\epsilon > 0$, there exists k_0 such that

(1) $$|\phi_{k'}(s) - \phi_{k''}(s)| < \epsilon$$

on the lines α and β if only $k' > k_0$, $k'' > k_0$. As $\phi_{k'}(s) - \phi_{k''}(s)$ is bounded in the strip $[\alpha, \beta]$, we conclude by the preceding theorem that (1) holds at all points of the strip, which proves the theorem.

8°. Denote by $L(\sigma)$ the upper bound of $|\phi(s)|$ on the line σ.

DOETSCH'S THEOREM. *If $\phi(s)$ is an analytic bounded function in a strip $[\sigma_1, \sigma_2]$, then for any σ of the strip*

$$(1) \qquad L(\sigma) \leqq L(\sigma_1)^{\frac{\sigma_2-\sigma}{\sigma_2-\sigma_1}} L(\sigma_2)^{\frac{\sigma-\sigma_1}{\sigma_2-\sigma_1}}.$$

In other words $\log L(\sigma)$ *is a convex function of* σ.

Take the function $\phi(s)e^{as}$, where a is real and is defined by the equation

$$L(\sigma_1)e^{a\sigma_1} = L(\sigma_2)e^{a\sigma_2},$$

so that

$$(2) \qquad e^a = L(\sigma_1)^{-\frac{1}{\sigma_1-\sigma_2}} L(\sigma_2)^{\frac{1}{\sigma_1-\sigma_2}}.$$

Applying the preceding theorem to the function $\phi(s)e^{as}$, we obtain

$$(3) \qquad L(\sigma)e^{a\sigma} \leqq L(\sigma_1)e^{a\sigma_1}.$$

Eliminating a from this inequality by means of the equation (2), we arrive at the inequality (1).

9°. THEOREM. *For an exponential polynomial*

$$\phi(s) = \sum_{n=1}^{N} a_n e^{\lambda_n s}$$

with only negative exponents λ_n, $L(\sigma)$ is a strictly decreasing function in the interval $(-\infty, +\infty)$.

In this case $L(+\infty) = 0$. Thus $\log L(\sigma)$ is a convex function of σ and is equal to $-\infty$ for $\sigma = +\infty$. From these two facts it follows that $\log L(\sigma)$ and consequently $L(\sigma)$ are strictly decreasing functions.

10°. THEOREM. *Given numbers $\alpha' < \alpha < \sigma_0 < \beta < \beta'$, $K > \epsilon > 0$, there exists a positive number δ depending only on the above numbers such that any function $\phi(s)$, analytic in the strip $[\alpha', \beta']$ and satisfying the conditions*

(1) $|\phi(s)| \leqq K$ *in the strip* $[\alpha', \beta']$,

(2) $L(\sigma_0) \leqq \delta$,

satisfies also the condition $|\phi(s)| \leqq \epsilon$ *in the strip* $[\alpha, \beta]$.

Define δ by the conditions that the point $(\alpha, \log \epsilon)$ lies above the straight line joining the points $(\alpha', \log K)$ and $(\sigma_0, \log \delta)$, and the point $(\beta, \log \epsilon)$ lies above the line joining the points $(\sigma_0, \log \delta)$ and $(\beta', \log K)$. From these two conditions we conclude that $L(\alpha) < \epsilon$ and $L(\beta) < \epsilon$, and then by the theorem of 7° that $|\phi(s)| < \epsilon$ in the strip $[\alpha, \beta]$.

11°. THEOREM. *If a function $\phi(s)$ satisfies the conditions*

(1) *it is analytic and bounded in a strip (α, β),*

(2) *on an interior line σ_0 there exists a sequence of points $\{\sigma_0 + it_n\}$ such that $\phi(\sigma_0 + it_n) \to 0$, as $n \to \infty$,*

(3) *there exist positive numbers d and l such that on any segment of the line σ_0 of length l there exists a point satisfying the inequality $|\phi(\sigma_0 + it)| > d$,*

then $\phi(s)$ has zeros in any strip $(\sigma_0 - \delta, \sigma_0 + \delta)$.

Writing $\phi_n(s) = \phi(s + it_n)$, we shall have the sequence $\{\phi_n(s)\}$ of analytic and uniformly bounded functions in the rectangle $\alpha < \sigma < \beta, -l < t < l$. By Montel's Theorem there exists a subsequence $\{\phi_{n_k}(s)\}$ $(k = 1, 2, \ldots)$ uniformly convergent in the rectangle C:

$$\sigma_0 - \delta < \sigma < \sigma_0 + \delta, \; -\tfrac{1}{2}l < t < \tfrac{1}{2}l,$$

where $$\delta < \min. \{\sigma_0 - \alpha, \beta - \sigma_0\}.$$

Let $\psi(s)$ be the limit of this subsequence. It is analytic in C and $\psi(\sigma_0) = 0$. As the upper bound of every $|\phi_{n_k}(s)|$ in the rectangle C is $\geqq d$, we conclude on account of the uniform convergence that *u.b.* $|\psi(s)|$ in C is also $\geqq d$. Thus $\psi(s)$ is not identically zero, and consequently there exists $r < \delta$ such that $\psi(s) \neq 0$ on the circle $|s - \sigma_0| = r$. Now there exists k_0 such that for all $k > k_0$

$$|\phi_{n_k}(s) - \psi(s)| < |\psi(s)|$$

on the circle $|s - \sigma_0| = r$. Thus by Rouché's Theorem every

$$\phi_{n_k}(s) = \psi(s) + \{\phi_{n_k}(s) - \psi(s)\} \qquad (k > k_0)$$

has in the circle $|s - \sigma_0| = r$ the same number of zeros as $\psi(s)$, i.e. not less than one. Returning now from the functions $\phi_{n_k}(s)$ to the function $\phi(s)$, we see that the theorem has been proved.

12°. THEOREM. *Given numbers* $\sigma_1 < \sigma_2$, $k > 0$, $c > 0$; *if a function* $f(s)$ *analytic in the half-plane* $\sigma > \sigma_1$ *satisfies the conditions:*

(i) $|f(s)| > c\,e^{k\sigma_1}$ *in the half-plane* $\sigma > \sigma_1$,

(ii) $|f(s)| \leqq c\,e^{k\sigma_2}$ *on the line* σ_2,

then it satisfies also the condition

$$|f(s)| \leqq c\,e^{k\sigma}$$

in the whole half-plane $\sigma > \sigma_2$.

By a trivial change of variable we can reduce the general case to the case of $\sigma_1 = 0$, $\sigma_2 = 1$ and $c = 1$. Then our data are

(1) $|f(s)| > 1$ *in the half-plane* $\sigma > 0$,

(2) $|f(s)| \leqq e^k$ *on the line* $\sigma = 1$,

and we have to prove that

(3) $|f(s)| \leqq e^{k\sigma}$ *in the half-plane* $\sigma > 1$.

If we prove the last inequality only for real $s > 1$, then we shall have proved it also for any s of the half-plane $\sigma > 1$. For, any function $f(s + ib)$ (b real) satisfies the conditions (1) and (2) together with $f(s)$, and thus we shall have that for any real $s > 1$ and for any real b

$$|f(s + ib)| < e^{ks},$$

which is the required inequality in the general case. Denote by $F(s)$ some branch of the function $\frac{1}{k}\operatorname{Log} f(s)$. Evidently $F(s)$ is analytic in the half-plane $\sigma > 0$. By (1) and (2)

(4) $R\{F(s)\} > 0$ for $\sigma > 0$,

(5) $R\{F(s)\} \leqq 1$ for $\sigma = 1$.

We write $F(1) = u_1 + iv_1$, where $0 < u_1 \leqq 1$. Now applying Cor. of 5° to the function

$$w = \phi(s) = \frac{F(s) - iv_1}{u_1},$$

we shall have $\left|\frac{\phi(\sigma)-1}{\phi(\sigma)+1}\right| \leqq \frac{\sigma-1}{\sigma+1}$

for any $\sigma > 1$, whence

$$R\{\phi(\sigma)\} \leqq \sigma. \tag{6}$$

But

$$R\{\phi(\sigma)\} = \frac{1}{ku_1}\log|f(\sigma)| \geqq \frac{1}{k}\log|f(\sigma)|. \tag{7}$$

By (6) and (7) $\qquad |f(\sigma)| \leqq e^{k\sigma},$

and the theorem is proved.

13°. We shall now quote Iversen's Theorem* on the set of values of an analytic function in a half-plane, which will enable us to prove an analogon of the Picard Theorem for the case of *u.a.p.* functions. We shall quote only a particular case of the theorem.

THEOREM. *Let $f(s)$ be analytic in the half-plane $[\sigma_1, +\infty)$ and bounded on the line σ_1. Let, further, E be the set of its values on the line σ_1 and E' the derivative set. If the set of values of $w = f(s)$ in any half-plane $(\sigma_2, +\infty)$, $(\sigma_2 > \sigma_1)$ is everywhere dense on the w-plane, then $f(s)$ takes in the half-plane $(\sigma_1, +\infty)$ all values which do not belong to the set $E + E'$ with at most one exception.*

§ 2. Definition of analytic almost periodic functions and their elementary properties.

1°. Let $f(s)$ be *a function analytic in a strip* (α, β), where each of the numbers α, β may be finite or infinite. A real number τ satisfying the condition

$$|f(s+i\tau) - f(s)| \leqq \epsilon$$

at all points s of the strip is called "a translation number of $f(s)$ belonging to ϵ." The set of all the translation numbers of $f(s)$ belonging to ϵ is denoted by $E\{\epsilon, f(s)\}$.

* "Sur quelques propriétés des fonctions monogènes au voisinage d'un point singulier," *Öfv. finska vet. soc.*, Bd 58, Nr 25 (1915–16).

If the set $E\{\epsilon, f(s)\}$ *is r.d. for any* $\epsilon > 0$, *then the function* $f(s)$ *is called uniformly almost periodic (u.a.p.) in the strip* (α, β).

Similarly can be defined a *u.a.p.* function in a strip $[\alpha, \beta]$.

A *u.a.p.* function $f(s)$ in a strip (α, β) is a *u.a.p.* function of the real variable t on any line of the strip.

2°. THEOREM. *A u.a.p. function* $f(s)$ *in a strip* $\langle\alpha, \beta\rangle$ *is bounded in this strip.*

Take a strip (α_1, β_1) $(\alpha < \alpha_1 < \beta_1 < \beta)$. The function $f(s)$ being analytic in the strip $[\alpha_1, \beta_1]$ is bounded in any finite part of it. We now prove that it is bounded in the whole strip (α_1, β_1) by the same argument as in 4°, § 1, Ch. I. The strip (α_1, β_1) being an arbitrary strip interior to (α, β), we have proved the theorem.

3°. THEOREM. *An analytic function* $f(s)$ *bounded in a strip* $\langle\alpha, \beta\rangle$ *(and consequently any u.a.p. function in* $\langle\alpha, \beta\rangle$*) is uniformly continuous in* $\langle\alpha, \beta\rangle$ *together with all its derivatives.*

Take two strips (α_1, β_1), (α_2, β_2) $(\alpha < \alpha_2 < \alpha_1 < \beta_1 < \beta_2 < \beta)$. Denote by M the upper bound of $|f(s)|$ in the strip (α_2, β_2) and put $\delta = \min. (\alpha_1 - \alpha_2, \beta_2 - \beta_1)$. By Cauchy's Theorem we have for any n

$$|f^{(n)}(s)| \leq \frac{n!\,M}{\delta^n}$$

at all points of the strip (α_1, β_1). Thus for any pair s', s'' of points of the strip (α_1, β_1)

$$|f^{(n-1)}(s') - f^{(n-1)}(s'')| = \left|\int_{s'}^{s''} f^{(n)}(s)\,ds\right| \leq \frac{n!\,M}{\delta^n}\,|s' - s''|,$$

whence $f(s)$ and all the derivatives are uniformly continuous in (α_1, β_1), i.e. in $\langle\alpha, \beta\rangle$ (but they do not form generally a uniformly continuous set of functions).

4°. We shall now prove a theorem by means of which it will be possible to generalise a number of theorems on *u.a.p.* functions of a real variable to the case of analytic *u.a.p.* functions.

THEOREM. *If a function* $f(s)$, *analytic in a strip* (α, β), *is bounded in the strip* $\langle\alpha, \beta\rangle$ *and if it is a u.a.p. function of the variable t on one line* σ_0 $(\alpha < \sigma_0 < \beta)$, *then it is u.a.p. in the strip* $\langle\alpha, \beta\rangle$.

Take two intervals $[\alpha_1, \beta_1]$, $[\alpha_2, \beta_2]$ $(\alpha < \alpha_2 < \alpha_1 < \beta_1 < \beta_2 < \beta)$. Denote by M the upper bound of $|f(s)|$ in the strip $[\alpha_2, \beta_2]$. Let τ be any number of the set $E\{\delta, f(\sigma_0 + it)\}$, where $\delta\,(>0)$ is to be defined later. The difference $f(s+i\tau) - f(s)$ satisfies the following conditions:

(1) $$|f(s+i\tau) - f(s)| \leqq 2M \text{ in } [\alpha_2, \beta_2],$$

(2) $$|f(s+i\tau) - f(s)| \leqq \delta \text{ on the line } \sigma_0.$$

From the theorem of 10°, § 1, we conclude that to any $\epsilon > 0$ corresponds $\delta = \delta(\epsilon) > 0$ such that from (1) and (2) follows the inequality

$$|f(s+i\tau) - f(s)| \leqq \epsilon \text{ in } (\alpha_1, \beta_1).$$

Thus for any $\epsilon > 0$ the set $E\{\epsilon, f(s)\}$ of translation numbers of $f(s)$ in the strip (α_1, β_1) contains a *r.d.* set $E\{\delta, f(\sigma_0 + it)\}$, which shows that $f(s)$ is *u.a.p.* in the strip (α_1, β_1). Since (α_1, β_1) is an arbitrary strip inside the strip (α, β), the theorem has been proved.

Remark 1. We see that for any analytic *u.a.p.* function $f(s)$ in a strip (α_1, β_1) there exists a largest strip of uniform almost periodicity $\langle\alpha, \beta\rangle$, which is the largest strip of boundedness of $f(s)$. Whether or not $f(s)$ possesses any kind of almost periodic properties beyond this strip we shall see later on.

Remark 2. We have deduced the almost periodicity in a strip of an analytic function from its almost periodicity on a line and from an additional condition of boundedness of the function in the strip. If we remove this additional condition, then the theorem is not true. In fact H. Bohr has constructed an analytic function which is *u.a.p.* on all lines of a strip except possibly one, and which is not *u.a.p.* in the strip.

5°. THEOREM. *The sum and the product of two u.a.p. functions* $f(s)$, $g(s)$ *in a strip* $\langle\alpha, \beta\rangle$ *are u.a.p. functions in the same strip.*

Let σ_0 be a line of the strip (α, β).

Each of the functions $f(s)$ and $g(s)$ is bounded in the strip

$\langle\alpha, \beta\rangle$ and *u.a.p.* on the line σ_0. Therefore so are the functions $f(s)+g(s)$ and $f(s)g(s)$. By the preceding theorem they are *u.a.p.* in the strip $\langle\alpha, \beta\rangle$.

Corollary. *An exponential polynomial*

$$f(s)=\sum_{n=1}^{N} a_n e^{\lambda_n s} \qquad (\lambda_n\text{'s real})$$

is u.a.p. in $\langle-\infty, +\infty\rangle$.

6°. THEOREM. *If a sequence* $\{f_n(s)\}$ *of u.a.p. functions in a strip* (α, β) *converges uniformly to a function* $f(s)$, *then* $f(s)$ *is also u.a.p. in* (α, β).

The proof is identical with that of 8°, § 1, Ch. I.

Corollary. *The sum of an exponential series*

$$f(s)=\sum_{n=1}^{\infty} a_n e^{\lambda_n s},$$

uniformly convergent in a strip $\langle\alpha, \beta\rangle$, *is u.a.p. in the same strip.*

7°. THEOREM. *The derivative* $f'(s)$ *of a function* $f(s)$, *u.a.p. in* $\langle\alpha, \beta\rangle$, *is also u.a.p. in* $\langle\alpha, \beta\rangle$.

We have proved in 3° that $f'(s)$ is bounded and uniformly continuous in $\langle\alpha, \beta\rangle$. Taking any σ_0 $(\alpha<\sigma_0<\beta)$ we see that $f'(\sigma_0+it)$ is uniformly continuous. By Bochner's Theorem of 14°, § 1, Ch. I, we conclude that $f'(\sigma_0+it)$ is *u.a.p.*, and then by the theorem of 4° that $f'(s)$ is *u.a.p.* in $\langle\alpha, \beta\rangle$.

8°. THEOREM. *If an indefinite integral* $F(s)$ *of a function* $f(s)$, *u.a.p. in* $\langle\alpha, \beta\rangle$, *is bounded in* $\langle\alpha, \beta\rangle$, *then it is u.a.p. in* $\langle\alpha, \beta\rangle$.

For on a line σ_0 $(\alpha<\sigma_0<\beta)$, $F(s)$ is *u.a.p.* on account of the theorem of 15°, § 1, Ch. I. Then our theorem follows from the theorem of 4°.

9°. THEOREM. *If* $f(s)$ *is u.a.p. in* (α, β) *and* G *is the set of all its values on a line* σ_0 $(\alpha<\sigma_0<\beta)$, *then in any strip* $(\sigma_0-\delta, \sigma_0+\delta)$ $f(s)$ *takes all values of the derivative set* G'.

Let w_0 be any point of G'. There may be two cases: either the function $f(s)-w_0$ vanishes at a point of the line σ_0, or it does not vanish but there exists a sequence $\{\sigma_0+it_n\}$ of points such that

$$f(\sigma_0+it_n)-w_0 \to 0,$$

as $n\to\infty$. We take in the second case a point σ_0+it', and we write

$$|f(\sigma_0+it')-w_0|=2d>0.$$

Let l_d be an inclusion interval of the set $E\{d, f(\sigma_0+it)\}$, so that any interval of length l_d of the line σ_0 contains a point at which

$$|f(\sigma_0+it)-w_0| \geqq d>0.$$

We see that the conditions of the theorem of 11°, § 1, are satisfied by the function $f(s)-w_0$ which therefore vanishes in any strip $(\sigma_0-\delta, \sigma_0+\delta)$.

Thus in either case $f(s)-w_0$ vanishes in any strip $(\sigma_0-\delta, \sigma_0+\delta)$ and the theorem is proved.

Corollary 1. *If a u.a.p. function $f(s)$ in (α, β) does not vanish in this strip, then l.b. $|f(s)|$ is positive in $\langle\alpha, \beta\rangle$.*

Corollary 2. *If $f(s)$ is u.a.p. in $\langle\alpha, \beta\rangle$ and does not vanish in (α, β), then $g(s)=\dfrac{1}{f(s)}$ is u.a.p. in $\langle\alpha, \beta\rangle$.*

For take an interval (α_1, β_1) and a line σ_0, $(\alpha<\alpha_1<\sigma_0<\beta_1<\beta)$. By Cor. 1 $g(s)$ is bounded in (α_1, β_1), and by the theorem of 7°, § 1, Ch. I, $g(\sigma_0+it)$ is *u.a.p.* Consequently by the theorem of 4°, $g(s)$ is *u.a.p.* in (α_1, β_1), from which the corollary follows.

10°. We shall now consider whether a definition of *a.p.* analytic functions, similar to that of Stepanoff, leads to a more general class of functions than that of *u.a.p.* functions.

Definition 1. *Let $f(s)$ be analytic in (α, β), and let τ be a real number such that*

$$\int_z^{z+i} |f(s+i\tau)-f(s)|\, dt<\epsilon \tag{1}$$

at all points z of (α, β). Then τ is called an S translation number of $f(s)$ belonging to ϵ.

The set of all S translation numbers of $f(s)$ belonging to ϵ is denoted by $SE\{\epsilon, f(s)\}$.

DEFINITION 2. *If* $SE\{\epsilon, f(s)\}$ *is r.d. for any* $\epsilon > 0$, *then* $f(s)$ *is said to be an S a.p. function in* (α, β).

Evidently a *u.a.p.* analytic function in a strip (α, β) is an S *a.p.* function. But the next theorem will show that Definition 2 does not lead to a generalisation of the class of *u.a.p.* functions.

LINFOOT'S THEOREM. *An S a.p. function* $f(s)$ *in a strip* (α, β) *is u.a.p. in* $\langle\alpha, \beta\rangle$.

Given $\epsilon > 0$, let l_ϵ be an inclusion interval of $SE\{\epsilon, f(s)\}$. Take a strip (α_1, β_1), $(\alpha < \alpha_1 < \beta_1 < \beta)$. The function $f(s)$ is bounded in any finite part of this strip. Denote by M the upper bound of $|f(s)|$ in the rectangle C: $\sigma = \alpha_1$, $\sigma = \beta_1$, $t = 0$, $t = l_\epsilon + 1$. By (1),

$$\int_z^{z+i} |f(s)|\,dt < \epsilon + \int_z^{z+i} |f(s+i\tau)|\,dt = \epsilon + \int_{z+i\tau}^{z+i(1+\tau)} |f(s)|\,dt. \tag{2}$$

Corresponding to any z of (α_1, β_1) we can define τ so that both the points $z + i\tau$, $z + i(1+\tau)$ belong to the rectangle C. Then

$$\int_{z+i\tau}^{z+i(1+\tau)} |f(s)|\,dt \leqq M.$$

Thus by (2)

$$\int_z^{z+i} |f(s)|\,dt < \epsilon + M,$$

for any z of the strip (α_1, β_1). Therefore by the theorem of 6°, § 1, $f(s)$ is bounded in $\langle\alpha_1, \beta_1\rangle$, and consequently in $\langle\alpha, \beta\rangle$. By the theorem of 3° it is uniformly continuous on any line

$$\sigma_0 \quad (\alpha < \sigma_0 < \beta).$$

Thus $f(\sigma_0 + it)$ is an S *a.p.* function and is also uniformly continuous. Consequently by Bochner's Theorem of 2°, § 3, Ch. II, it is a *u.a.p.* function of t. Then by the theorem of 4°, $f(s)$ is *u.a.p.* in $\langle\alpha, \beta\rangle$.

§ 3. Dirichlet series.

1°. As in the case of *u.a.p.* functions of a real variable, to any analytic *u.a.p.* function $f(s)$ corresponds an exponential series—"the Dirichlet series," which defines uniquely a *u.a.p.* function, and which represents the Fourier series of $f(s)$ on any line of the strip of almost periodicity. We shall see this from the following theorem.

THEOREM. *If $f(\sigma+it)$ is u.a.p. in a strip (α, β), then the Fourier series of $f(\sigma+it)$ considered as a function of t has the same expression,*

$$(1) \qquad f(\sigma+it) \sim \Sigma A_n e^{\Lambda_n \sigma} e^{i\Lambda_n t},$$

for all σ of the interval (α, β).

For any σ of the interval (α, β) the Fourier exponents of $f(\sigma+it)$ are the real values of λ for which

$$(2) \qquad M\{f(\sigma+it)e^{-i\lambda t}\} \neq 0.$$

We shall first prove that these values of λ are independent of σ. For let $\sigma_1 < \sigma_2$ be any two numbers of the interval (α, β). By Cauchy's Theorem

$$(3) \qquad \frac{1}{T}\int_{\sigma_1}^{\sigma_1+iT} + \frac{1}{T}\int_{\sigma_1+iT}^{\sigma_2+iT} + \frac{1}{T}\int_{\sigma_2+iT}^{\sigma_2} + \frac{1}{T}\int_{\sigma_2}^{\sigma_1} f(s)e^{-\lambda s}\,ds = 0,$$

for any $T > 0$. Let in this formula T tend to $+\infty$. Then the second and the fourth terms tend to zero, since $f(s)$ is bounded in (σ_1, σ_2), and we obtain

$$(4) \qquad e^{-\lambda\sigma_1} M\{f(\sigma_1+it)e^{-i\lambda t}\} = e^{-\lambda\sigma_2} M\{f(\sigma_2+it)e^{-i\lambda t}\},$$

which shows that if (2) is true for one value of σ in (α, β), then it is also true for all other values. *Thus the Fourier exponents of $f(\sigma+it)$ are the same for all σ in (α, β). Denote them by*

$$\Lambda_1, \Lambda_2, \ldots,$$

and write the Fourier series of $f(\sigma+it)$

$$f(\sigma+it) \sim \Sigma A_n(\sigma) e^{i\Lambda_n t},$$

where

$$A_n(\sigma) = M\{f(\sigma+it)e^{-i\Lambda_n t}\}. \qquad (n = 1, 2, \ldots)$$

But by (4) $A_n(\sigma)e^{-\Lambda_n\sigma} = \text{constant} = A_n,$
and thus

(5) $$f(\sigma + it) \sim \Sigma\, A_n e^{\Lambda_n\sigma} e^{i\Lambda_n t},$$

which gives the Fourier series of $f(\sigma + it)$ on all lines of (α, β).

2°. We may *conventionally* write (5) 1° in the form

(1) $$f(s) \sim \Sigma\, A_n e^{\Lambda_n s}.$$

The series (1) *is called the Dirichlet series of* $f(s)$ *in the strip* (α, β). We immediately obtain the following three theorems:

THEOREM 1. *A u.a.p. function* $f(s)$ *defined by the sum of an exponential series* $\Sigma\, a_n e^{\lambda_n s}$ *uniformly convergent in some strip has this series as its Dirichlet series.*

UNIQUENESS THEOREM. *To any analytic u.a.p. function corresponds a Dirichlet series and if two analytic functions, u.a.p. in the same strip, have the same Dirichlet series, then they are identical.*

FUNDAMENTAL THEOREM. *For any u.a.p. function*

$$f(s) \sim \Sigma\, A_n e^{\Lambda_n s}$$

in a strip (α, β) *the Parseval equation*

$$M_t\{|f(\sigma + it)|^2\} = \Sigma\, |A_n|^2 e^{2\Lambda_n\sigma}$$

holds for all σ *of the interval* (α, β).

3°. POLYNOMIAL APPROXIMATION THEOREM. *To any u.a.p. function in a strip* (α, β) *corresponds a sequence of exponential polynomials, Bochner-Fejér polynomials, converging uniformly to the function in* $\langle\alpha, \beta\rangle$.

Let $$f(s) \sim \Sigma\, A_n e^{\Lambda_n s}$$

be a *u.a.p.* function in the strip (α, β). Consider the *u.a.p.* functions of t:

$$f(\sigma + it) \sim \Sigma\, A_n e^{\Lambda_n\sigma} e^{i\Lambda_n t},$$

for all σ of the interval (α, β). *All these functions have the same Fourier exponents.* We write a Bochner-Fejér polynomial

$$\sigma_B(t) = \Sigma\, d_n A_n e^{\Lambda_n\sigma} e^{i\Lambda_n t},$$

where B is any set $\begin{pmatrix} n_1, n_2, \dots, n_p \\ \beta_1, \beta_2, \dots, \beta_p \end{pmatrix}$ of basic numbers and indices. By Remark of 2°, § 9, Ch. I, all the d_n are independent of σ. Let

$$N_1 < N_2 < \dots$$

be a sequence of positive integers and

$$\eta_1 > \eta_2 > \dots$$

a sequence of positive numbers converging to zero. By Remark of 4°, § 9, Ch. I, to any k there corresponds a Bochner-Fejér polynomial

$$\sigma_{B_k}(t) = \Sigma\, d_n^{(k)} A_n e^{\Lambda_n \sigma} e^{i\Lambda_n t},$$

such that

$$d_n^{(k)} > 1 - \eta_k$$

for $n = 1, 2, \dots, N_k$. Evidently the sequence of polynomials

$$(1) \qquad \sigma_{B_k}(t) \qquad (k = 1, 2, \dots)$$

converges in mean to $f(\sigma + it)$, and consequently converges uniformly on any line of the strip (α, β). Take any pair of lines α', β' of the strip. By the theorem of 7.1°, § 1, the sequence (1) converges uniformly in the strip $[\alpha', \beta']$, from which the theorem follows.

4°. We have given in 4°, § 2, sufficient conditions for the almost periodicity of an analytic function, one of them being the condition of boundedness. We shall now give other sufficient conditions for almost periodicity, not involving the boundedness condition. We first prove the following theorem by an argument similar to that of the preceding section.

THEOREM. *If the series* $\Sigma A_n e^{\Lambda_n \sigma} e^{i\Lambda_n t}$ *represents for* $\sigma = \alpha, \sigma = \beta$ *the Fourier series of two u.a.p. functions* $f_\alpha(t)$ *and* $f_\beta(t)$, *then there exists a function* $f(s)$ *u.a.p. in the strip* (α, β) *continuous in the strip* $[\alpha, \beta]$, *satisfying the conditions* $f(\alpha + it) = f_\alpha(t)$, $f(\beta + it) = f_\beta(t)$ *and having*

$$(1) \qquad \Sigma A_n e^{\Lambda_n s}$$

as its Dirichlet series.

Observe that any Bochner-Fejér polynomials $\sigma_B(t)$ of functions $f_\alpha(t)$ and $f_\beta(t)$ are values of the Bochner-Fejér polynomials $\sigma_B(s)$

of (1) on the lines $\sigma=\alpha$, $\sigma=\beta$. By the argument of the preceding section there exists a sequence

$$\sigma_{B_k}(s) \qquad (k=1, 2, \ldots)$$

of Bochner-Fejér polynomials of (1) uniformly convergent in $[\alpha, \beta]$, the limit on the lines being $f_\alpha(t), f_\beta(t)$. Denoting the limit function by $f(s)$ we see that it possesses the properties stated in the theorem.

5°. We shall now give the above-mentioned conditions for almost periodicity of a function in a strip.

THEOREM. *If a function $F(s)$ analytic in (α, β) and continuous in $[\alpha, \beta]$ is a u.a.p. function of t on the lines α and β, and if its Fourier series on these lines are represented by the series*

$$\Sigma A_n e^{\Lambda_n \sigma} e^{i\Lambda_n t}$$

for $\sigma=\alpha$, $\sigma=\beta$, then $F(s)$ is u.a.p. in (α, β) and its Dirichlet series is

$$\Sigma A_n e^{\Lambda_n s}.$$

By the preceding theorem there exists a *u.a.p.* function

$$f(s) \sim \Sigma A_n e^{\Lambda_n s}$$

in the strip (α, β) which is continuous in $[\alpha, \beta]$ and is equal to $F(s)$ on the lines α, β. By Cor. of 3°, § 1, $F(s)-f(s)=0$ at all points of (α, β), since the equation is true on the lines α, β. This proves the theorem.

This theorem was proved by Linfoot under more general conditions. In his case $F(s)$ is supposed to be only S *a.p.* on the lines α, β, but not *u.a.p.* His proof is based on the representation of $F(s)$ by Poisson integrals.

6°. The argument employed in 4° and 5° can be applied in some cases to define the region of almost periodicity of an exponential series.

THEOREM 1. *If a series with negative exponents*

(1) $$\Sigma A_n e^{\Lambda_n s},$$

is for some $\sigma=\alpha$ the Fourier series of a u.a.p. function $f_\alpha(t)$, then *the series* (1) *is the Dirichlet series of a function* $f(s)$ *u.a.p. in* $(\alpha, +\infty)$, *continuous in* $[\alpha, +\infty)$, *equal to* $f_\alpha(t)$ *on the line* α, *and converging to zero, as* $\sigma \to \infty$ *uniformly in* t.

For let

(2) $$\sigma_{Bk}(t) \qquad (k = 1, 2, \ldots)$$

be Bochner-Fejér polynomials uniformly convergent to $f_\alpha(t)$. These polynomials are values on the line α of the Bochner-Fejér polynomials

(3) $$\sigma_{Bk}(s) \qquad (k = 1, 2, \ldots)$$

of the series (1). From the uniform convergence of the sequence (2) and from the theorem of 9°, § 1, follows the uniform convergence of the sequence (3) in $[\alpha, +\infty)$, which proves the theorem.

THEOREM 2. *If a function*

$$f(s) \sim \Sigma A_n e^{\Lambda_n s}$$

is u.a.p. in a strip (α, β) *and if all the exponents* Λ_n *are negative, then* $f(s)$ *is u.a.p. in* $(\alpha, +\infty)$ *and it converges to zero, as* $\sigma \to +\infty$, *uniformly in* t.

Remark. Similar results hold for series with only positive exponents.

7°. THEOREM. *If a function*

$$f(s) \sim \Sigma A_n e^{\Lambda_n s}$$

is u.a.p. in (α, β) *and if the set of all the exponents* Λ_n *is bounded, then* $f(s)$ *is an integral function u.a.p. in* $\langle -\infty, +\infty \rangle$.

For let

$$k < \Lambda_n < K$$

for all n.

By Theorem 2 of 6° $f(s)e^{-Ks}$ is *u.a.p.* in $(\alpha, +\infty)$ and by Remark 6° $f(s)e^{-ks}$ is *u.a.p.* in $(-\infty, \beta)$ from which the theorem follows.

8°. THEOREM. *If a function $f(s)$ is u.a.p. in $(\alpha, +\infty\rangle$ and bounded in $(\alpha, +\infty)$, then it has only non-positive exponents.*

Let
$$f(s) \sim \Sigma A_n e^{\Lambda_n s},$$
and let C be the upper bound of $|f(s)|$ in $(\alpha, +\infty)$. We have
$$C \geqq |M_t\{f(\sigma+it)e^{-i\Lambda_n t}\}| = |A_n| e^{\Lambda_n \sigma}$$
for all n and all $\sigma > \alpha$, which is possible only if no Λ_n is positive.

By Theorem 2 of 6° $f(s)$ *is u.a.p. in $(\alpha, +\infty)$ and tends to the constant term of its Dirichlet series, as $\sigma \to +\infty$, uniformly in t.*

Combining this theorem with Theorem 2 of 6° we conclude that:

The class of functions bounded and u.a.p. in a half-plane $(\alpha, +\infty)$ and the class of functions with non-positive exponents are identical. Any function of this class tends to the constant term of its Dirichlet series, as $\sigma \to \infty$ uniformly in t.

9°. The above theorems on functions with Dirichlet exponents of the same sign permit us to establish a theorem on the almost periodicity of integrals of such functions.

THEOREM. *If a function*
$$f(s) \sim \Sigma A_n e^{\Lambda_n s}$$
is u.a.p. in $\langle\alpha, +\infty)$, and if
$$\Lambda_n < \lambda < 0$$
for all n, then an indefinite integral of $f(s)$ is u.a.p. in $\langle\alpha, +\infty)$.

We shall first prove that an indefinite integral of $f(s)$ is bounded in $\langle\alpha, +\infty)$. Take any numbers α_1, σ_1 such that $\alpha < \alpha_1 \leqq \sigma_1$. Denote *u.b.* $\Lambda_n = -\Lambda^*$. The function $f(s)e^{\Lambda^* s}$ has only non-positive Dirichlet exponents and consequently tends to a finite limit, as $\sigma \to +\infty$. There exists a positive number K such that
$$|f(s)e^{\Lambda^* s}| < K \qquad \text{in } [\alpha_1, +\infty),$$
i.e.

(1) $$|f(s)| < Ke^{-\Lambda^* \sigma} \qquad \text{in } [\alpha_1, +\infty).$$

We now have for any real T and any $\sigma_2 > \sigma_1$

$$(2) \qquad \int_{\sigma_1}^{\sigma_1+iT} f(s)\,ds + \int_{\sigma_1+iT}^{\sigma_2+iT} + \int_{\sigma_2+iT}^{\sigma_2} + \int_{\sigma_2}^{\sigma_1} = 0.$$

By (1)

$$\left|\int_{\sigma_1+iT}^{\sigma_2+iT} f(s)\,ds\right| < K\int_{\sigma_1}^{\sigma_2} e^{-\Lambda^*\sigma}\,d\sigma < \frac{K}{\Lambda^*}e^{-\Lambda^*\sigma_1} \leq \frac{K}{\Lambda^*}e^{-\Lambda^*\alpha_1},$$

$$\left|\int_{\sigma_2}^{\sigma_1} f(s)\,ds\right| < \frac{K}{\Lambda^*}e^{-\Lambda^*\alpha_1},$$

$$\left|\int_{\sigma_2+iT}^{\sigma_2} f(s)\,ds\right| < TKe^{-\Lambda^*\sigma_2}.$$

We may take σ_2 as large as we please; hence by (2)

$$\left|\int_{\sigma_1}^{\sigma_1+iT} f(s)\,ds\right| < 2\frac{K}{\Lambda^*}e^{-\Lambda^*\alpha_1}.$$

Thus an indefinite integral of $f(s)$ is bounded in $\langle\alpha, +\infty)$. Hence by the theorem of 8°, § 2, the integral $\int^s f(s)\,ds$ is *u.a.p.* in $\langle\alpha, +\infty\rangle$, and since all its Dirichlet exponents are non-positive it is *u.a.p.* in $\langle\alpha, +\infty)$ on account of Theorem 2 of 6°, § 3.

Ex. 1. Prove that if $f(s)$ is *u.a.p.* in $[\alpha, +\infty)$ and if $\Lambda_n < \lambda < 0$ for all n, then $\int^s f(s)\,ds$ is *u.a.p.* in $[\alpha, +\infty)$.

Ex. 2. Prove that if all the Fourier exponents of a *u.a.p.* function $f(t)$ of a real variable

$$f(t) \sim \Sigma A_n\, e^{i\Lambda_n t}$$

are $< \lambda < 0$, then $\int_0^t f(t)\,dt$ is *u.a.p.*

10°. The question of the convergence of the Dirichlet series of analytic *u.a.p.* functions in the general case is as difficult as in the case of *u.a.p.* functions of a real variable. We shall establish only some results concerning absolute convergence.

THEOREM. *If a function*

$$f(s) \sim \Sigma A_n e^{\Lambda_n s}$$

is u.a.p. in $\langle \alpha, \beta \rangle$ *and if one of the following conditions is satisfied:*

1. *The exponents* Λ_n *are linearly independent,*
2. *The coefficients* A_n *are all positive,*
3. *The series* $\Sigma e^{-|\Lambda_n|\delta}$ *converges for any* $\delta > 0$,

then the series $\Sigma A_n e^{\Lambda_n s}$ *converges absolutely in* (α, β).

The cases 1 and 2 follow immediately from the corresponding theorems on Fourier series (1°, 2°, § 10, Ch. I).

In the case 3, let σ_0 be any number of the interval (α, β). Take a $\delta_0 > 0$ so that $\alpha < \sigma_0 - \delta_0$ and $\sigma_0 + \delta_0 < \beta$. As the two series

$$\Sigma A_n e^{\Lambda_n(\sigma_0 - \delta_0)} e^{i\Lambda_n t}, \quad \Sigma A_n e^{\Lambda_n(\sigma_0 + \delta_0)} e^{i\Lambda_n t}$$

are the Fourier series of *u.a.p.* functions of t: $f(\sigma_0 - \delta_0 + it)$, $f(\sigma_0 + \delta_0 + it)$, their coefficients are bounded and there exists a constant $K > 0$ such that

$$| A_n e^{\Lambda_n(\sigma_0 \pm \delta_0)} | < K$$

for all n. We now write

$$| A_n e^{\Lambda_n \sigma_0} | = | A_n e^{\Lambda_n(\sigma_0 \pm \delta_0)} | e^{\mp \Lambda_n \delta_0} < K e^{-|\Lambda_n| \delta_0},$$

whence

$$\Sigma | A_n e^{\Lambda_n(\sigma_0 + it)} | < K \Sigma e^{-|\Lambda_n| \delta_0},$$

i.e. the series $\Sigma A_n e^{\Lambda_n s}$ is absolutely convergent on any line σ_0 of (α, β), which proves the theorem.

11°. The absolute convergence of the Dirichlet series in the case 2 permits us to establish the existence of singular points of certain *u.a.p.* functions. We have the following theorem, analogous to the Vivanti-Landau Theorem.

THEOREM. *If* $\langle \alpha, \beta \rangle$ *is the maximum strip of uniform almost periodicity of a function*

$$f(s) \sim \Sigma A_n e^{\Lambda_n s}, \tag{1}$$

all of whose Dirichlet coefficients A_n *are positive, then the two points* $s = \alpha$, $s = \beta$ *are singular points of* $f(s)$.

By the preceding theorem the series (1) is absolutely convergent in (α, β), *a fortiori* so are the two series

(2) $$f_1(s)=\sum_{\Lambda_n>0} A_n e^{\Lambda_n s}, \quad f_2(s)=\sum_{\Lambda_n\leqq 0} A_n e^{\Lambda_n s}.$$

By Theorem 1 of 6°, $f_1(s), f_2(s)$ are *u.a.p.* respectively in $(-\infty, \beta\rangle$ and in $\langle\alpha, +\infty)$. Since

$$f(s)=f_1(s)+f_2(s),$$

it is sufficient to prove that β is a singular point of $f_1(s)$ and α of $f_2(s)$. Suppose that the theorem is not true and that for instance β is a regular point of $f_1(s)$. By 7°, § 2, all the derivatives of $f(s)$ are *u.a.p.*, and clearly

$$f_1^{(\nu)}(s)\sim \sum_{\Lambda_n>0} A_n \Lambda_n^\nu e^{\Lambda_n s}$$

for any ν. The series on the right-hand side has again only positive coefficients and consequently it is absolutely convergent in $(-\infty, \beta)$ and it is easy to see that it is uniformly convergent in $(-\infty, \beta\rangle$. By Theorem 1 of 2°, § 3,

$$f_1^{(\nu)}(s)=\sum_{\Lambda_n>0} A_n \Lambda_n^\nu e^{\Lambda_n s}.$$

We now write the Taylor expansion of $f_1(s)$ at the point $\beta-1$

(3) $$f_1(s)=\sum_{\nu=0}^{\infty}\frac{(s-\beta+1)^\nu}{\nu!}f_1^{(\nu)}(\beta-1)$$
$$=\sum_{\nu=0}^{\infty}\frac{(s-\beta+1)^\nu}{\nu!}\sum_{\Lambda_n>0} A_n \Lambda_n^\nu e^{\Lambda_n(\beta-1)}.$$

If the point β is a regular point of $f_1(s)$, then the radius of convergence r of the above series is greater than 1. Write the series (3) at a point $s=\eta$, where η is real and satisfies the inequality $\beta<\eta<\beta-1+r$,

$$f_1(\eta)=\sum_{\nu=0}^{\infty}\frac{(\eta-\beta+1)^\nu}{\nu!}\sum_{\Lambda_n>0} A_n \Lambda_n^\nu e^{\Lambda_n(\beta-1)}$$
$$=\sum_{\Lambda_n>0} A_n e^{\Lambda_n(\beta-1)}\sum_{\nu=0}^{\infty}\frac{(\eta-\beta+1)^\nu}{\nu!}\Lambda_n^\nu$$
$$=\sum_{\Lambda_n>0} A_n e^{\Lambda_n(\beta-1)} e^{\Lambda_n(\eta-\beta+1)}$$
$$=\sum_{\Lambda_n>0} A_n e^{\Lambda_n \eta},$$

which shows that the series $\sum_{\Lambda_n > 0} A_n e^{\Lambda_n s}$ is absolutely convergent in $(-\infty, \eta]$ and thus that $f_1(s)$ is *u.a.p.* in $(-\infty, \eta)$ and consequently that $f(s)$ is *u.a.p.* in $\langle\alpha, \eta)$, which is contrary to our assumption. Thus β is a singular point of $f(s)$. By a similar argument it can be proved that α is also a singular point.

12°. On account of the established characteristic properties of *u.a.p.* analytic functions with the exponents of a constant sign, it is important to investigate when a *u.a.p.* function,

$$(1) \qquad f(s) \sim \sum A_n e^{\Lambda_n s},$$

with exponents of both signs, can be represented as the sum of two *u.a.p.* functions, each with exponents of a constant sign. This "bisecting the series" is similar to that for Laurent series. We can formulate this problem in the following way:

When are the two parts of the series (1),

$$\sum_{\Lambda_n > 0} A_n e^{\Lambda_n s}, \quad \sum_{\Lambda_n \leq 0} A_n e^{\Lambda_n s},$$

Dirichlet series of u.a.p. functions?

We shall prove two theorems concerning this problem.

THEOREM. *If*

$$(1) \qquad f(s) \sim \sum A_n e^{\Lambda_n s}$$

is u.a.p. in $\langle\alpha, \beta\rangle$ *and if its integral* $F(s)$ *is also u.a.p. in* $\langle\alpha, \beta\rangle$* *(which is true if* $F(s)$ *is bounded), then the series*

$$\sum_{\Lambda_n < 0} A_n e^{\Lambda_n s}, \quad \sum_{\Lambda_n > 0} A_n e^{\Lambda_n s},$$

are the Dirichlet series of two functions $f_1(s)$, *u.a.p. in* $\langle\alpha, +\infty)$, *and* $f_2(s)$, *u.a.p. in* $(-\infty, \beta\rangle$.

Take any strip (α_1, β_1), $(\alpha < \alpha_1 < \beta_1 < \beta)$. At any point s of this strip we have

$$2\pi i f(s) = \int_{\alpha_1+iT}^{\alpha_1-iT} \frac{F(z)\,dz}{(z-s)^2} + \int_{\alpha_1-iT}^{\beta_1-iT} + \int_{\beta_1-iT}^{\beta_1+iT} + \int_{\beta_1+iT}^{\alpha_1+iT},$$

where $T > |I(s)|$ ($I(s)$ being the imaginary part of s). Let T tend to $+\infty$, then on account of the boundedness of $F(z)$ in

* In this case the constant term in (1) is zero.

(α_1, β_1) the second and the fourth integral tend to zero and we obtain

$$f(s) = \frac{1}{2\pi i}\int_{\alpha_1+i\infty}^{\alpha_1-i\infty}\frac{F(z)\,dz}{(z-s)^2} + \frac{1}{2\pi i}\int_{\beta_1-i\infty}^{\beta_1+i\infty}\frac{F(z)\,dz}{(z-s)^2}$$
$$= f_1(s) + f_2(s).$$

We see that $f_1(s)$ is an analytic function bounded in $\langle\alpha_1, \infty)$ and tending to zero, as $\sigma \to +\infty$, uniformly in t. The function $f_2(s)$ has analogous properties to the left of the line β_1. Take now a line σ_0 of the strip (α_1, β_1) and let τ be any translation number belonging to ϵ of $F(z)$ in the strip (α_1, β_1). We shall have

$$|f_1(s+i\tau) - f_1(s)| = \frac{1}{2\pi}\left|\int_{\alpha_1+i\infty}^{\alpha_1-i\infty}\frac{F(z+i\tau)-F(z)}{(z-s)^2}dz\right|$$
$$\leq \frac{\epsilon}{2\pi}\int_{-\infty}^{+\infty}\frac{dt}{(\sigma_0-\alpha_1)^2+t^2} = \frac{\epsilon}{2(\sigma_0-\alpha_1)},$$

which shows that $f_1(s)$ is *u.a.p.* on the line σ_0. By the theorem of 4°, § 2, it is *u.a.p.* in $\langle\alpha_1, \infty)$ and by the theorem of 8° it has only negative exponents. In the same way we can prove that $f_2(s)$ is a *u.a.p.* function in $(-\infty, \beta_1\rangle$ with only positive exponents. As the Dirichlet series of $f(s)$ is the sum of the Dirichlet series of the functions $f_1(s)$, $f_2(s)$ we see that

(2) $$f_1(s) \sim \sum_{\Lambda_n<0} A_n e^{\Lambda_n s} \quad \text{in } \langle\alpha_1, +\infty),$$

(3) $$f_2(s) \sim \sum_{\Lambda_n>0} A_n e^{\Lambda_n s} \quad \text{in } (-\infty, \beta_1\rangle.$$

As these series remain unaltered when α_1, β_1 vary in the interval (α, β) we see that $f_1(s)$ and $f_2(s)$ are the functions whose existence is stated in the theorem.

13°. THEOREM. *If*

$$f(s) \sim \sum A_n e^{\Lambda_n s}$$

is u.a.p. in $\langle\alpha, \beta\rangle$ *and if*

$$|\Lambda_n| > \lambda > 0$$

for all n, then the series $\sum_{\Lambda_n<0} A_n e^{\Lambda_n s}$, $\sum_{\Lambda_n>0} A_n e^{\Lambda_n s}$ *are the Dirichlet series of two functions* $f_1(s)$, $f_2(s)$ *respectively u.a.p. in* $\langle\alpha, +\infty)$ *and in* $(-\infty, \beta\rangle$.

We write $$f'(s) \sim \Sigma A_n \Lambda_n e^{\Lambda_n s},$$
and as the integral of $f'(s)$ is *u.a.p.* we have, on account of the preceding theorem,
$$f'(s) = \phi_1(s) + \phi_2(s),$$
where
$$\phi_1(s) \sim \sum_{\Lambda_n < 0} A_n \Lambda_n e^{\Lambda_n s} \quad \text{in } \langle \alpha, +\infty),$$
$$\phi_2(s) \sim \sum_{\Lambda_n > 0} A_n \Lambda_n e^{\Lambda_n s} \quad \text{in } (-\infty, \beta\rangle.$$

By the theorem of 9°, the integrals of $\phi_1(s)$, $\phi_2(s)$ are *u.a.p.* in $\langle \alpha, +\infty)$ and $(-\infty, \beta\rangle$. Denoting these integrals by $f_1(s)$ and $f_2(s)$ we shall have
$$f_1(s) \sim \sum_{\Lambda_n < 0} A_n e^{\Lambda_n s} + C_1,$$
$$f_2(s) \sim \sum_{\Lambda_n > 0} A_n e^{\Lambda_n s} + C_2.$$

Obviously we may put $C_1 = C_2 = 0$ and the theorem is then proved.

Corollary. *If*
$$f(s) \sim \Sigma A_n e^{\Lambda_n s}$$
is u.a.p. in $\langle \alpha, \beta\rangle$ and if there exists a real γ such that
$$|\Lambda_n - \gamma| > \lambda > 0$$
for all n, then the two series
$$\sum_{\Lambda_n < \gamma} A_n e^{\Lambda_n s}, \quad \sum_{\Lambda_n > \gamma} A_n e^{\Lambda_n s},$$
are the Dirichlet series of two functions, u.a.p. in $\langle \alpha, +\infty\rangle$ and $\langle -\infty, \beta\rangle$.

§ 4. Behaviour of *u.a.p.* functions at $\sigma = \infty$.

1°. In this paragraph we shall study the behaviour at the "point $\sigma = \infty$" of *u.a.p.* functions defined in a half-plane $(\alpha, +\infty\rangle$ The results concerning this problem are analogous to two theorems of the general theory of functions: Weierstrass's Theorem and Picard's Theorem.

THEOREM. *For a function $f(s)$, u.a.p. in $(\alpha, +\infty\rangle$, there are only three possibilities concerning its behaviour at the "point $\sigma=\infty$":*

(A) *It tends to a finite limit, as $\sigma\to+\infty$, uniformly in t.*

(B) *Its modulus tends to infinity, as $\sigma\to+\infty$, uniformly in t.*

(C) *In any half-plane $\sigma>\alpha_1>\alpha$ it approximates to any given complex number arbitrarily closely.*

Corresponding to these possibilities we say that a function $f(s)$ belongs to the class (A), to the class (B) or to the class (C).

To prove the theorem, assume that the function $f(s)$ does not belong to either of the classes (A), (B). We have then to prove that it belongs to the class (C). Assume the contrary. Let there exist a number w_0 such that the lower bound of $|f(s)-w_0|$ in the half-plane $\sigma>\alpha_1$ is positive. Then by Cor. 2, 9°, § 2, $\dfrac{1}{f(s)-w_0}$ is *u.a.p.* in $(\alpha_1, +\infty\rangle$ and is bounded in $(\alpha_1, +\infty)$. Consequently by the theorem of 8°, § 3, $\dfrac{1}{f(s)-w_0}$ tends to a finite limit, as $\sigma\to+\infty$, uniformly in t, which is impossible, since $f(s)$ does not belong to either of the classes (A), (B). By this contradiction the theorem is proved.

2°. Given the Dirichlet series of a *u.a.p.* function we can easily determine to which of the three classes the function belongs.

THEOREM. *If $f(s)\sim\Sigma A_n e^{\Lambda_n s}$ is u.a.p. in $(\alpha, +\infty\rangle$, then it belongs*

(1) *to the class* (A), *if all the exponents are non-positive;*

(2) *to the class* (B), *if there are positive exponents and there is a largest among them;*

(3) *to the class* (C), *if there are positive exponents, but they have no largest one.*

We know already that the class (A) of *u.a.p.* functions is

identical with the class of *u.a.p.* functions with non-positive exponents (8°, § 3), which proves (1).

Passing to (2), assume that $f(s)$ has positive exponents and that Λ is the largest of them. Then the Dirichlet series of $f(s)\,e^{-\Lambda s}$ has only non-negative exponents and the constant term of the series is different from zero. Then $f(s)\,e^{-\Lambda s}$ tends to this term, as $\sigma \to +\infty$, uniformly in t (8°, § 3), whence the result (2) follows.

In proving the result (3) we shall consider two cases:

(*a*) there are positive exponents as large as we please;

(*b*) Λ, the upper bound of exponents, is finite, but Λ itself is not an exponent.

We shall give a separate proof in each of these cases, though the idea of the proof in each case is the same. It is clear that in each of these cases $f(s)$ does not belong to the class (A). We have to prove that it does not belong to (B) either. Assume the contrary: let $|f(s)|$ tend to infinity, as $\sigma \to \infty$, uniformly in t.

In the case (*a*) we take a constant $C_1 > 0$ and define σ_1 such that

$$|f(s)| > C_1 \quad \text{in} \quad (\sigma_1, +\infty).$$

Take now an arbitrary $\sigma_2 > \sigma_1$ and define a constant $C_2 > C_1$ such that

$$|f(s)| < C_2 \qquad \text{for } \sigma = \sigma_2.$$

Define positive numbers c, k from the equations $C_1 = ce^{k\sigma_1}$, $C_2 = ce^{k\sigma_2}$. We write then

$$|f(s)| > ce^{k\sigma_1} \qquad \text{in } (\sigma_1, +\infty),$$
$$|f(s)| < ce^{k\sigma_2} \qquad \text{for } \sigma = \sigma_2.$$

By the theorem of 12°, § 1,

$$(1) \qquad |f(s)| < ce^{k\sigma} \qquad \text{in } (\sigma_2, +\infty).$$

Take now an exponent $\Lambda_n > k$ and denote as before

$$L(\sigma) = \underset{-\infty<t<+\infty}{u.b.} |f(\sigma + it)|.$$

We have

$$L(\sigma) \geqq |M_t\{f(\sigma + it)\,e^{-i\Lambda_n t}\}| = |A_n|\,e^{\Lambda_n \sigma} \qquad \text{in } (\alpha, +\infty).$$

Thus for large σ

$$L(\sigma) > ce^{k\sigma},$$

which is impossible on account of (1). This shows that in the case (a) $f(s)$ does not belong to the class (B). If now it does in the case (b) we take a constant $C_1 > 0$ and define $\sigma_1 > 0$ so that

$$|f(s)| > C_1 \qquad \text{in } (\sigma_1, +\infty)$$

Writing $C_1 = ce^{\Lambda\sigma_1}$ we have

$$(2) \qquad |f(s)| > ce^{\Lambda\sigma_1} \qquad \text{in } (\sigma_1, +\infty).$$

On the other hand $f(s)e^{-\Lambda s}$ having only negative exponents tends to zero, as $\sigma \to \infty$, uniformly in t. Consequently there exists $\sigma_2 > \sigma_1$ such that $|f(s)e^{-\Lambda s}| < \frac{1}{2}c$ on the line $\sigma = \sigma_2$, i.e.

$$(3) \qquad |f(s)| < \tfrac{1}{2}ce^{\Lambda\sigma_2} \qquad \text{for } \sigma = \sigma_2.$$

Define $\Lambda' < \Lambda$ under the condition

$$\tfrac{1}{2}e^{\Lambda\sigma_2} < e^{\Lambda'\sigma_2}.$$

By (2), (3)

$$|f(s)| > ce^{\Lambda'\sigma_1} \qquad \text{in } (\sigma_1, +\infty),$$

$$|f(s)| < ce^{\Lambda'\sigma_2} \qquad \text{for } \sigma = \sigma_2.$$

Hence by the theorem of 12°, § 1,

$$(4) \qquad |f(s)| < ce^{\Lambda'\sigma} \qquad \text{in } (\sigma_2, +\infty).$$

Now in the same way as before we write for a $\Lambda_n > \Lambda'$

$$L(\sigma) \geqq |A_n| e^{\Lambda_n\sigma} \qquad \text{in } (\alpha, +\infty).$$

Thus for large values of σ

$$L(\sigma) > ce^{\Lambda'\sigma},$$

which is impossible on account of (4). This shows that also in the case (b) $f(s)$ does not belong to the class (B).

Having proved that $f(s)$ does not belong to the class (B) in either of the cases (a), (b), we have proved the theorem.

3°. We now shall prove theorems of the Picard type.

THEOREM. *If a function $f(s)$ is u.a.p. in $(\alpha, +\infty\rangle$ and belongs to the class* (C), *then in any half-plane $(\alpha_1, +\infty)$ it takes all values with at most one exception.*

For take a line $\sigma = \sigma_1 > \alpha_1$ and let G be the set of values of $f(s)$ on this line, and G' the derivative of this set. Since $f(s)$ belongs to the class (C) its values in any half-plane $(\sigma_2, +\infty)$ are everywhere dense. Consequently by Iversen's Theorem of 13°, § 1, $f(s)$ takes in the half-plane $(\sigma_1, +\infty)$ all values, which do not belong to $G + G'$ with at most one exception. On the other hand, by the theorem of 9°, § 2, $f(s)$ takes all the values of $G + G'$ in any strip $(\sigma_1 - \delta, \sigma_1 + \delta)$. Hence the theorem follows.

4°. We shall now prove a theorem which will give a valuable addition to the above theorem.

THEOREM. *Let $f(s)$ be a u.a.p. function with negative exponents only. Then, if the upper bound of the exponents is also an exponent, $f(s)$ has no zeros with arbitrary large abscissa; if on the contrary the upper bound is not an exponent, $f(s)$ has zeros in any half-plane $(\alpha, +\infty)$.*

Let Λ be the upper bound of the exponents. In the first case the constant term of the Dirichlet series of $f(s)e^{-\Lambda s}$ is different from zero. Denoting it by A we shall have by 8°, § 3,

$$\lim_{\sigma \to \infty} |f(s)e^{-\Lambda s}| = |A|.$$

Thus there exists σ_1 such that

$$|f(s)e^{-\Lambda s}| > \tfrac{1}{2}|A| \qquad \text{in } (\sigma_1, +\infty)$$

which shows that in the first case $f(s)$ has no zero with the abscissa $> \sigma_1$.

Passing now to the second case we consider again the function $f_1(s) = f(s)e^{-\Lambda s}$ which has now only negative exponents, and consequently tends to zero, as $\sigma \to +\infty$, uniformly in t. Suppose that it has no root in the half-plane $(\sigma_1, +\infty)$. Then by Cor. 2 of 9°, § 2, the function $g(s) = \dfrac{1}{f_1(s)}$ is *u.a.p.* in $\langle \sigma_1, +\infty \rangle$. It obviously belongs to the class (B) and consequently its Dirichlet series has a largest positive exponent. Let the corresponding term be Be^{Ms} $(M > 0)$. Then $g(s)\, e^{-Ms} \to B$, as $\sigma \to \infty$, uniformly in t. Consequently there exists a $\sigma_2 > \sigma_1$ such that

$$|g(s)\, e^{-Ms}| > \tfrac{1}{2}|B| \qquad \text{in } (\sigma_2, +\infty).$$

Hence

$$(1) \qquad |f(s)| < \frac{2}{|B|} e^{(\Lambda - M)\sigma} \qquad \text{in } (\sigma_2, +\infty).$$

Take now $\Lambda_n > \Lambda - M$. We have

$$L(\sigma) \geqq |A_n|\, e^{\Lambda_n \sigma},$$

and thus for large values of σ

$$L(\sigma) > \frac{2}{|B|} e^{(\Lambda - M)\sigma},$$

which is impossible on account of (1). Thus in the second case $f(s)$ has zeros with abscissa as large as we please.

Thus we have proved both parts of the theorem.

5°. THEOREM. *If $f(s)$ belongs to the class* (C) *and if its exponents are bounded above, then it takes all values in any half-plane $(\alpha, +\infty)$ (i.e. there is no exceptional Picard value).*

Let $\Lambda > 0$ be the upper bound of the exponents. Λ itself is not an exponent since $f(s)$ belongs to the class (C). Take any number a and consider the function

$$f_1(s) = \{f(s) - a\}\, e^{-\Lambda s}.$$

By the preceding theorem it has zeros in any half-plane $(\alpha, +\infty)$, which shows that $f(s)$ takes the value a in any half-plane $(\alpha, +\infty)$.

§ 5. On the behaviour of analytic functions outside the strip of uniform almost periodicity.

1°. We know from 4°, § 2, that any *u.a.p.* function possesses a maximum strip of uniform almost periodicity, which is the maximum strip of boundedness of the function. Now the following question arises:

If a u.a.p. function $f(s)$ can be analytically continued on a strip adjacent to the maximum strip of uniform almost periodicity, *does it possess any type of almost periodic properties, and if it does, is it still connected with its Dirichlet series and does the Parseval equation remain true?*

This problem is analogous to that of F. Carlson for ordinary Dirichlet series

$$\Sigma A_n e^{\Lambda_n s} \qquad (\Lambda_1 > \Lambda_2 > \ldots, \Lambda_n \to -\infty)$$

and its solution and the results are also similar to those of F. Carlson.

2°. THEOREM. *If* $f(s) \sim \Sigma A_n e^{\Lambda_n s}$ *is u.a.p. in a strip* (α, β) *and if it is analytic in a wider strip* (α_1, β_1) $(\alpha_1 \leqq \alpha < \beta \leqq \beta_1)$ *and satisfies the following conditions:*

(i) $\bar{M}_t\{|f(\sigma+it)|^2\} = K_\sigma$ *is finite for all* σ *of the interval* (α_1, β_1),

(ii) *there exists a positive integer m and a positive constant C such that*

$$(1) \qquad |f(\sigma+it)| < C\left|\frac{t}{2}\right|^{m-\frac{1}{2}}$$

for $\qquad \alpha_1 < \sigma < \beta_1, \quad |t| > 1,$

then it is B^2 *a.p. on any line* σ_0 *of the strip* (α_1, β_1) *and its Fourier series is derived from the Dirichlet series* $\Sigma A_n e^{\Lambda_n s}$ *in the usual way.*

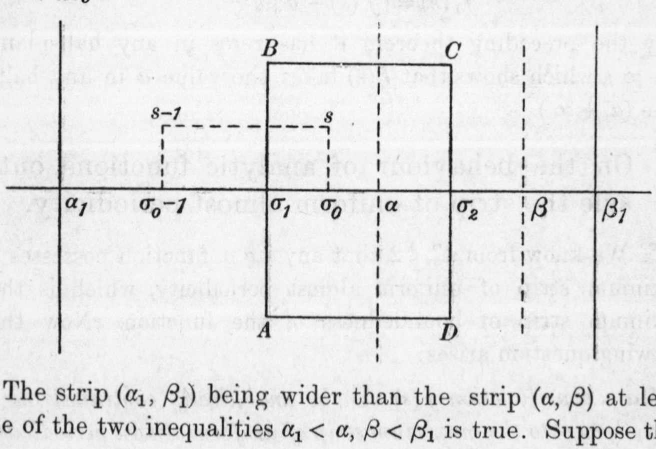

The strip (α_1, β_1) being wider than the strip (α, β) at least one of the two inequalities $\alpha_1 < \alpha$, $\beta < \beta_1$ is true. Suppose that

$\alpha_1 < \alpha$ and take a line σ_0 of the strip (α_1, α). We choose two fixed abscissae σ_1, σ_2 so that

$$\text{Max.}(\alpha_1, \sigma_0 - 1) < \sigma_1 < \sigma_0$$

and $\alpha < \sigma_2 < \beta$, for instance $\sigma_2 = \dfrac{\alpha+\beta}{2}$.

Corresponding to an arbitrary point $s = \sigma_0 + it$ of the line σ_0 we take a number $T > |t|$ and consider the rectangle $ABCD$:

$$A = \sigma_1 - iT, \quad B = \sigma_1 + iT, \quad C = \sigma_2 + iT, \quad D = \sigma_2 - iT.$$

We write $f(s) = -\dfrac{1}{2\pi i}\displaystyle\int_{ABCDA} \frac{f(z) e^{\lambda(z-s)}\, dz}{(z-s)(z-s+1)^m}$,

where λ is a positive number. We have

$$f(s) = -\frac{1}{2\pi i}\int_{\sigma_1 - iT}^{\sigma_1 + iT} + \frac{1}{2\pi i}\int_{\sigma_2 - iT}^{\sigma_2 + iT} - \frac{1}{2\pi i}\int_{\sigma_1 + iT}^{\sigma_2 + iT} + \frac{1}{2\pi i}\int_{\sigma_1 - iT}^{\sigma_2 - iT}.$$

We now let T tend to infinity. By (1) the third and the fourth integral tend to zero and thus

$$f(s) = -\frac{1}{2\pi i}\int_{\sigma_1 - i\infty}^{\sigma_1 + i\infty} + \frac{1}{2\pi i}\int_{\sigma_2 - i\infty}^{\sigma_2 + i\infty}$$

3°. Consider now the second integral on the right-hand side

$$\psi(s, \lambda) = \frac{1}{2\pi i}\int_{\sigma_2 - i\infty}^{\sigma_2 + i\infty} \frac{f(z) e^{\lambda(z-s)}\, dz}{(z-s)(z-s+1)^m}.$$

We shall prove *that* $\psi(s, \lambda)$ *is u.a.p. in* $(\alpha_1, \sigma_2\rangle$. Let γ be any number of the interval (α, σ_2). We have to prove that $\psi(s, \lambda)$ is *u.a.p.* in (α, γ). Given $\epsilon > 0$, take any number τ of

$$E\{\epsilon, f(\sigma_2 + it)\}.$$

We shall have for any point $s = \sigma + it$ of the strip (α_1, γ)

$$\psi(s + i\tau, \lambda) = \frac{1}{2\pi i}\int_{\sigma_2 - i\infty}^{\sigma_2 + i\infty} \frac{f(z)\, e^{\lambda(z-s-i\tau)}\, dz}{(z-s-i\tau)(z-s-i\tau+1)^m}$$
$$= \frac{1}{2\pi i}\int_{\sigma_2 - i\infty}^{\sigma_2 + i\infty} \frac{f(z+i\tau)\, e^{\lambda(z-s)}\, dz}{(z-s)(z-s+1)^m},$$

and thus

$$\psi(s + i\tau, \lambda) - \psi(s, \lambda) = \frac{1}{2\pi i}\int_{\sigma_2 - i\infty}^{\sigma_2 + i\infty} \frac{\{f(z+i\tau) - f(z)\}\, e^{\lambda(z-s)}\, dz}{(z-s)(z-s+1)^m},$$

whence

$$\begin{aligned}|\psi(s+i\tau,\lambda)-\psi(s,\lambda)| &\leq \frac{\epsilon}{2\pi}\int_{\sigma_2-i\infty}^{\sigma_2+i\infty}\left|\frac{e^{\lambda(z-s)}}{(z-s)(z-s+1)^m}\right||dz| \\ &< \frac{\epsilon}{2\pi}e^{\lambda(\sigma_2-\alpha_1)}\int_{\sigma_2-i\infty}^{\sigma_2+i\infty}\frac{|dz|}{|z-s|^{m+1}} \\ &< \frac{\epsilon}{2\pi}e^{\lambda(\sigma_2-\alpha_1)}\int_{-\infty}^{+\infty}\frac{dy}{|(\sigma_2-\gamma)+iy|^{m+1}} \\ &= B\epsilon,\end{aligned}$$

where B is a constant independent of s and ϵ. Thus all numbers of $E\{\epsilon, f(\sigma_2+it)\}$ are translation numbers of $f(s)$ in the strip (α_1, γ) belonging to $B\epsilon$, which proves that $\psi(s, \lambda)$ is *u.a.p.* in (α_1, γ) and consequently in (α_1, σ_2).

4°. Consider now the function

$$(1)\quad \phi(s)=f(s)-\psi(s,\lambda)=-\frac{1}{2\pi i}\int_{\sigma_1-i\infty}^{\sigma_1+i\infty}\frac{f(z)\,e^{\lambda(z-s)}\,dz}{(z-s)(z-s+1)^m}.$$

We shall show that $\bar{M}\{|\phi(\sigma_0+it)|^2\}$ is small for large positive values of λ.

Take a constant $T>1$. We write for any point

$$s=\sigma_0+it \qquad (-T<t<T)$$

$$\begin{aligned}(2)\qquad \phi(s) &= -\frac{e^{\lambda(\sigma_1-\sigma_0)}}{2\pi i}\int_{\sigma_1-i\infty}^{\sigma_1+i\infty}\frac{f(z)\,e^{i\lambda(y-t)}}{(z-s)(z-s+1)^m}dz \\ &= -\frac{e^{\lambda(\sigma_1-\sigma_0)}}{2\pi i}(\phi_1+\phi_2),\end{aligned}$$

where

$$\phi_1(s)=\int_{\sigma_1-2Ti}^{\sigma_1+2Ti}, \quad \phi_2(s)=\int_{\sigma_1+2Ti}^{\sigma_1+i\infty}+\int_{\sigma_1-i\infty}^{\sigma_1-2Ti}.$$

Writing $a=\min.(\sigma_0-\sigma_1, \sigma_1-\sigma_0+1)$ we shall have on account of (1) 2°

$$\begin{aligned}\left|\int_{\sigma_1+2Ti}^{\sigma_1+i\infty}\frac{f(z)\,e^{i\lambda(y-t)}}{(z-s)(z-s+1)^m}dz\right| &\leq \int_{2T}^{\infty}\frac{C\,(y/2)^{m-\frac{1}{2}}\,dy}{\{a^2+(y-t)^2\}^{(m+1)/2}} \\ &< C\int_{2T}^{\infty}\frac{(y/2)^{m-\frac{1}{2}}\,dy}{(y/2)^{m+1}} \\ &= \frac{4C}{\sqrt{T}}.\end{aligned}$$

Similarly

$$\left|\int_{\sigma_1-i\infty}^{\sigma_1-2Ti} \frac{f(z)\, e^{i\lambda(y-t)}\, dz}{(z-s)(z-s+1)^m}\right| < \frac{4C}{\sqrt{T}},$$

and thus

(3) $$|\phi_2(s)| < \frac{8C}{\sqrt{T}}.$$

Consider now $\phi_1(s)$. We have

$$|\phi_1(s)| \leqq \int_{-2T}^{+2T} \frac{|f(\sigma_1+iy)|\, dy}{\{a^2+(y-t)^2\}^{(m+1)/2}},$$

and by Schwarz's inequality

$$|\phi_1(s)|^2 \leqq \int_{-2T}^{+2T} \frac{|f(\sigma_1+iy)|^2\, dy}{a^2+(y-t)^2} \int_{-2T}^{+2T} \frac{dy}{\{a^2+(y-t)^2\}^m}.$$

But

$$\int_{-2T}^{+2T} \frac{dy}{\{a^2+(y-t)^2\}^m} < \int_{-\infty}^{+\infty} \frac{du}{(a^2+u^2)^m}$$

$$< \frac{1}{a^{2m-2}} \int_{-\infty}^{+\infty} \frac{du}{a^2+u^2} = \frac{\pi}{a^{2m-1}},$$

thus $$|\phi_1|^2 \leqq \frac{\pi}{a^{2m-1}} \int_{-2T}^{+2T} \frac{|f(\sigma_1+iy)|^2\, dy}{a^2+(y-t)^2}.$$

Putting $$\frac{1}{2T}\int_{-T}^{+T} |f(\sigma_1+iy)|^2\, dy = K_{\sigma_1}(T),$$

we shall have

(4)

$$\frac{1}{2T}\int_{-T}^{+T} |\phi_1|^2\, dt < \frac{\pi}{a^{2m-1}} \frac{1}{2T}\int_{-2T}^{+2T} |f(\sigma_1+iy)|^2\, dy \int_{-T}^{+T} \frac{dt}{a^2+(y-t)^2}$$

$$< \frac{2\pi^2}{a^{2m}} K_{\sigma_1}(2T).$$

By (3)

$$|\phi_1+\phi_2|^2 \leqq |\phi_1|^2 + \frac{16C}{\sqrt{T}}|\phi_1| + \frac{64C^2}{T}.$$

By Schwarz's inequality and (4)

$$\frac{1}{2T}\int_{-T}^{+T} |\phi_1|\, dt \leqq \left(\frac{1}{2T}\int_{-T}^{+T} |\phi_1|^2\, dt\right)^{\frac{1}{2}} < \frac{\pi}{a^m}\sqrt{2K_{\sigma_1}(2T)}.$$

Thus

$$\frac{1}{2T}\int_{-T}^{+T} |\phi_1+\phi_2|^2\,dt < \frac{2\pi^2}{a^{2m}} K_{\sigma_1}(2T) + \frac{16C\pi}{\sqrt{T}a^m}\sqrt{2K_{\sigma_1}(2T)} + \frac{64C^2}{T}$$

whence

$$\bar{M}\{|\phi_1+\phi_2|^2\} \leqq \frac{2\pi^2}{a^{2m}} K_{\sigma_1}.$$

By (2)

$$\bar{M}\{|\phi(\sigma_0+it)|^2\} = \frac{e^{2\lambda(\sigma_1-\sigma_0)}}{4\pi^2}\bar{M}\{|\phi_1+\phi_2|^2\},$$

and thus

$$(5) \qquad \bar{M}\{|\phi(\sigma_0+it)|^2\} \leqq \frac{1}{2a^{2m}} e^{2\lambda(\sigma_1-\sigma_0)} K_{\sigma_1}.$$

Take now an increasing sequence $\{\lambda_n\}$ of positive numbers such that $\lambda_n \to \infty$. By (5) and (1)

$$f(\sigma_0+it) = B^2 \lim_{n\to\infty} \psi(\sigma_0+it, \lambda_n).$$

As all $\psi(\sigma_0+it, \lambda_n)$ are *u.a.p.* we conclude that $f(\sigma_0+it)$ is B^2 *a.p.*

5°. To complete the proof we have to show that the Fourier series of $f(\sigma_0+it)$ is given by

$$(1) \qquad f(\sigma_0+it) \sim \Sigma A_n e^{\Lambda_n\sigma_0} e^{i\Lambda_n t}.$$

We shall prove this without any new calculations by the following argument.

The functions $\psi(s, \lambda_m)$ have been proved to be *u.a.p.* in (α, σ_2) and B^2 convergent to the function $f(s)$, which is B^2 *a.p.* on any line of (α_1, σ_2) and even *u.a.p.* on the lines of (α, σ_2). Consequently the Fourier series of the functions $\psi(s, \lambda_m)$ on any line of (α_1, σ_2) are formally convergent to the Fourier series of $f(s)$ on the same line. On the other hand the Fourier series of the functions $\psi(s, \lambda_m)$ on all lines of (α_1, σ_2) are derived from their Dirichlet series in (α_1, σ_2). Thus the Dirichlet series of the functions $\psi(s, \lambda_m)$ are formally convergent to an exponential series which gives the Fourier series of $f(s)$ on any line of (α_1, σ_2). But we know that the Dirichlet series of $f(s)$ in (α, σ_2) gives the Fourier series of $f(s)$ on the lines of this strip; consequently it also gives it on the lines of (α_1, σ_2), which proves (1), and thus the theorem of 2° is proved.

6°. We now remark that the condition for the function $f(s)$ to be analytic in (α_1, β_1) can be replaced by the less stringent condition that $f(s)$ may have only a finite number of poles and no other singularity in (α_1, β_1). For we write then

$$f(s)-\psi(s, \lambda) = -\frac{1}{2\pi i}\int_{\sigma_1-i\infty}^{\sigma_1+i\infty} \frac{f(z)\, e^{\lambda(z-s)}\, dz}{(z-s)(z-s+1)^m} - P(s),$$

where $P(s)$ is the sum of residues of the poles of

$$\frac{f(z)\, e^{\lambda(z-s)}}{(z-s)(z-s+1)^m}$$

in the strip (σ_1, σ_2).

It can be easily seen that $P(s)$ is the product of $e^{-\lambda s}$ by a rational fraction of s tending to zero, as $s\to\infty$. Consequently

$$M_t\{|P(\sigma_0+it)|^2\} = 0.$$

Thus in this case also

$$f(s) = B^2 \lim_{n\to\infty} \psi(s, \lambda_n)$$

and the argument of the preceding section remains unaltered.

§ 6. On the behaviour of analytic functions on the boundary of the strip of uniform almost periodicity.

We shall now consider a boundary problem connected with the problem of the preceding paragraph. We proved there that if a *u.a.p.* function

$$(1) \qquad f(s) \sim \Sigma A_n e^{\Lambda_n s}$$

in a strip (α, β) satisfies the conditions (i), (ii) of 2°, § 5, in

$$(\alpha_1, \beta_1), \qquad (\alpha_1 \leqq \alpha < \beta \leqq \beta_1)$$

then $f(s)$ is B^2 *a.p.* on any line of (α_1, β_1) and consequently the Parseval equation

$$(2) \qquad M_t\{|f(\sigma+it)|^2\} = \Sigma |A_n|^2 e^{2\Lambda_n \sigma}$$

is true for any σ of (α_1, β_1).

The question may now be raised: if (i), (ii) are true not only in (α_1, β_1) but even in $[\alpha_1, \beta_1]$ is it necessarily true that (2) also holds in $[\alpha_1, \beta_1]$?

We shall show that neither (i), (ii) in $[\alpha_1, \beta_1]$, nor even some much stronger conditions, are sufficient to ensure the truth of (2). We shall, in fact, construct a Dirichlet (exponential) series representing a function *u.a.p.* in $\langle 0, +\infty)$, bounded in $[0, +\infty)$

$$f(s) = \Sigma\, a_n e^{-\lambda_n s},$$

and even possessing a mean value $M\{|f(it)|^2\}$, which, however, does not satisfy the equation (2) on the line $\sigma = 0$.

Let $\chi(t)$ be a positive continuous function of bounded variation, periodic and with period 1, and let

$$\chi(0) = \chi(1) = 0, \quad \chi(t) > 0, \qquad (0 < t < 1)$$

(3) $$\int_0^1 [\chi(t)]^2\, dt = 1.$$

We have

(4) $$M\{|\chi(t)|^2\} = 1.$$

For any positive integer l we next define the periodic function $\phi(t, l)$, with period l, in the following way:

$$\begin{aligned} \phi(t, l) &= \chi(t) \quad (0 \leq t \leq 1) \\ &= 0. \qquad (1 < t < l) \end{aligned}$$

Now let

(5) $$\Phi(t) = \phi(t, 2^{k_1}) + \phi(t, 2^{k_2}) + \phi(t, 2^{k_3}) + \ldots,$$

where $2 \leq k_1 < k_2 < k_3 < \ldots$ are positive integers, and a_2 is the nearest point to the origin (or one of the two nearest points) for which $\phi(t, 2^{k_1})$ is zero throughout the interval $(a_2, a_2 + 1)$; a_3 is the nearest point to the origin (or one of the two nearest points) for which the functions $\phi(t, 2^{k_1})$ and $\phi(t - a_2, 2^{k_2})$ are both zero throughout the interval $(a_3, a_3 + 1)$, and so on. Writing for shortness

$$\phi(t, 2^{k_1}) = \phi_1(t), \quad \phi(t - a_2, 2^{k_2}) = \phi_2(t), \ldots$$

we have

(6) $$\Phi(t) = \phi_1(t) + \phi_2(t) + \ldots.$$

We shall now show that

$$\Phi(t) = \chi(t). \tag{7}$$

Let us first observe that the function ϕ_j differs from zero only in the intervals

$$(a_j + n2^{k_j},\ a_j + n2^{k_j} + 1) \qquad (n \text{ any integer}). \tag{8}$$

The functions $\phi_1, \phi_2, \ldots, \phi_{j-1}$ are all identically zero in the interval $(a_j, a_j + 1)$, and so, since they have period 2^{k_j}, they are identically zero in all the intervals (8). Thus in any interval $(a, a+1)$ (a integer) where ϕ_j differs from zero, all the preceding functions $\phi_1, \phi_2, \ldots, \phi_{j-1}$ are identically zero, and consequently in any interval $(a, a+1)$ (a integer) only one term of the series (6) can differ from zero. Now it is easy to see that there always is such a term. For, for every j, the interval $(a_j, a_j + 1)$ is the nearest to the origin (or one of the two nearest) throughout which all the functions $\phi_1, \phi_2, \ldots, \phi_{j-1}$ are zero. Therefore if all the terms of the series (6) were zero throughout the interval $(a, a+1)$, all the intervals $(a_j, a_j + 1)$ would be at least as near to the origin as $(a, a+1)$, which is evidently impossible, since all the intervals $(a_j, a_j + 1)$ are different. Now from the definition of the function $\phi(t, l)$ it is easy to see that in every interval $(a, a+1)$ (a integer) the function is equal throughout the interval to zero or to $\chi(t)$. The same is true for all the functions ϕ_j. Since in every interval $(a, a+1)$ just one term of the series (6) differs from zero, the equation (7) follows immediately. Hence

$$M\{|\Phi(t)|^2\} = 1. \tag{9}$$

Let us consider the Fourier series of the function $\phi(t, l)$

$$\phi(t, l) = \sum_{\nu=-\infty}^{+\infty} b_\nu e^{(2\pi/l)\nu t i}, \tag{10}$$

where
$$b_\nu = \frac{1}{l}\int_0^l \phi(u, l)\, e^{-(2\pi/l)\nu u i}\, du.$$

Let t be some point outside the set of intervals of values t' for which $\phi(t', l) > 0$, and d the distance from this set to the point t. Also let n_0 and n be any positive integers. We shall have

$$\sum_{\nu=n_0}^{n_0+n-1} b_\nu e^{(2\pi/l)\nu t i}$$
$$=\frac{1}{l}\int_0^l \phi(u,l)\, e^{-(\pi/l)(2n_0+n-1)(u-t)i}\,\frac{\sin\{(\pi/l)\,n\,(t-u)\}}{\sin\{(\pi/l)(t-u)\}}\,du,$$

$$\left|\sum_{\nu=n_0}^{n_0+n-1} b_\nu e^{(2\pi/l)\nu t i}\right|<\frac{1}{l}\int_0^l \phi(u,l)\,\frac{1}{\sin\{(\pi/l)(t-u)\}}\,du$$
$$=\frac{1}{l}\int_0^1 \chi(u)\,\frac{1}{|\sin\{(\pi/l)(t-u)\}|}\,du$$
$$=\frac{1}{l\,|\sin\{(\pi/l)(t-u_0)\}|}\int_0^1 \chi(u)\,du. \quad (0<u_0<1)$$

But from Schwarz's inequality we have

$$\int_0^1 \chi(u)\,du \leqq \sqrt{\int_0^1 \{\chi(u)\}^2\,du}=1,$$

and from our assumption about t

$$\left|\sin\frac{\pi}{l}(t-u_0)\right|>\frac{2d}{l};$$

consequently

$$\left|\sum_{\nu=n_0}^{n_0+n-1} b_\nu e^{(2\pi/l)\nu t i}\right|<\frac{1}{2d}. \tag{11}$$

Thus (11) gives an upper limit for the modulus of the sum of any number of consecutive terms of the series (10). We shall use (11) later on.

Now suppose

$$\phi_j(t)=\sum_{\nu=-\infty}^{+\infty} b_{\nu,j}\, e^{\nu(2\pi/2^{k_j})ti}=s_j(ti)+r_j(ti), \tag{12}$$

where

$$s_j(ti)=\sum_{\nu=-n_j}^{+n_j} b_{\nu,j}\, e^{\nu(2\pi/2^{k_j})ti}, \tag{13}$$

and n_j is a positive integer chosen large enough to make

$$|r_j(ti)|<\frac{\epsilon}{2^j}, \tag{14}$$

ϵ being some small positive number; this is evidently possible, since all the series (12) are uniformly convergent. Thus we shall have

$$(15) \qquad | s_j(ti) | < \frac{\epsilon}{2^j}$$

for all values of t which satisfy the equation $\phi_j(t) = 0$.

Let us suppose the terms in each of the sums s_j arranged in order of decreasing exponents. We can choose μ_1, a positive multiple of $2\pi/2^{k_1}$, so that all the exponents of the product $s_1(ti)\, e^{-\mu_1 ti}$ are negative. We can then choose μ_2, a positive multiple of $2\pi/2^{k_2}$, so that all the exponents of $s_2(ti)\, e^{-\mu_2 ti}$ are negative and smaller than any of the exponents of the first product, and so on. We may suppose further that $\mu_n \to \infty$, as $n \to \infty$. The products

$$s_1(ti)\, e^{-\mu_1 ti}, \quad s_2(ti)\, e^{-\mu_2 ti}, \ldots$$

have the same periods as the functions $\phi_1, \phi_2, \ldots$ respectively.

Let us now consider the series

$$(16) \qquad \Psi(t) = b_1 s_1(ti)\, e^{-\mu_1 ti} + b_2 s_2(ti)\, e^{-\mu_2 ti} + \ldots,$$

where $b_1, b_2, \ldots$ are positive constants whose values will now be chosen. Since we have

$$\int_0^1 | s_1(ti)\, e^{-\mu_1 ti} |^2\, dt = \int_0^1 | s_1(ti) |^2\, dt = \int_0^1 | \phi_1(t) - r_1(ti) |^2\, dt$$

$$= \int_0^1 | \phi_1(t) |^2\, dt + \theta_1' \int_0^1 \{ | 2r_1(ti)\, \phi_1(t) | + | r_1(ti) |^2 \}\, dt$$

$$= 1 + \tfrac{3}{2}\theta_1 \epsilon \qquad (| \theta_1' | < 1, \ | \theta_1 | < 1)$$

we can choose the positive number b_1 so that

$$(17) \qquad \int_0^1 | b_1 s_1(ti)\, e^{-\mu_1 ti} |^2\, dt = 1.$$

b_1 is evidently near to 1 and *a fortiori less* than 2. In the same way we have

$$\int_{a_2}^{a_2+1} | s_2(ti)\, e^{-\mu_2 ti} |^2\, dt = 1 + \tfrac{3}{4}\theta_2 \epsilon,$$

$$\int_{a_3}^{a_3+1} | s_3(ti)\, e^{-\mu_3 ti} |^2\, dt = 1 + \tfrac{3}{8}\theta_3 \epsilon,$$

$$\dots\dots\dots\dots\dots\dots\dots\dots\dots,$$

and we can thus choose the positive numbers b_2, b_3, ... so that

$$(18)\quad \begin{cases} \displaystyle\int_{a_2}^{a_2+1} |b_1 s_1(ti)\, e^{-\mu_1 ti} + b_2 s_2(ti) e^{-\mu_2 ti}|^2 dt = 1, \\ \displaystyle\int_{a_3}^{a_3+1} |b_1 s_1(ti) e^{-\mu_1 ti} + b_2 s_2(ti) e^{-\mu_2 ti} + b_3 s_3(ti) e^{-\mu_3 ti}|^2 dt = 1, \\ \dots\dots\dots\dots\dots\dots\dots\dots\dots\dots\dots\dots \end{cases}$$

Observing that, in the first of these integrals,

$$|s_1(ti)| < \frac{\epsilon}{2},$$

in the second

$$(19)\qquad |s_1(ti)| < \frac{\epsilon}{2}, \quad |s_2(ti)| < \frac{\epsilon}{4},$$

and so on, we conclude that when ϵ is small all the numbers b_2, b_3, ... are near to 1 and *a fortiori* less than 2.

The series (16) converges at every point of the whole interval $-\infty < t < +\infty$. For at every point t only one of the functions ϕ_1, ϕ_2, ... can differ from zero, and therefore for all values of j, except perhaps one, $j = j'$, the inequality (15) holds, and consequently

$$\begin{aligned} |\Psi(t)| &\leqq |b_1 s_1(ti)| + |b_2 s_2(ti)| + \dots \\ &< b_{j'} |s_{j'}(ti)| + 2\epsilon. \end{aligned}$$

Thus we see that the series (16) is convergent and represents a bounded function. If we now replace each term of the series (16) by its explicit expression as the sum of a finite number of exponential functions, we obtain a series of exponentials whose arguments are ti multiplied by a sequence of decreasing constants tending to $-\infty$:

$$(20)\quad \Psi(t) = c_1 e^{-\lambda_1 ti} + c_2 e^{-\lambda_2 ti} + \dots \quad (0 < \lambda_1 < \lambda_2 < \dots;\ \lambda_n \to \infty)$$

We shall next show that the series (20) is also convergent.

Let t_0 be any fixed value of t and let

$$\Psi(t) = \sigma_n(t) + \rho_n(t),$$

where

$$\sigma_n(t) = \sum_{j=1}^{n} c_j e^{-\lambda_j ti}.$$

For any n we have

$$(21) \qquad \sigma_n(t) = \sum_{j=1}^{\nu-1} b_j s_j(ti) e^{-\mu_j ti} + b_\nu s_\nu'(ti) e^{-\mu_\nu ti},$$

$$(22) \qquad \rho_n(t) = b_\nu s_\nu''(ti) e^{-\mu_\nu ti} + \sum_{j=\nu+1}^{\infty} b_j s_j(ti) e^{-\mu_j ti},$$

where $s_\nu'(ti)$ is the sum of the terms of $s_\nu(ti)$ up to and including some particular term, and $s_\nu''(ti)$ is the sum of the remaining terms (if any) of $s_\nu(ti)$. The series (16) being convergent, the $\rho_n(t)$ of (22) has a definite value for every t, and to prove the convergence of the series (20) it is sufficient to show that to any given pair of numbers t_0, η_0 (η_0 positive) corresponds a number n_0 such that $|\rho_n(t_0)| < \eta$ for $n \geqq n_0$. Let d be a positive number such that

$$(23) \qquad \frac{1}{d} < \frac{\eta_0}{2}.$$

Let, as before, $(a_j, a_j + 1)$ be the interval nearest to the origin (or one of the intervals) in which $\phi_j(t)$ differs from zero. We know that $|a_j| \to \infty$ as $j \to \infty$. Therefore there exists a number ν_0 such that $\epsilon/2^{\nu_0 - 1} < \eta/2$ and that, for $\nu \geqq \nu_0$, $\phi_\nu(t) = 0$ throughout the interval $(t_0 - d, t_0 + d)$. Let the first term of $b_{\nu_0} s_{\nu_0}(ti) e^{-\mu_{\nu_0} ti}$ have the suffix n_0 in the series (20). Then for $n \geqq n_0$ we shall have $|\rho_n(t_0)| < \eta_0$. For in the first place from $n \geqq n_0$ we have $\nu \geqq \nu_0$ and therefore $\phi_\nu(t) = 0$ in the interval $(t_0 - d, t_0 + d)$ and from (11) we have

$$|s_\nu''(t_0 i)| < \frac{1}{2d},$$

and consequently

$$|b_\nu s_\nu''(t_0 i) e^{-\mu_\nu t_0 i}| < \frac{1}{d} < \frac{\eta_0}{2}$$

by (23). Secondly we have from (15), since $\phi_j(t_0) = 0$,

$$\left| \sum_{j=\nu+1}^{\infty} b_j s_j(ti) e^{-\mu_j ti} \right| < \frac{\epsilon}{2^{\nu-1}} \leqq \frac{\epsilon}{2^{\nu_0 - 1}} < \frac{\eta_0}{2}.$$

Hence $|\rho_n(t_0)| < \eta_0$. Thus the series (20) is convergent.

We shall now show that the mean value $M\{|\Psi(t)|^2\}$ exists. We can represent the function $\Psi(t)$ as the sum of two functions:

$$\Psi(t) = \Psi_1(t) + \Psi_2(t),$$

where $\Psi_1(t)$ is defined by

$$(24) \qquad \Psi_1(t) = \sum_{j=1}^{n} b_j s_j(ti) e^{-\mu_j ti},$$

when t belongs to the intervals where

$$(25) \qquad \sum_{j=1}^{n} \phi_j(t) > 0$$

and

$$(26) \qquad \Psi_1(t) = 0$$

for all other values of t; n is chosen arbitrarily and will ultimately be infinitely great. Let L_1 be the set of intervals in which (25) holds, and L_2 the complementary set of intervals. $\Psi_1(t)$ is a periodic function with period 2^{k_n}. For suppose $\Psi_1(t_0)$ is different from zero. Then for $t = t_0$ the inequality (25) holds; but, 2^{k_n} being a period of the left-hand side of (25), it holds also for $t = t_0 + 2^{k_n}$ and consequently $\Psi_1(t_0)$ and $\Psi_1(t_0 + 2^{k_n})$ are both defined by (24) and are equal, since the expression of the right-hand side of (24) has 2^{k_n} for a period. If $\Psi_1(t_0) = 0$, then neither t_0 nor $t_0 + 2^{k_n}$ satisfies (25), and thus

$$\Psi_1(t_0) = \Psi_1(t_0 + 2^{k_n}) = 0.$$

Let us now consider the function $\Psi_2(t)$. In the intervals L_1 we have $\phi_j(t) = 0$ for $j > n$, and therefore, from (15),

$$|\Psi_2(t)| = \left| \sum_{j=n+1}^{\infty} b_j s_j(ti) e^{-\mu_j ti} \right| < \frac{\epsilon}{2^{n-1}}.$$

Now let $(k, k+1)$ (k integer) be any interval of L_2, and let $\phi_l(t)$ $(l > n)$ be the function which differs from zero in this interval. Then by (18)

$$\int_k^{k+1} |b_1 s_1(ti) e^{-\mu_1 ti} + \ldots + b_l s_l(ti) e^{-\mu_l ti}|^2 dt = 1,$$

and in the interval $(k, k+1)$ we have also

$$\left| \sum_{j=l+1}^{\infty} b_j s_j(ti) e^{-\mu_j ti} \right| < \frac{\epsilon}{2^{l-1}} \leq \frac{\epsilon}{2^{n-1}}.$$

We now define the function $\Omega(t)$ as follows:

$\Omega(t)$ is to be equal to $\Psi_1(t)$ in L_1. Let $(k, k+1)$ (k integer) be any interval of L_2 and let ϕ_l be the function which can differ from zero in this interval. We take

$$\Omega(t) = b_1 s_1(ti) e^{-\mu_1 ti} + \ldots + b_l s_l(ti) e^{-\mu_l ti}$$

for $k < t < k+1$.

Then, for all values of t, we have

$$|\Psi(t) - \Omega(t)| < \frac{\epsilon}{2^{n-1}}. \tag{27}$$

Let now $g(t)$ be the characteristic function of the set L_2. The function $g(t)$ is periodic. Plainly

$$\Omega(t) = \Psi_1(t) + g(t)\Omega(t)$$

and

$$|\Omega(t)|^2 = |\Psi_1(t)|^2 + g(t)|\Omega(t)|^2,$$

so that

$$\frac{1}{2T}\int_{-T}^{+T} |\Omega(t)|^2 dt = \frac{1}{2T}\int_{-T}^{+T} |\Psi_1(t)|^2 dt + \frac{1}{2T}\int_{-T}^{+T} g(t)|\Omega(t)|^2 dt. \tag{28}$$

$\Psi_1(t)$ is periodic, and hence it possesses a mean value. Therefore the first integral of the right-hand side of (28) tends to a limit, as $T \to \infty$. As for the second integral, the function $g(t)|\Omega(t)|^2$ differs from zero only in the intervals L_2 which are disposed periodically, and the value of the integral of this function over any interval of L_2 between two consecutive integers is 1. Therefore the second integral also tends to a limit as $T \to \infty$. Thus the limit

$$\lim_{T\to\infty} \frac{1}{2T}\int_{-T}^{+T} |\Omega(t)|^2 dt = C_n$$

exists and, as we can easily see, its value is near to 1.

The function $\Omega(t)$ being bounded, we deduce from (27) that the oscillation of the integral

$$\frac{1}{2T}\int_{-T}^{+T} |\Psi(t)|^2 dt, \tag{29}$$

as T tends to infinity, is of the order $\epsilon/2^n$ and, since n was chosen arbitrarily, we conclude that the expression (29) tends to a limit, as $T \to \infty$, and that its value is near to 1.

Let us now consider the Dirichlet series

(30) $s(z) = b_1 s_1(z) e^{-\mu_1 z} + b_2 s_2(z) e^{-\mu_2 z} + \dots \quad (z = \sigma + it)$

which coincides with the series (16) for $\sigma = 0$ and thus for $\sigma \geqq 0$ represents an analytic function bounded in the half-plane $\sigma \geqq 0$ and passing continuously to its values on the boundary $\sigma = 0$. By an elementary property of Dirichlet series, $s(z)$ is uniformly convergent in $\langle 0, +\infty)$ and consequently *u.a.p.* in $\langle 0, +\infty)$. Thus the Parseval equation holds in $(0, +\infty)$. We shall now show that it does not hold on the line $\sigma = 0$. For, all the coefficients of the series (30) are among the numbers $b_j b_{\nu, j}$, where

$$j = 1, 2, \dots \text{ and } \nu = \dots, -2, -1, 0, +1, +2, \dots.$$

$b_j < 2$, and the $b_{\nu, j}$ are given by (12). Every function ϕ_j being periodic, we have

$$M\{|\phi_j|^2\} = \sum_{\nu=-\infty}^{\infty} |b_{\nu,j}|^2,$$

and from the definition of ϕ_j we have

$$M\{|\phi_j|^2\} = \frac{1}{2^{k_j}}$$

and consequently

$$\sum_{\nu=-\infty}^{+\infty} |b_{\nu,j}|^2 = \frac{1}{2^{k_j}}.$$

Thus the sum of squares of the coefficients of (30) is less than

$$4\left(\frac{1}{2^{k_1}} + \frac{1}{2^{k_2}} + \dots\right)$$

and so, if $k_1 = 4$, $k_2 = 5, \dots$, the sum is less than $\frac{1}{2}$.

But the mean value of (30) is near to 1; hence the Parseval equation does not hold for $\sigma = 0$.

MEMOIRS REFERRED TO IN THE TEXT

A. Besicovitch. "On generalised almost periodic functions." *Proc. London Math. Soc.* (2), 25 (1926), pp. 495–512.

—— "On Parseval's theorem for Dirichlet series." *Proc. London Math. Soc.* (2), 26, pp. 25–34.

—— "Über die Parsevalsche Gleichung für analytische fastperiodische Funktionen." *Acta Math.* 47, pp. 283–295.

—— "Analysis of conditions of generalised almost periodicity." *Acta Math.* Bd. 58.

A. Besicovitch and H. Bohr. "Some remarks on generalisation of almost periodic functions." *Det Kgl. Danske Videnskabernes Selskab., Math.-fys. Meddelelser*, VIII, 5, pp. 1–33.

—— —— "On almost periodic properties of translation numbers." *Journal London Math. Soc.* 3, pp. 172–176.

—— —— "Almost periodicity and generalised trigonometric series." *Acta Math.* Bd. 57.

S. Bochner. "Beiträge zur Theorie der fastperiodischen Funktionen, I, II." *Math. Ann.* 96 (1926), pp. 119–147, 383.

—— "Konvergenzsätze für Fourierreihen grenzperiodischer Funktionen." *Math. Zeitschr.* 27, pp. 187–211.

—— "Properties of Fourier series of almost periodic functions." *Proc. London Math. Soc.* (2), 26, pp. 433–452.

—— "Über Fourier-Reihen von fastperiodischen Funktionen." *Sitzungsber. d. Berl. Math. Ges.* 26, pp. 49–65.

H. Bohr. "Zur Theorie der fastperiodischen Funktionen, I, II, III." *Acta Math.* 45 (1924), pp. 29–127; 46 (1925), pp. 101–214; 47 (1926), pp. 237–281.

—— "Über die Verallgemeinerungen fastperiodischen Funktionen." *Math. Ann.* 100 (1928), pp. 357–366.

—— "Bericht über die Theorie der fastperiodischen Funktionen." Comunicazioni. *Atti Cong. Int. Math. in Bologna.*

—— "Sur le théorème d'unicité dans la théorie des fonctions presque périodiques." *Bull. d. Sc. math.* 2e série, t. 50 (1926).

—— "Über analytische fastperiodische Funktionen." *Math. Ann.* 103 (1930), pp. 1–14.

Ph. Franklin. "Approximation theorems for generalised almost periodic functions." *Math. Zeitschr.* 29 (1929), pp. 70–86.

F. Iversen. "Sur quelques propriétés des fonctions monogènes au voisinage d'un point singulier." *Öfv. finska vet. Soc.* Bd. 58, Nr. 25.

Linfoot. "Generalisation of two theorems of Bohr." *Journal L.M.S.*

C. de la Vallée Poussin. "Sur les fonctions presque périodiques de H. Bohr." *Ann. de la Soc. Sc. de Bruxelles*, 47 (1927), pp. 140–158.

R. Schmidt. "Die trigonometrische Approximation für eine Klasse von verallgemeinerten fastperiodischen Funktionen." *Math. Ann.* 100 (1928), pp. 333–356.

W. Stepanoff. "Über einigen Verallgemeinerungen der fastperiodischen Funktionen." *Math. Ann.* 95 (1926), pp. 473–498.

H. Weyl. "Integralgleichungen und fastperiodische Funktionen." *Math. Ann.* 97 (1926–7), pp. 338–356.

N. Wiener. "On the representation of functions by trigonometrical integrals." *Math. Zeitschr.* 24, pp. 576–616.

—— "The spectrum of an arbitrary function." *Proc. L.M.S.* (2), 27 (1927–8), pp. 483–496.